BUILD YOUR OWN ENERGY-SAVER HOME
OR
UPGRADE YOUR EXISTING HOME

By Roy L. Wilson

ENERGY-SAVER HOMES CO.
P.O. BOX 10083
AUSTIN, TEXAS 78766

Foreword

"Energy Shortage"—these words are used so often in relation to our energy crisis. Yet, the words are misleading for we have something worse, much worse—we have an energy-depletion problem. We are using up—at an ever increasing rate—the fossil fuels developed millions of years ago and which, when used, can never be replaced.

Today, somewhere between 30 and 35 percent of the energy consumed in this country is used to heat or cool buildings (homes, apartments, offices, etc.). Regretfully, the vast majority of already-built buildings are energy hogs. Built in the days of cheap energy they reflect the then-popular opinion that low-cost energy would always be available. Now we know (or should know) that the days of cheap energy are over, perhaps forever.

Today—all too little is being done as to energy conservation as it relates to the home. Regretfully, the old energy-is-cheap thinking seems to prevail. Yet, most meaningful energy savings (and thus dollar savings) can be gained if a house is constructed or upgraded (retrofitted) to be a true energy saver.

In response to the energy shortage numerous articles have appeared over the last few years in newspapers, magazines, government pamphlets, manufacturer's literature, etc. as to how to build or upgrade a house to achieve a very high level of energy efficiency. However, the various articles, mostly excellent in themselves, do not seem to educate and inform to the degree one would think they should. The author has discussed these articles and pamphlets with numerous people and found they were thought excellent and useful by those who had some experience with energy-saving materials and techniques as related to home construction. However, those who did not have such experience were somewhat confused by the articles and pamphlets and just did not seem to understand how the very high energy (and dollar) savings mentioned would be realized.

The author, as a result of his findings, considers that a "full-coverage" manual is needed on the subject of energy-saving home construction and upgrading. A manual that will serve as a sort of primer—that starts from the bottom level of needed knowledge and brings the reader up gradually to gain a full understanding of what must be done to realize excellent energy savings and how both a dollar and comfort return will be gained by an energy-saver home.

For knowledgeable persons, this manual may seem to be too detailed. For those with little or no experience with energy-saving techniques and materials, the information level should be "just right."

Copyright © 1979 by Roy L. Wilson

Library of Congress Number 78-53845
ISBN-9601696-1-X

Third Edition
Printed September 1979

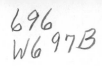

Table of Contents

Section 1

Manual Purpose

GENERAL

Today, most regretfully, few homes will be built to achieve the very high level of energy efficiency made possible when a home is constructed using the latest of building techniques and energy-saving materials. All too many of the homes being built even today (1979) are being built to outmoded insulation and air-infiltration standards—resulting in unnecessarily high energy bills. This is most regrettable since, for an added construction cost of between 5 and 10 percent, energy savings as high as 65 percent (or more) can be realized as related to heating and cooling of the home.

"A savings as high as 65 percent (or more) can be realized." Sounds far fetched, doesn't it? Yet, the statement is true and provable. Here is what the American Institute of Architects said in a recently issued pamphlet:

> "New buildings initially designed to be energy efficient could save as much as 80 percent of the fuel they would consume at present levels (of insulation and air-infiltration prevention)."

> "In existing buildings, fuel consumption could be reduced by as much as 50 percent from current levels (if upgraded as to insulation and air-infiltration prevention)."

> "By conservative estimates, 30 to 50 percent of the energy consumed in a (low-efficiency) building goes up in smoke (is wasted)."

While the energy-use experts may differ somewhat as to the amount of energy saved when a house is built to the "now-required" standards of insulation and air-infiltration prevention, all agree as to the absolute necessity to build houses to these new standards.

The purpose of this manual is to inform as to how a house may be constructed and equipped to achieve a very high order of energy efficiency and how an already-built home may be upgraded to achieve a comparable order of energy efficiency. The energy-saving material and information detailed in this manual was gathered from various sources and all have been proven to be practical as tested under actual living conditions. In the majority they were used by the author in the construction of his energy-saver homes.

The gathered and experienced material and information has been assembled, detailed, and illustrated in a manner to impart maximum useful information to you—the prospective new-home buyer or the existing-home owner. The material and information should educate and inform you to the end you may make meaningful decisions as to the desired energy-efficiency level of your home. The manual should prepare you to talk knowledgeably with architects, home-building contractors, and home-loan officials.

ENERGY-SAVING INFORMATION

Generally, for a home equipped with a central air-conditioning system as much as half (50%) of the energy costs of that home may relate to its use. The greatest energy savings possible in a home will thus be realized if the load on the heating and cooling system is reduced to an absolute minimum. As to this—the name of the game is:

- Prevent heat transfer (into the house in the summer and out of the house in the winter).

- Prevent air infiltration (into the house in the summer and out of the house in the winter).

- Select an efficient heating and cooling system.

Information on how to reduce heat transfer (with insulation) and to reduce or prevent air infiltration (drafts) along with information on how to select an efficient air-conditioning system is given in this manual.

The second largest use of energy in the home relates to hot-water heaters, with the major appliances (stove, dishwasher, clothes-dryer, etc.) being next as to energy use. Here the energy-saving answer is:

- Wise choice and wise use

Information on how to lay out an energy-efficient hot-water system and how to select and use energy-saving appliances is included.

Electrical lighting generally uses the smallest part of the energy consumed in a home. Yet, meaningful energy savings can be achieved while still maintaining adequate lighting levels by:

- Wise choice and wise use

This manual will give facts on energy-saving lighting systems.

Two other factors directly affect the energy efficiency of a home. They are:

- Orientation of the house to the sun's path
- Landscaping, designed to reduce the heating and cooling loads

These will be discussed under a separate section.

And then there is the human factor—the living habits of the occupants. That is, living habits extremely wasteful of energy have been developed over the many years cheap energy was available. In general, most people are not naturally "conservative minded," wasting energy at a great rate while not being aware of its loss. Not understanding how energy can be wasted the occupants of a house can—by wasteful use—increase their energy costs by a considerable amount.

This manual will point out many of these wasteful habits and will suggest up-to-date methods and means to allow each individual in the home to make meaningful reduction of energy use.

INFORMATION INTENT

This manual is generally written on a non-technical basis. Actual construction methods are not given in full detail. It was felt that full-detail information would be excessively lengthy and was not warranted of inclusion since any building contractor would already know the basic techniques.

If additional installation, material and equipment details are desired, these can be obtained from informative pamphlets developed by various manufacturing companies and by the government. A list of such pamphlets and other material is given in the Bibliography at the end of this manual. Appropriate addresses and prices (where applicable) are also given. Much of the listed material can be obtained (for free) at any large lumber yard or hardware store or they can be requested by mail. It is suggested that you obtain all that interests you.

CONFIDENCE IN INFORMATION

As the author of this book I feel it of utmost importance that you, the reader, have confidence in the material. Much of the material may be completely new to you; some other material may clarify a particular viewpoint and still other material may act to confirm an already-held belief. The big question at this point is: "Are you, the author, a real expert?" A good question.

A careful analysis of the home building energy-saving articles appearing in newspapers and magazines will reveal that even the "experts" do not always agree on all points. For example, the author (as a serious student of the subject) has read conflicting statements as to the worth of storm windows, double-glazed windows, heat pumps, etc. Each author surely felt their article to be factual and correct in all respects. But, how can each expert see things from a different viewpoint when there should only be one true viewpoint? Further, the author has seen the "experts" raise their prediction of the amount of energy that can be saved if a house is built to the "new" standards of energy-use efficiency. That is, about three years ago, the experts were stating that "a savings as high as 35%" could be achieved if a house was built the "new" standards. Today (1979), these same experts now confidently state "savings as high as 85% are possible" when comparing a non-standard house with a new-standard house.

Why do the experts disagree somewhat—why have they changed their outlook? For a variety of reasons. In particular, because as more and more experience is gained in building true energy-saver homes and their excellent energy bills are examined, it is clear that energy savings far in excess of those expected are being obtained. Experience has proven that double-glazed windows, for example, both function as energy savers because of their inherent resistance to heat flow and because they are better built and thus permit less air infiltration. Metal-clad doors, using magnetic weather-stripping, both save energy on an energy-flow basis and because the weatherstripping so effectively seals off drafts on a permanent basis. Most wonderfully, actual experience revealed that as more energy-saving features were built into a house, the energy savings increased to a higher-than-calculated basis. Also, many experts do not really take into account the very great increase in energy costs per unit and thus arrive at unrealistically low dollar savings.

A point to be made here is that many "experts" still hold to viewpoints that were accepted as "gospel" in the past but are now known to be incorrect in part or in the whole.

While writing this book, I based my statements on information obtained from:

- my own review in depth of all energy-saving features, materials and building methods—with this review dictating the design and construction of our house.

- my own personal experience in building a home that demonstrates energy savings entirely in line with the latest predictions.

- my wide experience gained while acting as an energy-consultant to a large number of people desirous of building a true energy-saver home.

As the author of this book, I feel I entered into the field of energy-efficient house construction with an open mind and thus was able to easily accept all the "new" thoughts. That is, I was able to research, review, test in practice and advise others how to build an energy-saver home with an open mind.

The very low energy bills realized by our home should give you, the reader, confidence that what you read is correct, practical and up-to-date. And, that you need but follow the recommendations made in this book to realize comparable energy (and dollar) savings.

YOU MUST DO YOUR PART

The author has talked with many people who recently have either built an energy-saver home or have retrofitted their existing home to achieve a very high level of energy-use efficiency. These people all have three things in common: they believe in, are enthusiastic about and knowledgeable as to energy-saving home construction or retrofitting. Their belief and enthusiasm stems from their broad knowledge of the subject, gained (mainly) by a careful study of energy-saving articles appearing in newspapers and magazines. As their knowledge of the subject increased, they became believers and, with belief came enthusiasm.

Few homes builders are really knowledgeable and/or enthusiastic about energy-saving home construction. Most contractors engaged in energy-saving retrofitting are knowledgeable in a broad sense and are usually up to date with the newest materials and techniques to improve the energy-use efficiency of a home. Ridiculous as it may seem, you — who desire to have a true energy-saver home built or to have a home retrofitted — must supply some of the knowledge and much (if not, all) of the enthusiasm and belief. Of course, you need not instruct the contractor as to technical details and he would resent it if you did. What you must supply is the specialized knowledge, the enthusiasm and the firm belief that energy-saving home construction or retrofitting is vitally needed today, it's cost

is well worthwhile and that your extra dollar outlay will be returned in a very short time.

Actually, we are in a pioneering stage. There is no question that in just a few years (five or less) *all* homes, apartments, offices, schools, factories, etc. will be built (as a standard thing) to achieve a high order of energy-use efficiency. In fact, rigid standards — far in excess of today's — will make it mandatory to build to save energy. Much stricter regulations are now being issued or considered by the various government agencies, lending institutions are now learning it does not pay to loan money on an energy-hog home and the public will be aware of the wonderful energy and dollar savings that can be gained.

Your part is then to make a serious study of the subject. You must read this book as a manual (which it really is). It is not meant to be browsed through in an afternoon. You must spend some time with the book, you must study and review the material until you become convinced that energy-saving home construction or existing-home retrofitting is vitally needed and that it will result in excellent savings in energy use. You must be both knowledgeable and convinced. Then, in any talks with your contractor you can talk with confidence, with full belief based upon your newly-gained knowledge. Should your contractor be less than enthusiastic or even have a strong negative feeling for certain energy-saving equipment, materials or building techniques, you can make firm reply based upon your knowledge and belief.

So it will take a few weekends plus a few nights to really study this book — this manual — but it will be well worth it. You will benefit every day thereafter as long as you live in your energy-saver home and, when the day comes to sell it, you will be doubly thankful you spent some time in study today.

YOUR ENERGY-SAVING HABITS

The best designed, best built and best equipped energy-saver home cannot realize its inherent energy-saving potential if the living habits of the occupants are wasteful of energy. This is dramatically highlighted by government studies that clearly prove the energy-using habits of the house occupants play a very large role in the overall energy-use efficiency of the house. The studies compared energy usage (natural gas, heating oil and electricity) of identical (or nearly identical) homes equipped with the same heating and cooling systems, hot-water systems and appliances and built with the same amount of insulation, the same care for weatherization, etc. In brief, identical homes with the same number of occupants. The comparison produced some startling results.

The results—a difference of as high as 50 percent in total energy used between one identical house against another, both having the same size family. Energy savings of 30 and 40 percent by one house versus another identical house were even common. A recent university study made a strong case for energy conservation, theorizing that if all—business, government, private citizens—practiced basic economy as to energy usage our use of energy could be reduced by half. Energy savings of 50 percent.

And—here is the most wonderful part of the identical-house study. The occupants of homes that used from 10 to 50 percent less energy than the highest users did not feel they were "living a life of hardship," they did not "freeze in the dark." That is, they did not feel they were living in a substandard way. Their energy-saving habits were ingrained, accepted and adjusted to in a mild sense. A bit of care here, a little thoughtfulness there and their energy bills were markedly lower than the "average" home. Meaningful savings in energy and thus in dollars.

Impossible—not so. Consider, many people keep their thermostats on 68°F during the summer and raise it to 78°F in the winter. If they can tolerate (and even want) 78°F in the winter, why must their home be cooled to 68°F in the summer? The 20-minute shower, the open door or window during the air-conditioning season—all very wasteful of energy. Key examples of energy-wasting living habits are as follows:

Bad Habits	**Good Habits**
Summer-time setting of 68°F	Summer-time setting of 75-78°F
Winter-time setting of 78°F	Winter-time setting of 65-68°F
Deep, warm tub soakings	Shallower tub soakings
Long (20-minute) showers	Shorter showers
Full-power shower spray (5 gallons per minute)	Water reducer valve used (1½ gallons per minute)
Doors and windows left open during a/c season	Doors and windows carefully closed during a/c season
Careless use of hot water in kitchen and bathrooms	Careful use of hot water in kitchen and bathrooms
Careless use of lights — TV and radio on when no one is looking or listening	Careful use of light, TV and radio. Any not in use are shut off.
Careless use of ventilation in kitchen and bathrooms — fans left on too long	Careful use of ventilation in kitchen and bathrooms — fans turned off as soon as possible
Windows not shaded from sun by drawn curtains during summer — open in winter	Window curtains and drapes used to keep sun from entering in summer — open to allow sun in during winter
Careless use of kitchen range and oven during summer, appearing as a heat load on the cooling system	Careful use of kitchen range and oven to keep heat built up in kitchen to a minimum in the summer — use built-in fan to pull heat out of kitchen
Careless use of dishwasher—use electric-heat drying cycle	Careful use of dishwasher — full loads only — use air dry method
Careless opening and closing of refrigerator doors — doors opened many times for single items	Careful opening and closing of refrigerator doors — fewest door openings possible by planning ahead
A/C filters seldom cleaned — unit seldom serviced	A/C filters cleaned at regular intervals — unit serviced as recommended.

What savings can be made? Figure 19-1 shows the extra heating and cooling costs of keeping a house temperature above or below normal. During the winter, if the thermostat is set to 79°F, the heating cost is increased by 65% above that related to the "new" normal setting of 65°F. During the summer, if the thermostat is set to 68°F instead of to the "new" normal setting of 78°F, the cooling bill is increased by 75%.

Heating hot water uses more energy than any other household function except air conditioning and is especially expensive if electric heating is used. Consider the following:

24.5 KWH used to heat 100 gallons of water to 135°F

With an average cost of 4.5¢ per KWH = 24.5 KWH x 4.5¢ = $1.10 per 100 gallons

$1.10/100 = 1.1¢ per gallon

10 minute shower at 4 GPM = 40 gallons x 1.1¢ = 44¢ per shower

30 showers per month = 30 x 44¢ = $13.20

5 minute shower at 1.5 GPM = 7.5 gallons x 1.1¢ = 8.25¢ per shower

30 showers per month = 30 x 8.25¢ = $2.48

   Savings = $13.20 - $2.48 = $10.72 per person

             or

5 minute shower at 4 GPM = 5 x 4 = 20 gallons x 1.1¢ = 22¢ x 30 = $6.60

5 minute shower at 1.4 GPM = 1.5 x 5 = 7.5 gal. x 1.1¢ = 8.25¢ x 30 = -$2.48

                                    Savings per person = $4.12

Section 2

New Words—New Trends

NEW WORDS

As a result of the energy shortage, three phrases are being increasingly used and reflect the importance of energy savings in our daily life. These three phrases are:

- *MPG — Miles Per Gallon* — is of major importance in the selection of a car. The higher the MPG figure, the more practical the car. The MPG figure is developed by the Federal government for each car on a size and weight basis.

  All other things being somewhat equal, the MPG figure is usually the deciding factor in the purchase of a car, new or used. The net result is—the manufacturers build a more efficient car, the public pays less for gasoline and our energy crisis is lessened.

- *EPM — Energy Per Month* — relates to the amount of energy used per month in a home to heat and cool the house. The measurement value is the BTU (British Thermal Unit) and is given in BTU's per square foot per month. This figure can be calculated directly from the house plans on a yearly basis, being divided by 12 to arrive at the monthly figure.

  While not yet used as a measure of air-conditioning efficiency, experts in the energy conservation field consider it will come into mandatory use in the near future. It is thought the Federal government will establish maximum EPM figures for houses in much the same manner as is now done for MPG.

  Too high an EPM figure will identify a house that will be costly to air condition and that will be hard to sell should the need arise. A low EPM figure will identify a house that is less expensive to air condition and that would easily sell at an advantageous price should the need arise.

  The EPM figure can be calculated by an architect from the house plans, with the results converted into air-conditioning costs in dollars and cents. A family can thus determine the air-conditioning cost for a home before it is built and can decide if the cost is within their budget. But note that the decision should not be based upon today's energy costs—they will be much higher in the future.

- *PDL — Peak Demand Load* — is an energy-conservation measure that will limit the maximum amount of electrical power a home may use at any time. If the assigned peak power for the house is exceeded, even for just a very short time, a flag is set on the meter. The net result, the KWH rate for that house will be increased for the entire month by a certain amount.

  PDL is important to generation efficiency since if the power plant need only generate electrical power for a foreseen maximum, it need not generate excess power that is not used and is thus a total loss. The PDL method will require government permission but it is considered so important to energy conservation that it will certainly come about in the near future. The method is already under test in several cities.

  A house with a low EPM figure would be less likely to exceed its PDL figure.

Another conservation measure now being tested in some cities is a variation of the PDL method. That is, with the consumer's permission, the electric-power company fits special switches (controllable circuit breakers) in the power wiring to the hot-water heater, clothes-dryer, dishwasher and (sometimes) to the air-conditioning equipment. At certain times during the day when the power company anticipates an increased demand for electricity, the power company sends a special tone signal out over the electric wires. This is picked up by the special switches, acting to open the switch to turn off the unit (if on). When the power load drops to "normal," the power company sends another signal over the lines that acts to close the special switches.

Lastly, rationing of electricity will certainly occur. Recent newspaper articles state the rationing of electricity is forseen for California and the Northwest at some time during 1977. Other experts state that rationing of electricity will be nationwide to a certain degree by or before 1980. Brownouts (lowering the voltage on the power lines) has already occurred in the East and it has been predicted that it will occur widely across the nation in future years.

Thus, we must build houses that have a very high level of energy efficiency and we must upgrade the energy efficiency of existing houses so that when (not, if) rationing etc. occurs, the amount of electricity allowed each home will suffice for normal or near-normal living.

NEW TRENDS

As a result of the energy shortage, two major trends are appearing in the home-construction and home-sales fields. These trends are:

- Knowledgeable owners of homes that have high energy costs are planning "to sell them right now, before everyone starts to ask for the energy bills." These knowledgeable home owners are planning on selling their energy-hog home and building a new energy-saver home.

  Just note how many large homes, with vast expanse of glass, vaulted ceilings and with large areas of living space are appearing on the market. Some of these homes are less than a year old, lived in long enough for the owners to see that their energy bills will eat up too much of the family budget.

  But, as of now, these energy-hog homes do not sell readily, staying vacant while new houses of comparable size and quality are being built right next door, constructed to the "new" standards of air-infiltration prevention and insulations. The people building the new energy-saver home have said, "We looked at the house up the street that is up for sale. It is a fine house in every respect except that it has a very high energy cost. So, we decided to build a house with a higher level of energy efficiency; it really doesn't cost that much more."

- Knowledgeable home-building contractors (all too few) are now starting to build homes to a higher level of energy efficiency than in the past. That is, above the present FHA Minimum Property Standards. These up-to-date contractors have seen the need and are responding. But, most unfortunately, these contractors report the public (in general) does not respond too well in the energy-saving features since they do not really believe in the energy crisis and do not understand the real dollar savings that will be gained—now and in the future. The buyers are all too interested in getting maximum size and appearance for their dollar and do not (as yet) see the wisdom of building or buying an energy-saver home.

  An education is needed here and it is hoped this manual will help fill that need.

At the risk of being repetitious, a home being built today should not be built to the existing standards of energy efficiency. The house must be built with an eye to the future. Clearly, energy prices will never return to their low level of just a few years ago. Obviously, energy prices will rise to levels that cannot be foreseen today.

When building or buying a home today, one should keep two things firmly in mind:

- Energy costs will never drop—the time to build for energy efficiency is when the house is being built, not afterwards on a upgrade basis since this is more costly and less efficient.

- You will almost certainly sell your home at some time and an energy-hog home will be just about unsaleable in a few years. An energy-saver home, on the other hand, will certainly sell much faster and at a better price.

PUBLIC REACTION

An energy-knowledge survey made in 1976 by the Houston (Texas) Lighting and Power Company provides insights into the public's reaction to the energy crisis. Some 700 respondents to the statewide survey listed their thoughts as given by Tables 2-1 and 2-2.

Table 2-1
Seriousness of Energy Crisis

	Yes
Serious problem	51%
Minor problem	26%
No problem	17%
No opinion	6%

Table 2-2
Overall View of Energy Crisis

	Yes
World is running out of fuel	82.4%
Energy waste in home results from improper house design and operation	78.3%
Citizens have been wasteful of energy	71.6%
Have made efforts to reduce use of electricity	73%
Energy-saving design features are desirable in a home	61.6%

The survey showed that only 51% actually believed that there is a real energy shortage—a real crisis. Since the people who respond to surveys are usually those who are generally well informed and only 51% of such people believed the energy problem actually exists, the true number of disbelievers must be greater than 51% of the public. This disbelief must be corrected since the energy crisis is real and will certainly increase in severity as our remaining fossil fuel supplies are used up. Sections 2 and 3 are thus included in the hope the material and information they present may turn disbelievers into believers.

ENERGY COSTS

The unit price for natural gas, oil and coal as used in the home has risen at an ever increasing rate over the last few years. Similarly, the price of electricity has risen sharply. Even more serious, shortages are occurring in many parts of the nation. Spot shortages of natural gas and heating oil were a serious problem during the winter of 1978 and may be an even worse problem during this winter and into the future. These energy shortages have even caused many homeowners to install a heat pump to replace a gas or heating oil furnace, reasoning that electricity will "always be available if gas and oil run short". Regretfully, this may not be always true.

No one seems to be able to predict the future cost of energy, not even for next year let alone 5 years, 10 years from now, etc. One thing is certain, energy costs will increase and spot shortages will become more serious.

The future is most uncertain, much depends upon how the American public and the business world enter into energy conservation, how the OPEC nations act and how many new fields of oil and natural gas are found and developed. Clearly, the energy costs will rise — somewhat slowly if consumption is held down, more rapidly if we continue our wasteful ways. What it all really comes down to is this:

Spend a little more today to make your house an Energy Saver and realize high energy and dollar savings now and into the future.

Keep the present and possible future cost of electricity, natural gas, oil and coal in mind when considering the payback period for the energy-saving features and materials you may build into your new home or have retrofitted into your existing home. When computing the payback time, figure that energy costs may double in 10 years, or even less.

Section 3

Need for Energy Saving

THE NEED

Why must we from this day and on build only houses that are designed, constructed and equipped to permit an excellent level of home comfort and appliance use with an absolute minimum expenditure of energy developed from fossil fuels? Why must we bring the energy-efficiency level of existing houses up to the "new" standards required because of the energy shortage? Why? Because:

- Morally it is wrong to wastefully use (as we too often now do) the precious gift of fossil fuels developed for us during the billions of years the sun has shone on our planet. These fossil fuels are irreplaceable and if we use them all up, what will be left for our children?

- Financially—you may not be able to support the energy costs of the future if you build or live in a home that is wasteful of energy. Energy costs—unacceptably high today, certain to rise next year—may soon reach the point you will say:

Our energy bills now exceed our house payments.

As to the future—what may be the energy costs five years from now, 10 years, 25 years, etc. If your home is an energy hog, in a few years you may be saying:

Our energy bills now exceed our house payments.

Even today, many home owners are worriedly saying:

Our energy bills are so high we may be forced to sell our home and move into a smaller one.

Another reason relates to solar-energy systems that are certain to be put into use, now and in the future. When these systems are practical on a dollar basis, the size of the solar-energy gathering array and the energy-storage facilities required to satisfy the heating and cooling requirements of a home will be directly proportional to:

- the square footage of living space
- the energy efficienty level of the house

If a home is inefficient of energy use as to heating, the solar-gathering array needed may exceed in size the capacity of the roof to mount it. Thus, building to a high energy-efficiency level today means a smaller (and less costly) solar array and storage system when the time comes to install such a system.

THE COST

What will be the extra cost to build an energy-saver home over a "standard" home—that is, one built to FHA Minimum Property Standards. The extra cost, on a square-foot of living-space basis, will add somewhere between 5% and 10% to the "standard" house cost depending on:

- Square footage of living space to be heated and cooled.
- Level of energy efficiency planned above the FHA Minimum Property Standards, with this being related to climatic conditions at the house locale and the type of fuel used for heating (gas, oil, electric-strip furnace or heat pump).
- Labor costs in house area.

For discussion sake, consider that the 50 States have climatic conditions that fall into or between four levels of winter-summer temperature. These being:

- *Very mild winters and summers,* such as enjoyed in Hawaii and some parts of Florida and California plus small areas along the Gulf Coast in favored spots.

  Insulation to FHA Minimum Property Standards should suffice, even if electric-strip heating (the most costly of all means) is used.

- *Mild winters and summers,* where the air-conditioning heating and cooling loads will be low as in parts of Florida and California plus certain favored areas in the West and Southwestern States and along the Gulf Coast.

Insulation to FHA Minimum Property Standards along with care to reduce air infiltration should suffice. If electric-strip heating is to be used, the energy-efficiency level should be raised by installing double-glazed windows and metal outer doors.

- *Moderate winters and summers*, such as experienced in the majority of the 48 States (excluding Hawaii and Alaska).

Increased insulation (R15+ walls and R30 ceilings) should be used, with metal outer doors, double-glazed windows and extreme care to reduce air infiltration to an absolute minimum. An insulated foundation is also recommended. If gas is not available and oil heating is not desired, a heat pump is highly recommended. If electric-strip heating must be used, treat house as for severe winter and/or summer conditions.

- *Severe winters and/or summers*, where the air-conditioning load for either heating or cooling can be high and for long periods. Such conditions will be found in Alaska and in the East, Northeast, North and Northwest areas plus some of the very hot parts of the desert States.

Maximum insulation (R20 walls and R40 ceilings) should be used, with metal outer doors, double-glazed windows and even triple-glazed windows, heavily insulated foundation (or floors) and with extreme care taken to reduce air infiltration to a minimum. Electric-strip heating should be avoided. If the house must be all-electric, use of a heat pump is highly recommended.

To build a conventional house to the FHA Minimum Property Standards of insulation and air-infiltration prevention would add not more than five percent to the building cost over that related to a house built without insulation or with less than the FHA minimum (R11 in walls, R19 over ceilings).

To raise the energy-efficiency level of the house to that required for areas experiencing moderate winters and summers would add between three and five percent to the FHA Minimum Property Standards cost. For those areas experiencing very severe winters and/or hot summers, the extra cost might rise to a maximum of 10 percent greater than the FHA Minimum Property Standards figure.

For further information on energy-efficiency levels and extra building costs, refer to "Energy-Saver Home Examples," Section 9.

INTEREST ON INTEREST

The author's energy-saving home (detailed in Section 7) saved $401.28 per year on an extra cost of $2,000.00 for energy-saving materials and construction. This savings results in a payback period of about 5 years at today's energy costs. However, since energy costs are certain to rise, the real payback period will more likely be 3 or 4 years.

Looking at the savings another way — a savings of $401.28 (at 1979 electrical rates) on an outlay of $2,000.00 is the same as receiving a 20% interest return yearly on the extra outlay. Assuming a possible interest rate on the home loan of 9%, the net interest rate related to the energy savings would be 20-9=11%. And this return will be higher in 1979, even higher in 1980 and so on. After the payback period, the savings is total and will continue as long as the house exists.

For additional details, refer to "Extra Cost vs. Energy Savings," Section 8 and to "Energy-Saver Home Examples," Section 9.

Section 4

Heat Transfer - Air Infiltration

GENERAL

Basically, to efficiently heat and cool a house that house must be:

- properly insulated to resist the conductive flow of heat out of the house in the winter and the conductive flow of heat into the house in the summer.

- properly caulked and weatherstripped around window and door openings in the house envelope and around other cracks and openings in the house envelope to prevent drafts—into or out of the house.

The two great enemies of energy efficiency in a home as related to air conditioning are thus: (1) conductive heat transfer and (2) air infiltration (drafts).

HEAT TRANSFER

Heat travels (is transferred) from a warmer to a colder temperature level. To understand how heat transfer relates to home heating and cooling energy costs, we must first examine heat. Heat is living energy, the product of:

- *Combustion* — the burning of gas, coal, oil, wood, etc.
- *Resistance* — the flow of electrical current through a resistive material.
- *Radiation* — the sun's rays and certain rays emitted by an open fire. Radiation is converted to heat only when the rays striking an absorbent material which then gives off the absorbed heat.

Cold is not the opposite of heat—it is simply the reduction of heat within a substance (a material or air) from a higher to a lower temperature level. Heat, for example, exists down to absolute zero (–459.6°F).

To understand the role insulation and sun shading play in reduction of heat transfer into or out of a house, the principle of heat transfer must be understood. Heat is transferred in three ways:

- *Conduction* — by being passed from one molecule to the next of a material or air. The denser the material, the more tightly packed the molecules and thus the easier (faster) heat can travel through the subject material.

  Thus, heat travels faster through metal than wood and faster through wood than air. In fact, non-moving (dead) air is an excellent insulator and is, actually, the basic principle of all highly-efficient insulation material.

- *Convection* — heated air expands, tends to rise and, in so doing, sets up an air current that distributes the warmer air throughout the room (such as warm air rising for a radiator or register, for example).

- *Radiation* — heat is also transferred by wave motion, in the same manner the sun's rays stream down to earth at the speed of light. The heat rays (either from the sun or any other heat source) are turned to actual heat only when the radiation strikes an absorbent material. An example of radiant heat is that felt when one stands in front of a fireplace or a sun-lit window.

Heat transfer into and out of a house through the house envelope is largely by conduction. Heat transfer by conduction can never be entirely eliminated but the rate at which heat passes through a material can be greatly reduced if the material is made up of widely-spaced molecules. An excellent insulation material is one containing a large number of small air pockets for a given thickness of material. An insulating material is said to "exhibit a *resistance* to the transfer of heat," thus all such material is rated by its heat-flow *resistance* (R) factor.

Heat transfer by radiation relates mainly to the sun's rays passing through the windows. This radiant heat can be of use in the winter but will appear as a load on the cooling system in the summer. If the radiant heat is desired as a part of the winter heating, radiant heat is considered as a winter-time gain. In areas having warm to hot summers, radiant heat will appear as a summer-time load on the cooling system and must thus be kept out of the house.

AIR INFILTRATION

Air infiltration is simple to understand and easy to correct, being nothing more or less than drafts. That is, air flowing into or out of the house through holes, gaps, cracks, etc. in the building envelope and around the windows and outer doors. *Only recently* has the *extreme effect drafts* have on the heating and cooling loads of a house been recognized. With careful attention, drafts can be almost entirely eliminated.

Drafts were (and still are) too often considered necessary in that it was felt that the air within a house should change "at least twice per hour if the air is to be clean and non-odorous." However, a little thought will reveal that it is most wasteful to expensively heat or cool air inside a house and then let it escape. Recent tests have demonstrated that an air change every two hours is sufficient except under exceptional conditions such as unusually high levels of smoke or cooking odors, etc. The new thinking is:

- Make the house as tight as possible, without any real concern that the house may be "too tight." If the resulting air change within the house is not sufficient for unusual conditions, a window can be opened as needed.

- If cooking odors or tobacco smoke are a problem, an air filter (electronic) is recommended.

- The very large volume of air needed by a gas-fired hot-water heater, a fireplace, or a furnace (gas or oil type) has, in the past, been drawn from within the house. This is a most inefficient means of obtaining combustion air since it results in expensively conditioned air being pulled from every part of the house to be sent wastefully up the flue or chimney.

- New thinking now states that combustion air for any fuel-fired unit installed inside the living area must be supplied from outside the living area. This means that the conditioned air within the house will not be drawn out through the flue or chimney and wasted.

Reduction or elimination of drafts is inexpensive as to material and labor, easy to do and results in excellent energy savings as related to the heating and cooling loads of a home.

For additional details on the importance of eliminating or reducing drafts, see Section 14, Air Infiltration.

SUMMARY

Basically, it's all very simple. The energy efficiency level of a house is determined by it's ability to reduce to a practical minimum heat flow out of the house envelope in the winter and heat flow into the house envelope in the summer. Secondly, the energy efficiency level of a house envelope is determined by it's ability to reduce to a practical minimum the flow of air into or out of the house. Let us consider a house envelope insulated to recommended level and having a very low air infiltration (draft) rate. Assume the house envelope is empty of occupants and that no appliances or lights are turned on. Clearly, the heating and cooling system will have to counter only the very low flow of heat out of the house in the winter and into the house in the summer. An absolute minimum use of energy is thus predictable and can be realized. Now, let us open a window slightly in each of two outside walls, simulating a draft. Now, some of the heated or cooled air within the house envelope will flow out the windows to be replaced by outside air that must be either heated (winter time) or cooled (summer time). The net result is an almost constant need for the heating or cooling system to counter a steady loss of conditioned air with a drop in energy efficiency in almost direct proportion to the volume of the air flow. In a drafty (leaky) house, the effect is the same with the windows closed.

The insulation in the walls, ceiling and floor of a drafty house will hold the thermal (heat) flow to the designed minimum but cannot counter the loss of conditioned air due to the drafts. Thus, a house to be truly energy efficient must be both well insulated and as draft free as possible.

Section 5

Insulation and Vapor Barriers

INSULATION REVIEW

Recent studies made by government agencies and private firms have shown quite clearly that the role of insulation in the construction of energy-saver homes has been overstressed and even oversold. In general, insulation manufacturers, energy experts, consultants and building contractors regard insulation as the top energy saver in home construction. Which it is up to a point — this point being where the energy dollars saved by adding "extra" insulation does not warrant the extra cost. Of course, insulation plays a very vital role in making a home an energy saver. A house without insulation can never be made energy efficient no matter what other energy-saver materials and features might be built into it. But, insulation is not the whole picture. The emphasis on insulation in the past years has reached a high point today. This emphasis has caused many home builders and those buying a new home or retrofitting an existing home to overspend on insulation and thus to "skimp" on other energy-saving features that must be incorporated into a house if it is to be a true energy saver. The emphasis on "over" insulating is not really justifiable on either a dollar or energy-saving basis.

Here are some comments related to studies made by the government and others:

Chemical Week, Feb. 8, 1978 Issue: 'A new five-year study by the Dept. of Energy and the National Science Foundation may well deflate the booming home-insulation business. "The study of air infiltration in urban buildings", says a DOE official, "indicates that 'insulation is not what it's cracked up to be'." The study revealed that cracks and holes in the wall sheathing and improper house design, for example, are much more important factors in loss of heat and energy in buildings than lack of adequate insulation. The study also indicated that adding insulation (above the recommended R value for the climatic area) is not particularly effective in decreasing cold air flow."

Air Conditioning, Heating and Refrigeration News, March 6, 1978 Issue: 'A recent study of home heating dynamics indicates the current faith in insulation may be based on erroneous assumptions, and the home owners pouring money into the burgeoning insulation industry won't see the savings they are promised' according to Dr. Jay McGrew, president of Applied Science and Engineering.'

...The study for a house with three inches of attic insulation, heat losses were as follows:

Windows	17%
Ceiling	11%
Walls	6%
Infiltration	66%

For an uninsulated house, the heat losses were as follows:"

Windows	15%
Ceiling	23%
Walls	5%
Infiltration	57%

The overemphasis, the oversell of insulation relates to the projected thought "if six inches of insulation will save X dollars, won't 12 inches save 2X dollars?". That is, if six inches of attic insulation will save 80% of the heat lost through the ceiling, wouldn't 12 inches save it all? One would then just have to increase wall, ceiling and floor insulation to the "100% saved" point and do likewise with the outer doors and windows to construct a house that will not lose or gain heat. Most obviously, an impossibility. The ability of an insulating material to resist the flow of heat (known as resistance or R) is directly related to it's thickness. But, the first inch of insulation has a greater effect on the reduction of heat flow than the next inch does, and the third inch has less again than the second. This is because the molecular flow is in direct relation to the temperature difference across the insulating material. Consider a six-inch thick piece of insulation with a high R value and a temperature differential across the material as illustrated below:

Inches Thick   1" 2" 3" 4" 5" 6"

Vapor barrier →

6"-thick insulation batt — seen on edge ←

Temperature   70° 65° 60° 55° 50° 45° 40°

The above is not entirely correct since the temperature drop across the insulation does not occur in a straight mathematical ratio as shown but the sketch does reveal why doubling the thickness of a given insulating material does not double the actual insulating value. For example, a 3″ batt of insulation (as we shall see) can have an R-11 value while a 6″ piece of the same material has only an R-19 value and not an R-22 value.

Most seriously, the point of maximum dollars-saved for dollars-spent is reached when the recommended R value for a given climatic area is installed. The various studies reveal that "extra" insulation should not be installed above the recommended value for the house area. In actual fact, if money is scarce for energy-saving features, each dollar spent on air infiltration will return a larger savings than if it had been spent on "extra" insulation above that recommended. For further details on the effect of air infiltration on energy saving in the home, refer to Air Infiltration, Section 14.

Of course, insulation must be used — installed to recommended R values — if a house is to realize a worthwhile level of energy savings. All the above simply states "don't over insulate and expect miracles".

INSULATION — WHY IT WORKS

Heat Flow. Heat flows through any material (air, wood, stone, etc.) on a molecular basis, always traveling from the warmer to the cooler side. A temperature difference must exist across a material for a flow of heat to occur. If a temperature difference does not exist, no heat flow can occur. The heat-flow rate through a particular material is always in direct proportion to the temperature difference across the material and in somewhat direct proportion to the thickness of the material. If a material is a "good" insulator, little heat will flow — if it is a "bad" insulator, a larger heat flow will occur under the same temperature-thickness conditions. Heat flow is measured in British Thermal Units (BTUs). A value of one BTU defines the amount of heat (energy) required to raise one pound of water by one degree Fahrenheit (F). Since heat is a product of expended energy, the BTU value (figure) thus expresses an energy-used measurement. For example, one kilowatt (KW) of electricity contains enough energy to develop 3,412 BTUs of heat. A value of one BTU per hour is termed one BTUH, with the "H" signifying per hour.

Insulation Value. The ability of a given material to resist the flow of heat through it is expressed as its resistance (R) value. The insulation efficiency of a given material is specified by its R rating. By virtue of its ability to resist the flow of heat, any material that has a marked ability to restrict the flow of heat is said to "insulate". The walls of a well-insulated house, for example, act to "insulate" the interior from the climatic changes of the exterior.

Since a temperature difference must exist across a given material if a flow of energy (heat) is to occur, the R value of a material thus actually states the constant temperature difference that must exist across the material for a flow of one BTU to occur through each square foot of the material. The R value for commonly-used building materials are given by Table 5-1 and have been established by precise tests made by the manufacturer and others. The test temperature is usually taken to be 75°F. As an R example, Table 5-1 gives an R1.25 value for a 1-inch thick board of softwood (fir or pine). The R value actually states:

- If the temperature on one side of the board is 75°F and on the other side is higher or lower by 1.25°F, a heat flow to the value of 1 BTU will occur through each square foot of the board as long as the temperature difference remains.

As another example, consider a well-insulated wall having an R value of R20. This R value specifies that a temperature difference of 20°F must exist across the wall for a flow of 1 BTU to occur through each square foot of wall. Note that the higher the R value, the higher (the better) the insulation efficiency of the material. Also note that if the temperature difference across the material is doubled, the heat flow (BTU flow) is doubled. Of course, if the temperature difference is halved, the heat-flow rate is also halved. Further, all materials having the same R value, regardless of composition, are equal in their insulation value per inch of thickness.

WHERE TO INSULATE

Insulation can be thought of as an energy-saving "blanket" that is wrapped around a house to reduce heat loss or gain to an acceptable value. The blanket must be complete, without any gaps or holes, if true energy saving is to be gained. The "holes" in the blanket related to window and door openings must be "closed" by installation of insulating windows and doors. A house having many walls and ceilings to insulate is illustrated by Figure 5-1.

RECOMMENDED INSULATION VALUES

When building a new home, if an Federal Housing Admininistration (FHA) or Federal Farm Housing Administration (FMHA) loan is to be obtained, the house must be insulated to the standards set up by the related agencies for the climatic conditions of the house area. These will be known by your building contractor. Here are some examples:

- FHA — Ceilings (i.e. attic floors)   = R22
  for areas with less than 8000
  degree days total #   = R19
  Exterior walls —   = R13
  for areas with less than
  8000 degree days total   = R11
  Floors over unheated   = R11
  basement or unsealed
  crawl space
  # For degree days details, see Section 6

Table 5-1. R Values - Building Materials

Wood bevel siding, 1/2 x 8, lapped	R-0.81
Wood siding shingles, 16", 7½" exposure	R-0.87
Asbestos-cement shingles	R-0.03
Stucco, per inch	R-0.20
Building paper	R-0.06
1/2" nail-base insul. board sheathing	R-1.14
1/2" insul. board sheathing, regular density	R-1.32
25/32" insul. board sheathing, regular density	R-2.04
1/4" plywood	R-0.31
3/8" plywood	R-0.47
1/2" plywood	R-0.62
5/8" plywood	R-0.78
1/4" hardboard	R-0.18
Softwood, per inch	R-1.25
Softwood board, 3/4" thick	R-0.94

Concrete blocks, three oval cores

Cinder aggregate, 4" thick	R-1.11
Cinder aggregate, 12" thick	R-1.89
Cinder aggregate, 8" thick	R-1.72
Sand and gravel aggregate, 8" thick	R-1.11
Lightweight aggregate (expanded clay, shale, slag, pumice, etc.), 8" thick	R-2.00

Concrete blocks, two rectangular cores

Sand and gravel aggregate, 8" thick	R-1.04
Lightweight aggregate, 8" thick	R-2.18

Common brick, per inch	R-0.20
Face brick, per inch	R-0.11
Sand-and-gravel concrete, per inch	R-0.08
Sand-and-gravel concrete, 8 inches thick	R-0.64
1/2" gypsumboard	R-0.45
5/8" gypsumboard	R-0.56
1/2" lightweight-aggregate gypsum plaster	R-0.32
25/32" hardwood finish flooring	R-0.68
Asphalt, linoleum, vinyl, or rubber floor tile	R-0.05
Carpet and fibrous pad	R-2.08
Carpet and foam rubber pad	R-1.23
Asphalt roof shingles	R-0.44
Wood roof shingles	R-0.94
3/8" built-up roof	R-0.33

Glass

Single glass (winter)	U = 1.13
Single glass (summer)	U = 1.06
Insulating glass (double)	
1/4" air space (winter)	U = 0.65
1/4" air space (summer)	U = 0.61
1/2" air space (winter)	U = 0.58
1/2" air space (summer)	U = 0.56
Storm windows	
1" to 4" air space (winter)	U = 0.56
1" to 4" air space (summer)	U = 0.54

Insulation

2" – 2½" thick	R-7.00
3" – 4" thick	R-11.00
5" – 7" thick	R-19.00

Air Spaces (3/4")

Heat flow UP	
Non-reflective	R-0.87
Reflective, one surface	R-2.23
Heat flow DOWN	
Non-reflective	R-1.02
Reflective, one surface	R-3.55
Heat flow HORIZONTAL	
Non-reflective (also same for 4" thickness)	R-1.01
Reflective, one surface	R-3.48

Note: The addition of a second reflective surface facing the first reflective surface increases thermal resistance values of an air space only 4 to 7 per cent.

Surface Air Films

INSIDE (still air)	
Heat flow UP (through horizontal surface)	
Non-reflective	R-0.61
Reflective	R-1.32
Heat flow DOWN (through horizontal surface)	
Non-reflective	R-0.92
Reflective	R-4.55
Heat flow HORIZONTAL (through vertical surface)	
Non-reflective	R-0.68
OUTSIDE	
Heat flow any direction, surface any position	
15 mph wind (winter)	R-0.17
7.5 mph wind (summer)	R-0.25

Example calculations
(to determine the U value of an exterior wall)

Wall Construction	Uninsulated Wall Resistance	Insulated Wall Resistance
Outside surface (film), 15 mph wind	0.17	0.17
Wood bevel siding, lapped	0.81	0.81
½" ins. bd. sheathing, reg. density	1.32	1.32
3½" air space	1.01	
R-11 insulation		11.00
½" gypsumboard	0.45	0.45
Inside surface (film)	0.68	0.68
Totals	4.44	14.43

For uninsulated wall, $U = \frac{1}{R} = \frac{1}{4.44} = U = 0.22$

Therefore, heat loss for the above uninsulated wall section at a +10° F. outside design temperature is equal to 0.22 x 60 (or 70-10) equals 13.2 Btuh per sq. ft. of wall section.

For insulated wall, $U = \frac{1}{R} = \frac{1}{14.43} = U = 0.07$

Therefore, heat loss for the above insulated wall section at a + 10° F. outside design temperature is equal to 0.07 x 60 (or 70-10) equals 4.2 Btuh per sq. ft. of wall section.

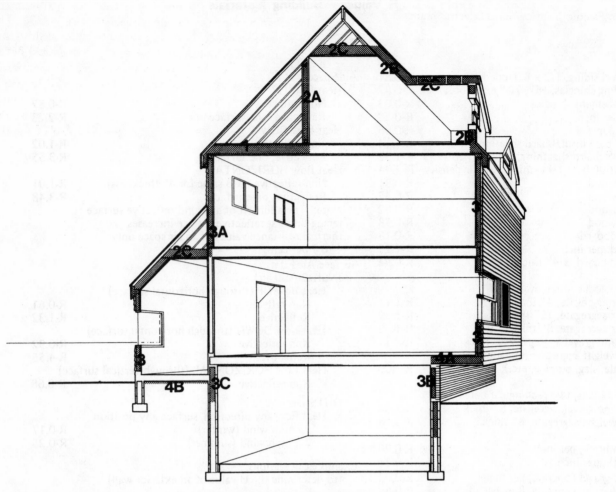

1. In unfinished attic spaces insulate between the floor joists to seal off living spaces below.[1]

2. In finished attic rooms with or without dormers, insulate . . .
   2A   between the studs of "knee" walls;
   2B   between the studs and rafters of exterior walls;
   2C   ceilings with cold spaces above.

3. All exterior walls, including . . .
   3A   walls between living spaces and unheated garages or storage areas;
   3B   foundation walls above ground level;
   3C   foundation walls in heated basements. These need only be insulated to 2 feet below ground level. (In certain extremely cold climates of northern Maine, Minnesota, and Alaska, specialists should be consulted for foundation wall insulation.)

4. Floors above cold spaces, such as vented crawl spaces and unheated garages. Also insulate . . .
   4A   any portion of the floor in a room that is cantilevered beyond the exterior wall below;
   4B   slab floors built directly on the ground.[2]

---

1 Well-insulated attics, crawl spaces, storage areas, and other closed cavities should be well-ventilated to prevent excessive moisture build-up.

2 Slabs on grade are almost always insulated, in accordance with building codes, when the house is constructed.

Figure 5-1. Where to Insulate

- Edison Electric Institute (for all-electric homes):

Ceilings	= R30
for areas with less than	
3500 degree days total	= R19
Exterior walls	= R11
Floors over unheated basement or sealed crawl space	= R11

Figure 5-2 gives the heating zones of the country and recommended insulation levels. Except for those areas where summer-time cooling is the sole problem, the indicated heating values hold equally well for cooling. That is, the temperature spread between the indoor and outdoor temperatures during the winter is almost always much wider than that which occurs during the summer. As an example, with the indoor temperature held to 68°F, if the outdoor temperatue drops to 30°F, a 38°F spread results. In the summer, with the indoor temperature held to 75°F, if the outdoor temperature rises to 95°F, a spread of only 20°F occurs.

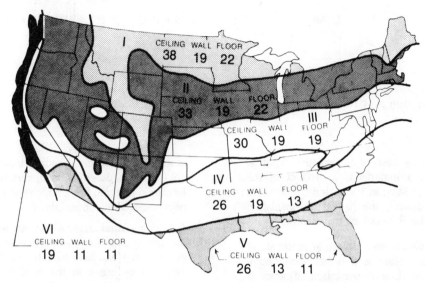

Figure 5-2. Recommended Insulation Values

DOLLARS SAVED BY INSULATION

The energy saved (and thus the dollar saved) by insulating a house to the recommended insulation level can be calculated rather accurately on a heat loss (winter-time) and heat gain (summer-time) basis. The effect of a complete blanket of insulation around, under and above the living area can be calculated on an energy-saved and dollar-saved basis. For complete details on heat gain or loss calculations, refer to "BTU Calculation Example", Section 6, page 6-1.

The energy and dollar savings that can be gained by insulating a house to various levels of energy-use efficiency are graphically illustrated by Table 5-2. The calculation (estimates) of KWH used and the savings gained are based upon the 1972 ASHRAE Book of Fundamentals and the following conditions:

15°F outdoor temperature	4,792 degree days, heating
70°F indoor temperature	Portland, Oregon area
1260 sq. ft. house built over a crawl space	200 sq. ft. windows & doors
Electric heating used — not a heat pump	

For additional details on energy and dollars saved by energy-saving home construction, refer to Section 7, Dollar Benefits of Energy-Saving Construction.

INSULATION MATERIAL

Insulation for building construction is made from many materials and in many manufactured forms. In fact, so many types of insulation of various basic materials and insulation (R) values are available that a person can easily become confused. The following is an attempt to clarify the insulation picture.

Most commonly-used building insulation falls into one of the following categories as to manufactured form.

1. Batts or Rolls
2. Loose-Fill or Blown-in
3. Foamed-In
4. Rigid-Foam

Before detailing the major types of insulation currently available, certain facts on insulation should be discussed. This information will make the insulation facts to follow more meaningful.

Table 5-2. Dollar Savings vs. Added Insulation

House Construction	KWH Used	Estimated Annual Cost			Total Saved*
		3¢ KWH	4¢ KWH	5¢ KWH	
No insulation	40,381	$1121.43	$1615.24	$2019.05	
R-19 ceiling	23,840	$ 715.20	$ 953.60	$1192.00	$ 661.64
R-19 ceiling R-11 walls	19,977	$ 599.31	$ 799.08	$ 998.85	$ 816.16
R-19 ceiling R-11 walls R-9 floors	14,263	$ 427.89	$ 570.52	$ 713.15	$1044.72
R-19 ceiling R-11 walls R9 floors Storm doors Storm windows	11,848	$ 355.44	$ 473.92	$ 592.40	$1141.32

*Total saved with a 4¢ KWH rate = 28,533 KWs x .04 = $1.141.32

- Entrapped (dead) air is the basis of all insulation. That is, the insulation value of a material is a product of the number of air pockets existing in the material. The more and smaller the air pockets, the higher the insulation efficiency (the higher the R value) of the material.

- Except for rigid-foam panels and foamed-in material, all insulation is "fluffy" in nature and rather easily compressed. When compressed, some insulation efficiency is lost since compression will reduce the number of air pockets. Insulation should thus not be compressed. When loose-fill or blown-in insulation is used in thicknesses of 10" or higher, some compression will occur simply by weight of the insulation material. This can be compensated for by adding an extra inch or two of the insulation material.

- Most insulation can absorb and hold water. Water (in the form of water vapor) will act to fill the air pockets in the insulation, with this acting to greatly reduce the insulation efficiency of the material. For water-absorbable insulation materials, a vapor barrier must be provided if the house is in an area where the January temperature drops below 45°F for even a short period. For full details on vapor barriers, refer to "Vapor-Barriers, page 5-9.

- To be totally effective, any area being insulated must be covered completely with the insulation. No holes, gaps or breaks in the insulation coverage (however small) should be allowed. If batts or roll insulation (to be discussed) is used, the ends must butt into each other. If installed between wood framing (wall studs or ceiling floor joists), the insulation must fit tightly against the wood framing. If batt or roll material is laid between the ceiling joists, each piece must fit tightly against the other. Small areas around window and door framing (regardless of how small the area) must be stuffed with insulation (try to avoid compression) or the small areas might be filled with a foamed-in material (to be discussed). If blown-in or loose-fill material (to be discussed) is used, care must be taken that the insulation material fills all openings and voids to the thickness required to obtain the desired R value.

- Any uninsulated area within an insulated area can be thought of as a hole that permits heat to escape outdoors in the winter and heat to enter the house in the summer. Any gap or break in the insulation "blanket" will thus materially reduce the insulation efficiency of the insulated area.

- Some insulation is provided with an aluminized-foil facing. This facing acts to reflect radiant energy, helping to prevent the entry of radiant energy into the house. The net result is an increase in the total insulation efficiency of the insulation material. However, the foil-face must not be less than ¾" from any other material (a ¾" air space must be maintained) for this benefit to be gained.

- Insulation should not be measured in "inches-of-thickness". Instead, it must be measured by R value. That is, to insulate an attic to an R22 value, the following can be used:

  6" batt-roll of rock wool   10" loose-pour glass fiber
  6½" batt-roll of glass fiber   7½" loose-pour rock wool
  6" loose-pour cellulosic fiber

- For blown-in material, the R value can only be established from the number of bags of insulation material used. That is, each bag *must* have a table specifying how many square feet can be covered per bag to achieve various R values. The number of square feet to be covered is thus divided by the number of bags required to cover that area to the desired R value. A bag count plus or minus 5 of the calculated value is considered acceptable. Regretfully, it would be best to personally see each counted bag opened and used. The R value for loose-pour material is also given in table form on each bag on an "inch-thickness" basis.

- For foamed-in material, the R value must be established on a "wet-weight" basis. That is, the insulation foam can be pumped in at various densities, with the R value being directly related to this density (weight). The test method is: a small amount of foam is pumped onto a board and allowed to set to a cutable density. A particular-size cube of the material is then cut out and weighed. If the weight does not equal that needed for the desired R value, the foam-mixture rate is varied and the test repeated until the proper foam weight is obtained. This test is very important as it will determine the overall insulation efficiency of the wall. Ask the applicator for the table giving the weight-to-R value relationship of the foam being used and personally supervise the cube test.

- Batt, roll or rigid-foam panels provided with a vapor barrier must not be used to cover any other vapor barrier. If vapor-barrier provided insulation, batts or rolls, must be used over another vapor barrier, the vapor-barrier covering on the added insulation must be slashed to a fair degree to make the covering ineffective. If this is not done, moisture can collect in the insulation between the two vapor barriers since an exit is not provided. For rigid-foam panels, manufacturer-supplied vents must be installed at the top of each panel. Literature on the proper method to use is provided by each manufacturer. For additional information, refer to "Vapor Barriers", Page 5-9.

Full details on the four major types of building insulation are as follows:

Table 5-3
R-Values for Various Thickness of Insulation

	Batts Or		Loose-Fill Poured In			
	Glass Fiber	Rock Wool	Glass Fiber	Rock Wool	Cellulosic Fiber	
R11	3½ - 4"	3"	5"	4"	3"	R11
R13	4"	4½"	6"	4½"	3½"	R13
R19	6" - 6½"	5¼"	8 - 9"	6 - 7"	5"	R19
R22	6½"	6"	10"	7 - 8"	6"	R22
R26	8"	8½"	12"	9"	7 - 7½"	R26
R30	9¼ - 10½"	9"	13 - 14"	10 - 11"	8"	R30
R33	11"	10"	15"	11 - 12"	9"	R33
R38	12 - 13"	10½"	17 - 18"	13 - 14"	10 - 11"	R38

Blown-In = by bag count per R-table on bag

Foamed-In = by test cube weight per manufacturer's specifications.

BATTS (4' OR 8' LONG) AND ROLLS (UP TO 57' LONG

- made in 15" and 23" widths - and in thickness from 1" to 9¼", in ½" steps.

- for use between wall studs and ceiling or floor joists. Made in two installation types: Pressure-Fit, fits between stud pairs or joist pairs to achieve a pressure-tight fit—Stapled-Fit, has a paper flange that permits stapling to the stud or joist pairs.

- Insulation material may be either glass fiber (R3.17 per inch) or rock wool (R3.67 per inch). Material is both fire and vermin proof and has a low settling factor. Can absorb water thus a vapor barrier is needed. Can be obtained in following types:

Kraft-Faced - provides own vapor barrier—if used over another vapor barrier, second vapor barrier must be slashed.

Foil-Faced - same as Kraft-faced except has a heat-reflector facing.

Un-Faced - needs vapor barrier—can be used over other vapor-barrier type insulation but must then not have its own vapor barrier.

Reinsul - same as Un-Faced.

- Benefits: Manufactured as a unit, relatively easy to cut and install (dependent upon easy access to area). Made to rigid specifications and R value will always be the same for each bundle. This eliminates the R-value "guesswork" commonly found with blown-in or foamed-in material. No shrinkage problem as encountered with foamed-in insulation.

- Can be stacked to achieve desired R value—two-layer stacking being maximum. In two-layer installation, first layer must be vapor-barrier type and be installed with vapor barrier towards living area. Second layer must lay crosswise over the first layer (this to reduce volume compression and attendant loss of insulation efficiency).

- Problems: Can be hard to install in areas difficult of access—must be fitted under pipes and wiring, etc. Hard to fit into small gaps (1" or 2" wide). Takes more time to install in an attic, for example, than to have the equivalent R-value blown-in or covered with loose-fill. (For a 1500 square-foot attic: up to 8 man hours for batts or rolls, 4 hours or less for loose-fill, and about 1½ hours for blown-in. These figures are based on 6" thickness of material).

- For installation details, refer to page 23-5.

LOOSE-FILL INSULATION

- insulation material specially made to be poured into area between ceiling joists — can be poured into wall cavities between stud pairs if cavities are readily accessible (sheet rock and outer sheathing must be installed).

- material contained in bags, of a size and weight permitting easy handling. R-value measured in inches per R-value printed on bags. Made to rigid specifications to ensure reliable R value. Needs vapor barrier.

- material used includes:

    rock wool, about R2.8 per inch
    glass fiber, about R2.2 per inch
    cellulosic fiber, about R3.7 per inch
    vermiculite, about R2.7 per inch
    perlite, about R2.7 per inch

- rock wool and glass fiber are fire and vermin proof. All materials need vapor barrier.

- vermiculite and perlite are more expensive but can be poured into smaller areas.

- cellulosic fibers must be treated to be fire-retardant and vermin-proof. Treatment is now under study—it may eventually reduce R value in time and may be corrosive to metal. Material must meet Federal Specifications as clearly labeled on bags. Deal only with a known and reputable dealer and/or installer.

- Benefits: Easy to install and rapidly pours into small areas. Pour between ceiling joists and level with a board or rake. See Table 5-2 for R-values versus insulation thickness. R-value is same on a bag-by-bag basis.

- Problems: Rock wool, glass fiber and cellulosic fiber materials will compress slightly with time, especially if poured in thicknesses of 10" or more. This can be compensated for by adding an extra inch. Takes more time to install than blown-in but only about half the time required for batts or rolls.

- For installation details, refer to page 23-7.

BLOWN-IN INSULATION

- insulation material specially made to be blown in between ceiling joists, under finished attic floor, between finished frame wall and under finished floors (bottom of floor joists must be covered).

- material contained in bags—R-value measured in square-feet covered to a specific thickness—details must be printed on each bag in table form. Made to rigid specifications as to resultant R value if blown in as detailed by R-value table on bag.

- material used includes: rock wool - glass fiber - cellulosic fiber

- all materials have same physical properties as detailed for poured-in loose fill materials. All materials need vapor barrier.

- Benefits: very easy to install in readily accessible areas, such as an unfinished attic floor (1500 square-foot attic can be completed in as little as 1½ hours, dependent on ease of access—6" thickness). Somewhat more difficult to blow into walls and under flooring.

- Problems: Same as detailed for poured-in loose fill materials. (See figure 23-3 for installation details.)

- For installation details, refer to page 23-12.

FOAMED-IN INSULATION

- insulation material specially made to be pumped in between ceiling joists or between stud pairs of a finished or unfinished wall.

- material pumped in as a foam—R-value measured on a 4-inch cube weight ratio—details supplied by manufacturer. For a standard 4" exterior wall (actual cavity depth equals 3½"), R-values are as follows:

    4" cube weight = 30-35 grams – R-value = R11 total
                  = 50 grams – R-value = R18 total

Another manufacturer states an R factor of 5.0 at a standard density of 0.7 lbs./cu.ft. This would result in an R17.5 for a 3½" - deep wall cavity.

material is urea formaldehyde resin, treated under air pressure with a foaming agent to produce a foamy liquid. Hardens (sets) within 10 to 60 seconds after leaving applicator gun. Material is fireproof up to a temperature of 1208°F. Should not be exposed to temperatures in excess of 210°F for prolong periods.

- Benefits: can be pumped into finished wall cavity and flows around piping and wiring within cavity. Can be pumped into wall cavity if finished only on one side—material may need smoothing with a trowel before material sets.

- Problems: More expensive than blown-in materials but has higher insulation value per inch of thickness. Quality of application largely dependent upon expertise of contractor—choose a contractor who will gaurantee his work—ask for references. Difficult to pump fully into wall cavities that have obstructions. If fire blocking is used in wall cavities (2x4 pieces nailed across between stud pairs about halfway up wall), foam must be pumped in from top and bottom of wall. (See figure 23-3 for installation details.)

- For installation details, refer to page 23-12.

RIGID-FOAM BOARDS

- insulation boards, intended to replace gypsum (sheet rock) or fibre-board sheathing while increasing insulation value of wall can also be used to raise insulation value of ceiling. Also used to insulate concrete-slab foundation and crawl-space foundation walls.

- material in moulded-board form, in 24" and 48" widths, customarily in 8' lengths minimum, and a variety of thicknesses from ½" to 4".

- Material used includes:

    extruded polystyrene beads   glass fibers
    polystyrene foam   urethane

- polystyrene foam and urethane are vapor-barrier types as is; bead board and glass-fiber board require vapor barriers.

- Commonly used types are: (See figure 11-1 for installation details.)

    Styrofoam TG - R5.41 per inch at 40°F Mean Temp. and about R5.0 at 70°F. 2 x 8 foot sheets (boards), tongue-and-groove design to achieve tight fit.

    Available in ¾" (R4.06), 1" (R5.41) and 1½" (R8.12) thicknesses.

    Will burn - must be covered with ½" gypsum board or equivalent. Can be used over other vapor barrier.

- High R   — R8 per inch at 40°F Mean Temp. Covered on both sides with foil. Maximum thickness = 2 inches.

TF-400 - R8.0 per inch at 40°F Mean Temp. — covered on both sides with reflective foil which adds to total insulation value if installed over a ¾" or better air space.

Available in 4 x 8 foot sheets, in following thicknesses:

3/8", 1/2", 5/8" 3/4", 7/8", 1", 1-1/8", 1-3/8", 1-5/8" and 1-7/8", with an average R value of R1.0 per 1/8."

Will burn - must be covered with 1/2" gypsum board or equivalent. Must not be subjected to temperatures in excess of 210°F for prolonged periods. Must be ventilated if used over other vapor barrier—use manufacturer-provided ventilation strips.

• For installation details, refer to page 23-14.

Insulation Material Summary. Practical experience tends to suggest the use of batts (or roll) material for insulating a house during the construction phase. The batt (and roll) material is less likely to settle and generally permits easier access into the attic. It is almost universally used in walls and under floors. Installation cost is moderately higher than for loose-fill, blown-in or foam. For upgrading an existing home, batt (or roll) material is most often used in easily-accessible ceilings and under flooring (a special type is manufactured for floors). On an upgrading basis, cannot be fitted into walls unless wall cavities are opened (by removal of inner or outer sheathing).

Loose-fill poured in or blown in is most often used to insulate ceilings of homes under construction if batt (or roll) material is not used. Insulation value can be higher than for equivalent thickness in batt or roll material. It has the added advantage that material easily fits into small areas. It is often used over R19 of batt or roll material to raise ceiling R value to R26 plus. Blown-in is seldom used to fill wall cavities or used under flooring either on a new house or upgrading basis—foam is now being widely used to upgrade the insulation value of walls in existing homes. Loose-fill poured or blown in has a tendency to settle with age, with some attendant loss of insulation value.

Foamed-in insulation is mainly used to upgrade the energy efficiency of walls in existing homes. Can be used to cover ceiling and can be foamed into open cavities of a wall, requiring minor smoothing before material sets. Foam insulation, in the form of a small bead (¼" to ½"), is now being used to permanently seal around door and window framing, to seal joints of outer sheathing, around water pipes and wiring that penetrates walls or flooring, etc. This to achieve a really "tight" house.

INSULATION COMPARISONS

The resistance (R) value for most commonly-used building materials are given by Table 5-1. The given values indicate how the insulation efficiency of various building materials vary widely; even fantastically so. Since concrete, stone, wood, and aluminum are widely used in home construction, a comparative study of their ability to restrict the flow of heat will be most informative. The comparison will be made against an R20 wall. The R values for the materials under discussion were taken from Table 5-1 and are as follows:

Soft pine or fir - per inch	R1.25
Concrete, sand or gravel base - per inch	R0.08
Brick, common - per inch (average figure)	R0.20
Stone - per inch (average figure)	R0.15
Aluminum - per inch	R0.0007

By dividing the R value given above individually into the R20 figure for the example wall, we can find how thick an R20 - wall would have to be if made entirely of wood, concrete, brick, etc.

Table 5-4
Building Material Comparisons

Type of Wall	R Ratio	Wall Thickness Inches	Feet
Wood wall	20/1.25	16"	= 1' 4"
Concrete wall	20/0.08	250"	= 20' 8"
Brick Wall*	20/0.20	100"	= 8' 3"
Stone Wall*	20/0.15	133"	= 11' 11"
Aluminum Wall	20/0.0007	28,571"	= 2,381' #

*Somewhat average value

#Not a mistake, an actual figure

Of course, it is not suggested that a wall be made up entirely of wood, brick or stone, and most certainly, not of aluminum. The study does show that the log cabin of old, heavy logs caulked with a mixture of hay and mud, was a rather well insulated dwelling place. But, consider aluminum siding, usually being not over 3/16" thick. Its insulation value (by itself) is almost zero and can be considered only as an attractive outer sheathing but never as wall insulation (regardless of what the ads in the newspapers say).

For information related to the heat loss or gain through walls constructed as detailed above, refer to Section 6, page 6-5.

VAPOR BARRIERS

General. The well-insulated, very "tight" energy-saver house can, under certain circumstances, suffer from either excessive or insufficient humidity. The old expression, "It's not the heat but the humidity that hurts," can be an accurate statement. If the relative humidity — the amount of water vapor in the air — is too high, the human body's thermal control mechanism, such as perspiration, do not function properly. Consequently, we suffer more from the heat. Conversely, if the level of humidity is too low, a directly opposite result affects the body. too much skin evaporation takes place which can cause one to feel chilled and the skin may dry and peel.

The relative humidity level inside a home can affect other than the occupants. Too much humidity can cause rust, mold or mildew of materials, swell wood so doors, windows and drawers stick, and cause moisture to condense on the windows in the winter. Too little humidity can cause materials to dry out, wood to shrink and crack and other materials to deteriorate.

Many tests have shown that a relative humidity of between 25% and 50% is acceptable to most people and will not have any adverse effect upon the house. Within a house temperature range of 70°F to 75°F, a humidity range of between 30-40% is considered ideal.

Humidity Sources. Humidity as developed within a house originates mainly in the kitchen and bathrooms with the house occupants contributing. Another source of humidity can be water vapor rising from the ground under the house which can, unless prevented, pass through the floor into the house.

Condensation. Humidity becomes a problem when it is trapped and turned into water by condensation. For a house, this can occur within the walls and in the attic when the outdoor temperature is below about 45°F and the humidity level within the house is 35°F or higher. Some of the problems related to humidity condensation into water are as follows:

- Paint failure on outer walls, caused by water vapor trying to pass through the paint. Other signs are: paint blisters, stained wood or actual wood rot.

- White powdery (salt) stains on brick veneer walls, brought about by leaching of salts in the bricks under the influence of water vapor passing through the bricks.

- Water stains on ceiling. During the winter, house humidity can pass through the ceiling into an unheated attic, there to condense and form into ice a little at a time. When the weather warms up, the ice melts with the resultant water soaking the ceiling covering (usually gypsum board).

- Water vapor can also condense in the wall cavity, soaking the insulation and dramatically lowering the insulation value. This will be noticed only as an increase in the heating bills.

These problems can be eliminated by proper use of ventilation alone, of a vapor barrier alone, or of a vapor barrier used in conjunction with ventilation.

Need For Vapor Barrier. In a very general sense, a vapor barrier is needed if:

- the house is in a climatic area where the outdoor temperature during January is below about 45°F for even short periods.

- the house is within Zone 1 or Zone 2 as illustrated by Figure 5-3.

    Zone 1 - install a vapor barrier if attic is insulated. If signs of condensation occur after one heating season, add ventilation area equal to 1:300 of attic-floor area.

    Zone 2 - If attic is insulated, a vapor barrier must be installed. If house is not air conditioned and signs of condensation occur after one heating season, add ventilation area equal to 1:300 of attic-floor area.

    If house is air conditioned and signs of condensation occur after one heating season, add ventilation area equal to 1:150 of attic-floor area.

- If any of the humidity problems detailed above under "Condensation" occur.

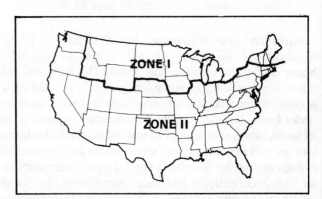

Figure 5-3. Vapor-Barrier Zoning

Agreed, the above "rules" are capable of various interpretation. In particular, the points that "ventilation should be added if condensation is noted" or a vapor barrier should be installed if any of the harmful problems detailed under "Condensation" are noted. This is sort of a "Close the barn door after the horse ran off" advice. One point should be made - a properly installed vapor barrier cannot cause any harm; lack of one can. Thus, if any doubt exists as to the need for a vapor barrier, it is much better to install one than not to. Local experience should be used as a guide line. For a home being built, it seems best that a vapor barrier should be planned on regardless of the house area.

Vapor Barrier Installation. A vapor barrier is defined as any material that reduces the flow of moisture to a rate of one perm or less. Such a material as—a polyethylene sheet (2-mil thick minimum), asphalt-coated paper or aluminum foil (such as found on insulation). Note that felt paper is not a vapor-barrier material.

The chosen vapor barrier material *must* be installed next to what is the warmest side of the house in the winter. For an insulated wall, for example, the vapor barrier must face the inside of the house and completely cover the entire insulated area. A second vapor barrier *must not* be installed past the insulation since this will act to partially defeat the purpose of the "true" vapor barrier. In fact, the insulation itself and any other material of the wall (outer sheathing, brick, stone, etc.) must be able to pass moisture at a rate of 5 perms or better. Note that if foil-covered insulation is used past the vapor barrier and other insulation (as when nailed on the outside of the studs), ventilation must be provided. For venting information, refer to manufacturer's literature.

Vapor barriers may be installed as follows:

- by using vapor-barrier-back insulation batt or roll material, either faced with kraft paper or foil. The insulation must be fitted between the wall stud-pairs or ceiling joist-pairs with the vapor barrier facing the living area. Care must be taken that the batt or roll material fits snugly to the wood framing. This also holds for underfloor installation.

- by nailing a continuous film of moderately heavy (4-mil minimum thickness) polyethylene film across the studs or joists before the sheet rock or other covering is installed. For walls, insulation must be installed first. For ceilings, insulation must be installed after the sheet rock or other ceiling covering is installed. For floors, film must be laid down on top of the floor joists after installation of the insulation if insulation is stapled. Alternately, insulation can be installed from underneath after the vapor barrier and flooring is laid down.

- In an existing house without insulation of any form between the ceiling joists (area is bare), the plastic film can be laid in strips between the joists before the insulation is installed (if non-vapor barrier type is to be used). Strips should be folded at the end seams and should lap up on the joists about 2 inches for stapling.

- In an existing house without ceiling insulation between the ceiling joists and where a vapor barrier would be difficult to install between the ceiling joists, paint of a low permeability (one perm or less) can be used to paint the ceiling material. Two coats are generally recommended and, if properly applied, this method provides an effective vapor barrier. This method may also be used for walls. Careful selection of paint is required to ensure an effective vapor barrier operation.

- The painted vapor barrier can also be used on insulated walls and ceilings that do not have a vapor barrier.

- Foil-back sheet rock (gypsum board) may also be used as a vapor barrier.

- For a concrete-slab foundation, a heavy (4 to 6 mil) plastic sheet must be laid down completely over the top fill before the floor is poured. For details, refer to Figure 10-1, Section 10.

- Crawl-space foundations are of two types: sealed and unsealed. For an unsealed foundation, natural air movement under the floor will tend to remove most of the moisture-ladened air. However, it is still recommended that a vapor barrier be laid down even if vapor-barrier insulation is installed under the floor. This vapor barrier, of heavy polyethylene film, is laid down on the ground to cover all the ground under the floor. The film must be folded at all seams to ensure a continuous film and brought up the foundation walls about 2 to 3 inches, being weighed down at the edges with sand or gravel, etc. Alternately, the seams may be overlapped by 6" and weighed down with sand, gravel, etc. at regular intervals.

- A vapor barrier MUST be laid down on the ground if a sealed crawl-space foundation is used. This is a positive requirement since a sealed crawl-space does not provide natural ventilation and a very high level of humidity can develop if a good vapor barrier is not laid down. This vapor barrier does *not* remove the need for a vapor barrier on top of the under-floor insulation. For details, refer to Figure 10-3, Section 10.

- If ground water is a problem under a sealed crawl-space foundation, a 2 to 3"-thick covering of concrete can be laid over the ground-cover vapor barrier. This flooring plus the concrete walls of the foundation can then be sprayed with a water sealant. This will ensure a very minimum movement of water vapor up from the ground into the sealed underfloor area. For details, refer to Figure 10-3, Section 10.

In all cases, regardless of the type of vapor barrier used, the barrier material must completely cover the insulated area and be without breaks, rips, holes, etc. If the barrier material is damaged in any way, the damage must be repaired. Aluminized tape is excellent for such repairs. If the barrier material must be joined at seams, the seams should either overlap about 6" or be folded to make a folded seam. Note that a folded seam must not land on a wall stud or a ceiling or floor joist since the thickened fold would prevent the sheet rock (walls and ceilings) or flooring material from laying flat.

A point to remember here is that any gap, even if very small, in the vapor barrier will have a detrimental effect entirely out of proportion to its size with relation to the entire barrier area. That is, the humidity will "travel" to the gap and move through into the insulation. On a long-term basis this can be enough to dampen the insulation such that a severe loss of insulation efficiency can occur.

EXCESSIVE HUMIDITY

The humidity level in a home should be checked at least once a week during any period the house is closed up and is being either heated or cooled. A humidity meter is usually used to determine the relative humidity of the house on a room by room basis. The small humidity meter generally used is not overly accurate but, unless damaged, will give a useable figure. Excessive humidity within a home almost always occurs during the period the house is being cooled. The air conditioner operates as a dehumidifier to a degree but it's effect is generally not sufficient to cope with a high level of household humidity.

Some "experts" recommend that a vapor barrier not be installed, particularly as regards to the ceiling. This, these experts state, will permit the water vapor to pass out of the house and thus will solve the water-vapor problem. This is entirely the wrong approach, of course, since the water vapor then soaks the ceiling insulation and lowers its insulation efficiency. The right approach is to produce less water vapor within the home by careful use of showers and by using area ventilation in the kitchen and bathrooms to remove water vapor as it is developed. In brief, the occupants should review their living habits to determine if they are producing water vapor on an unnecessary basis. If they are taking shorter showers, using area ventilation properly and are producing as little water vapor as possible in the kitchen.

If the above steps do not lower the humidity level to 50 percent or less, a dehumidifier may be needed. This unit is actually a small air conditioner in that the mechanism cools a pipe coil over which the house air is drawn. The water vapor in the air condenses on the coil and is drained off by a pipe running to the outside. The unit can be set to operate to hold the relative humidity level of the house to a desired figure (usually between 35-45%).

INSUFFICIENT HUMIDITY

The relative humidity level of a home can drop as low as 10 percent or less in the winter time because of the de-humidifying effect of the heating system. Actually, the air within the house can be drier even than that of the Sahara Desert. This is much too low for physical comfort and can cause damage to the house and furniture. If the air is "too dry" one is more prone to head colds (the nasal passages dry out), the skin will become too dry and one will feel cooler than the house temperature warrants. For the house, furniture will dry out causing the wood to shrink and crack, other material such as plastic and leather will deteriorate and a high level of static electricity will be noted.

The solution to all these problems is to install a humidifier. This can be used to raise the relative humidity level to around 40%, generally considered to be ideal. As a result, you will feel more comfortable at a lower thermostat setting and all the listed problems will be cleared. There are several types of humidifiers. Some fit into the ductwork of the hot-air system. Others look just like a piece of furniture and can be fitted into a room as such. Yet another type fits into a closet or the basement and delivers the water vapor into the house through a duct system. Type isn't important but capacity is. Local experience can be helpful and those who sell the units can help with sizing. As a rule of thumb, a gallon of water should be turned into water vapor per day for each room of the house. For a new, tightly sealed and well-insulated house, the requirements can be cut in half. For a drafty house, two gallons a day per room may be needed. Of course, the relative humidity level should be checked with a humidity meter and the unit should be equipped with a humidistat to automatically maintain the selected relative humidity level.

There are two basic types of humidifiers, evaporative or atomizing. Evaporative humidifiers are equipped with evaporator pads attached to a motor-driven wheel. The warm air in the house is them pumped past the evaporator pads (since the unit is mounted in the hot-air ducts) to extract moisture from the wet pads. This water vapor is then delivered to the entire house through the hot-air ducting system. The evaporator type requires water relatively free of mineral deposits. An evaporator-type humidifier contained in a furniture-like cabinet operates the same way but, of course, discharges the moisture-laden air only into the room where it is located. The air flow related to the hot-air system must then distribute the water vapor throughout the house.

Atomizing humidifiers shoot a fine mist into the air, have great capacity for their size and usually require less maintenance than the evaporator type. An atomizing humidifier, however, requires virtually mineral-free water otherwise it will clog up rather often and need cleaning. Also, the minerals in the fogged air shot out of the atomizer can deposit a chalky film throughout the house. If the water in your locale measures over eight grains of hardness (check with your water company), you are better off with an evaporative unit. Alternately, a mineral-flushing system can be installed to lower the hardness level of the water.

Of utmost importance, if the walls and ceiling of your home are not equipped with properly installed vapor barriers, do not use a humidifier. The humidity will simply pass through the walls and ceilings to soak the insulation.

Section 6

Measuring Heat Loss or Gain

GENERAL

The heat loss or gain through a particular building material or any combination of materials as assembled into a wall, floor, etc. can be rather accurately established. For example, the heat loss or gain through walls of various levels of insulation efficiency can be calculated and the results converted into actual dollar costs as related to the fuel needed for heating and cooling the house. The energy saved (and thus the dollars saved) by use of energy-efficient windows, doors, floors, walls, etc. can thus be easily established in both energy and dollar figures. These figures will clearly establish the dollar-saving worth of insulation and other energy-saving items.

ADMITTANCE (U) FACTOR

The R value of a material expresses its ability to restrict (resist) the flow of heat on a molecular basis. The ability of a material to pass heat on a molecular-flow basis is thus the opposite of the resistance (R) ability of the material. The ability to pass heat is expressed as the U (Admittance) factor of a material. It is the reciprocal of the R value and can be obtained by dividing R into 1 (U = 1/R).

All heat loss or gain calculations use the U factor. For example, the daily heat loss or gain through 25 square feet of pine wood for a temperature difference of 15° F would be as follows:

$$BTU = U \times F_t^2 \times Hr \text{ where, } U = \frac{1}{1.25} = 0.8$$
$$= 0.8 \times 25 \times 24 \times 15 = 7,200 \text{ BTU's per day}$$

Certain parts of a house (a wall, for example) may be made up of many materials, each having its own R value. A stud wall, for example, can consist of pine wood, insulation batts, sheet rock or paneling inner covering, an outer sheathing and a final covering (brick, stone, wood, etc.). To arrive at the resultant U factor for the entire wall, the individual R values of the various materials in the wall must be added up. The R total is then divided into 1 to arrive at the resultant U factor.

$$U = \frac{1}{R \text{ total}} = \frac{1}{R1 + R2 + R3 \ldots}$$

Note particularly that the U factors cannot be added up since they are reciprocals. If a material is only listed as having a U factor, the U factor must be converted into its equivalent R value before it can be added up with other R values.

$$R1 = \frac{1}{U_1} \qquad R2 = \frac{1}{U_2}$$

BTU CALCULATION EXAMPLE

To demonstrate how BTU's are calculated, let us take an R20 wall of 1500 square feet and find the total BTU flow per day through the wall for a 1°F temperature difference across the wall.

R20 = U0.05   Area = 1500 sq ft   Hrs = 24   Temp. Diff. = 1°F
$$BTU = U \times F_t^2 \times Hrs. \times °F$$
$$= 0.05 \times 1500 \times 24 \times 1 = 1800 \text{ BTU's per day per 1°F temp. diff.}$$

Simple enough so far—but—how can you determine the total BTU flow through the wall in one year, for a given climatic area, taking into account all temperature fluctuations outside the house for the full year. Since the BTU flow rate is directly related to the degree of temperature difference existing between the inside and outside of the house, we must:

- Determine the average temperaure maintained within the house. This is usually taken as 75°F.

- Determine how many hours the outside temperature was above (summer) or below (winter) a mean temperature of 65°F.

- Determine how many degrees of outside temperature change occurred during each hour of temperature change.

These two totals, when multiplied together, give a figure that expresses (1) the total number of 1°F temperature changes that occurred during every hour of

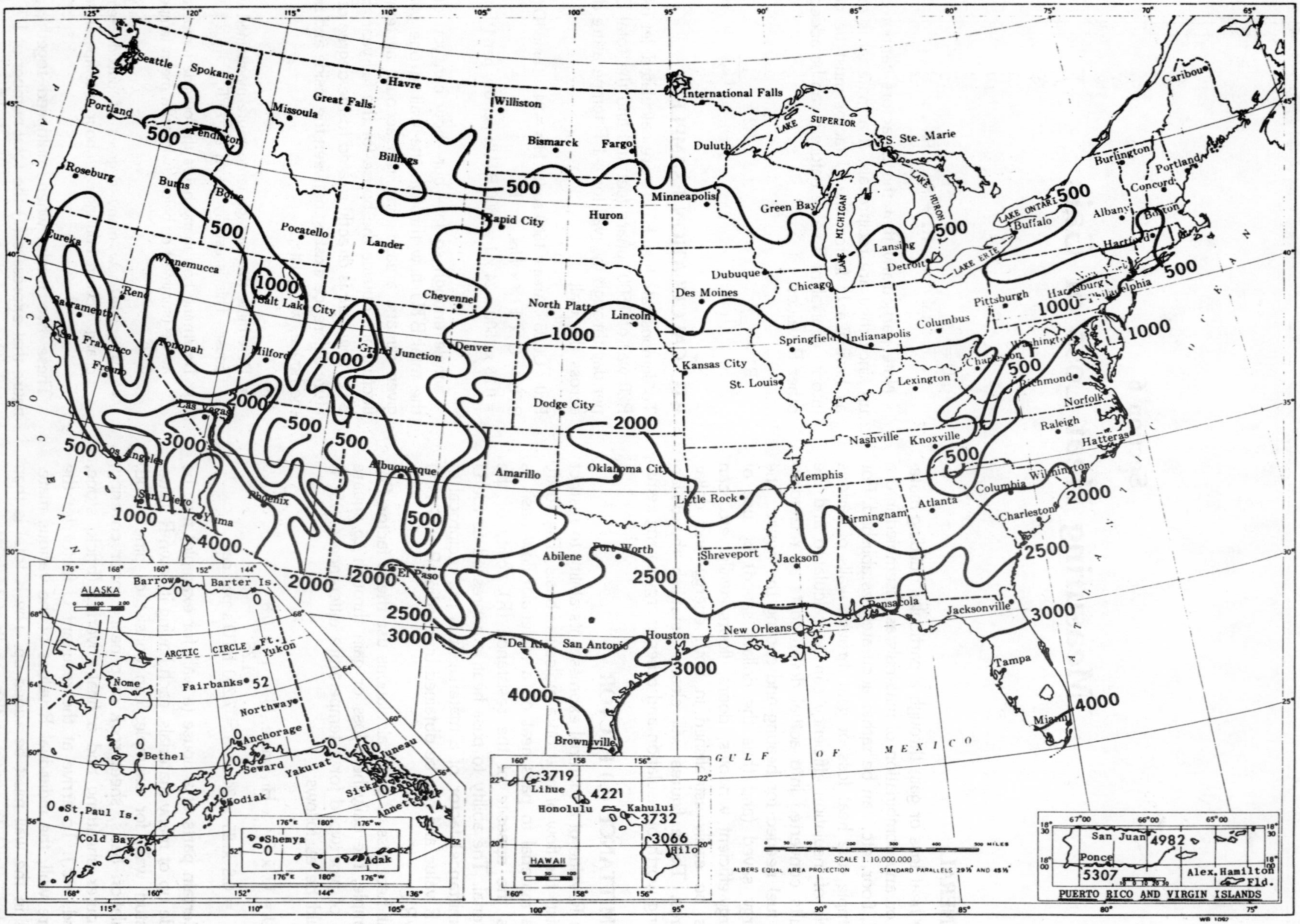

Figure 6-1. Degree Days, Cooling Chart

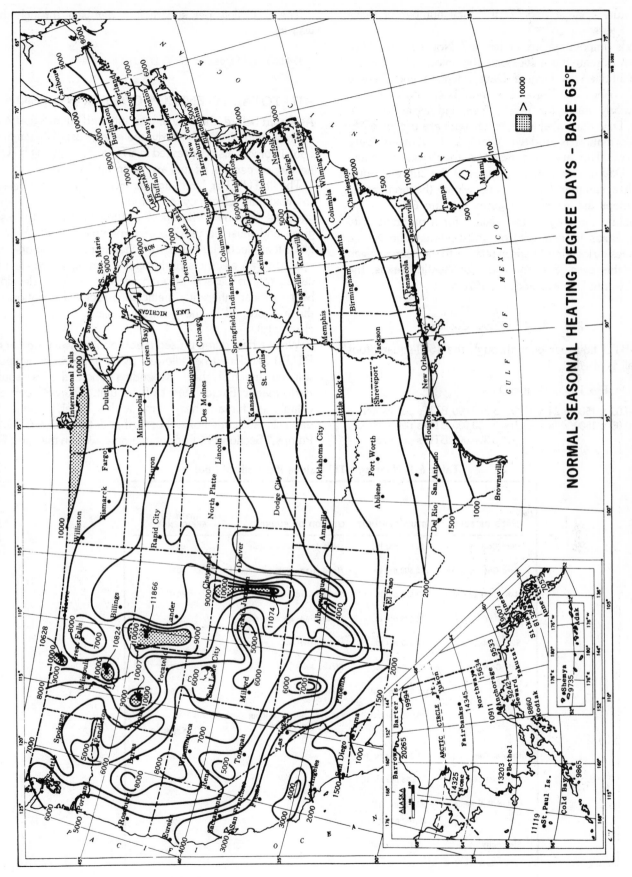

NORMAL SEASONAL HEATING DEGREE DAYS – BASE 65°F

> 10000

Figure 6-2. Degree Days, Heating

temperature change and (2) the total number of these change hours.

Sounds impossible to arrive at? Not so—the U.S. Weather Bureau has developed this information for us, being identified as Degree Days, Heating and Degree Days, Cooling. The Weather Bureau keeps daily records on a yearly basis for most cities and assembles the Degree Day data against a mean temperature of 65°F. This information is updated yearly and averaged every few years. The averaged result is then used to make Degree Day gradient lines on maps of the entire country on both a summer (cooling) and winter (heating) basis. These maps are given by Figures 6-1 and 6-2.

To obtain the Degree Day values for a particular city (Austin, Texas, for example), one must estimate the Degree Day values by locating Austin in relation to the nearest given city—in this case, San Antonio. For Austin, Texas, the yearly Degree Day averages for 1976 are:

1800 - Degree Days, Heating
2850 - Degree Days, Cooling

The BTU flow per year through the 1500-square foot R20 wall is then:

$$BTU = \frac{U}{t} \times F^2 \times Hrs. \times Degree\ Days$$
$$= 0.05 \times 1500 \times 24 \times 1800 = 3,240,000\ BTU's\ per\ winter$$
$$0.05 \times 1500 \times 24 \times 2850 = \underline{5,130,000}\ BTU's\ per\ summer$$
$$8,370,000\ BTU's\ per\ year$$

The BTU flow per square foot per year through the wall is:

$$\frac{8,370,000\ BTU's/year}{1500\ sq.\ ft.} = 5580\ BTU's$$

BTU TOTAL TO ENERGY-COST CONVERSION

As stated before, the flow of heat into and out of a house is expressed in BTU's. Similarly, the energy used to heat and cool a home is also expressed in BTU's. The heating BTU's developed per unit of fuel are given by Table 6-1.

The "BTU's Per Unit" figures given in Table 6-1 relate to maximum efficiency of combustion for coal, oil and gas. The "assumed efficiency" of the heating plant is also given and must be used in any energy-cost calculations. Note that electricity has a 100% heating efficiency only as related to an electric-strip furnace—that is, where electrical current is passed through resistor strips to develop heat (a most inherently inefficient process in relation to the fuel burned in the generating plants to develop the electricity).

When a heat pump is used the amount of heat (number of BTU's) developed per kilowatt (KW) of power consumed will be much higher, depending upon the Seasonal Performance Factor (SPF) of the unit. The SPF can be established for any heat pump and is largely dependent upon climatic conditions. (For further details, refer to "Heat Pumps," Section 19.) For our example, we can take an SPF

Table 6-1. Heating BTU Values Per Unit of Fuel

TYPES OF FUEL	BTU'S PER UNIT	METHOD OF BURNING	ASSUMED EFFICIENCY
Hard Coal or Coke	12,500 per lb.	Hand fired, no controls	65%
Hard Coal or Coke	12,500 per lb.	Hand fired, with controls	80%
Hard Coal or Coke	12,500 per lb.	Stoker fired	80%
Soft Coal	12,500 per lb.	Hand fired, no controls	55%
Soft Coal	12,500 per lb.	Hand fired, with controls	65%
Soft Coal	12,500 per lb.	Stoker fired	65%
Oil	140,000 per gal.	Units designed for oil	65-75%
Oil	140,000 per gal.	Pot type burner without forced draft and converted burners	60-70%
Natural Gas	1,000 per cu. ft.		80%
Manufactured Gas	525 per cu. ft.		80%
Liquid Petroleum Gas	92,000 per gal. or 21,700 per lb.		80%
Electricity	3,412 per kwh		100%

of 2.25 as a practical average for the Austin, Texas area.

The energy required to cool a home is indirectly proportional to the Energy Efficiency Rating (EER) of the cooling unit. The EER directly expresses the cooling efficiency of an air conditioner—the higher the EER, the more efficient the unit and the less electrical power (KW) needed. An EER of 7, for example, indicates the related air conditioner will remove 7 BTU's of heat from the air for every watt of electricity used. For our example, we can take an EER of 7 (a practical value for a heat pump and an average value for a "regular" air conditioner).

The following energy-cost conversions are based upon the 1500-square foot R20 wall just discussed.

Table 6-2 Heating Cost vs. Fuel Cost

Electricity (Strip Heaters) — $\dfrac{3,240,000 \text{ BTU's}}{* \ 3412 \times 1.0 \text{ eff.}}$ = 950 KWH per winter

Electricity (Heat Pump) — $\dfrac{3,240,000 \text{ BTU's}}{* \ 3412 \times 2.25 \text{ eff.}}$ = 422 KWH per winter

Natural Gas (Heating) — $\dfrac{3,240,000 \text{ BTU's}}{** \ 1,000 \times 0.8 \text{ eff.}}$ = 4050 cu ft per winter

Hard Coal (Heating) — $\dfrac{3,240,000 \text{ BTU's}}{\# \ 12,500 \times 0.8 \text{ eff.}}$ = 324 lbs per winter

Oil (Heating) — $\dfrac{3,240,000 \text{ BTU's}}{\#\# \ 140,000 \times 0.7 \text{ eff.}}$ = 33 gallons per winter

Electricity (Cooling) — $\dfrac{5,130,000 \text{ BTU's}}{*\# \ 1,000 \times 7.0 \text{ EER}}$ = 733 KWH per winter

* Electricity - develops 3412 BTU's of heat per KW
** Natural gas - develops 1,000 BTU's of heat per cut ft
\# Hard coal - develops 12,500 BTU's of heat per lb
\#\# Oil - develops 140,000 BTU's of heat per gallon
*\# Cooling, electrical - removes 1,000 BTU's of heat per KW x EER

For all-electric heating and cooling at a 5¢ KWH rate, the costs are:

Heat Pump - 422 KWH x .05 = $21.10
Cooling - 733 KWH x .05 = $36.65
Total = $57.75

El. Strip - 950 KWH x .05 = $47.50
Cooling - 733 KWH x .05 = $36.65
Total = $84.15

The insulation efficiency of a 3½" wall made of wood, brick, stone or concrete was discussed on page 5-7, Section 5. The BTU drain per winter through these 1500 square-feet walls are calculated below and show some startling examples of how energy can be wasted through a wall.

Wood wall — R1.25 per inch x 3.5 = R4.375 total = U0.23
Brick wall — R0.20 per inch x 3.5 = R0.700 total = U1.43
Stone wall — R0.15 per inch x 3.5 = R0.525 total = U1.90
Concrete wall — R0.08 per inch x 3.5 = R0.280 total = U3.57

BTU = U x Sq Ft x Degree Days (Austin, Tx)
R20 wall = 0.05 x 1500 x 24 x 1800 = 3,240,000 BTU's per winter

Wood wall = 0.23 x 1500 x 24 x 1800 = 14,904,000 BTU's per winter
Brick wall = 1.43 x 1500 x 24 x 1800 = 92,664,000 BTU's per winter
Stone wall = 1.90 x 1500 x 24 x 1800 = 123,120,000 BTU's per winter
Conc. wall = 3.57 x 1500 x 24 x 1800 = 231,336,000 BTU's per winter

The BTU loss through a bare concrete wall per winter is thus 71.4 times that of an R20 composite wall

The fantastic BTU drain related to brick, stone or concrete walls illustrates how these materials must be used sparingly in house construction if they are exposed to the outside air. Further aspects of a house will be covered under the separate sections related to foundation, doors, windows, floors, wall and ceilings to follow.

It should be particularly noted that the calculated heat gain or loss values relate *only* to the flow of heat on a molecular basis through the wall in relation to the temperature difference across the wall and that the calculations do not take into account:

1. solar energy effect (loss in the summer, gain in the winter)

2. appliance use (heat gain in winter - cooling loss in summer)

3. occupants (heat gain in winter, cooling loss in summer)

4. air infiltration standards of home

5. wind conditions

6. loss through windows and doors

Items 1 through 3 above are difficult to arrive at, requiring rather elaborate calculations to obtain meaningful figures. In a very general sense, items 1 to 3 effect upon the heating and cooling load of a home can be thought to somewhat cancel out. That is, whereas solar energy entering the home in the summer acts to present a load to the cooling system, the solar energy entering the home in the winter will act to reduce the heating load. The loss-gain effect of appliances and occupants (only considered here as heat-producing units) also somewhat cancel out on a yearly basis.

The wind conditions of the house locale and—most certainly—the air infiltration standards of the home play a very large part in the actual heating and cooling bills of the home. The BTU loss and gain calculations are based upon BTU flow under "still air" conditions. The rate at which the cold outside air of winter flows across the house walls, windows, doors, roof and foundation introduces a "chill factor" in that the heat passing out through the building envelope is always "looking" at cold air. That is, the temperature of the outer surface of the walls, windows, doors, roof and foundation is never raised by the heat passing out and thus the heat drain through the material is accelerated in direct proportion to the wind speed.

The air infiltration standards (the tightness) of a house have a *very large* effect upon the energy efficiency of the house and thus on the energy used for heating and cooling. Even if built to very high standards of draft prevention, the air within the house will change (be replaced by outside air) at a rate sufficient to appear as an added load to the air conditioning system. For a "loose" house, the added load can be very great.

Section 7

Dollar Benefits of Energy-Saving Construction

GENERAL

As previously mentioned and repeated for emphasis, a recent pamphlet by the American Institute of Architects said in part:

"In existing buildings, fuel consumption could be reduced by as much as 50 percent from current levels. New buildings initially designed to be energy efficient could save as much as 80% of the fuel they would consume at present levels."

The last figure seems extreme—"an 80% savings on fuel costs." Yet, the figure is true—an 80% savings is possible as to heating and cooling costs over an identical building that is not properly insulated, contains single-glazed windows and which was not built to the "new" standards of draft prevention.

Most houses built today conform to FHA Minimum Property Standards of insulation and general construction techniques as related to energy efficiency. In relation to the energy crisis, these standards are much too low and will surely be increased in the near future. Very large savings in energy use can be gained by houses that are built to a higher level of insulation and energy-saving construction than that now specified by the FHA. This is illustrated by the following study of four houses in the Austin, Texas area.

HOUSE COMPARISON—CONSTRUCTION FACTS

The energy-saving comparison to follow was made against four houses, all on the same street and all observed during construction by the author. Basic house facts are:

HOUSES A & B

Insulated to FHA Min. Prop. Stds. on an uninsulated slab foundation. Features single-glazed windows (covered with storm windows in mid 1976). Have dark-colored shingles, with attic ventilated by two turbine ventilators in conjunction with gable-end and eave vents. House A has wood front door, with rear door and door into garage being metal clad. House B has all-wood outer doors. Extra attention paid by owners to improving weatherstripping. Screen doors installed to use natural ventilation during moderate-summer period. Both houses are all-electric, use electric-strip heating and have a stone-faced fireplace built into an outer wall. Both installed storm windows in 1976 and improved weatherstripping. Both houses are rated at somewhat better than FHA Min. Prop. Stds. Two occupants in A, five in B.

HOUSE C

Insulated to somewhat better than FHA Min. Prop. Stds. on an uninsulated slab foundation. Features double-glazed windows, brown-colored asphalt shingles and an attic ventilated with a power-drive roof ventilator and gable-end vents. All outer doors are solid wood and a stone-faced fireplace is built into an outer wall. House is all-electric, using a heat pump for both heating and cooling. Extra care was taken to reduce drafts. Two occupants.

HOUSE D

Built by author and insulated to better than FHA Min. Prop. Stds. (R13 walls, R38 ceiling and R13 under floor). Built on an insulated crawl-space foundation. Features wood shingles, double-glazed windows and a fireplace built into an inner wall. Uses a free-standing fireplace in winter. Attic ventilated by a power-driven fan and gable-end vents. All outer doors are metal-clad with magnetic weatherstripping. Uses a screen door on front door to gain natural ventilation. *Extreme* care was taken to reduce drafts. All-electric home and uses a heat pump for both heating and cooling. Two occupants. For additional details, refer to page 7-5.

HOUSE COMPARISON—DOLLAR BENEFITS

The four-house comparison to follow illustrates the energy (and dollar) savings that can be realized by building an energy-saver home. The comparison is not exact and does not give precise answers for the following reasons:

- The air conditioning units are not on separate meters thus the actual electrical power (KWH's) used by each house for heating and cooling cannot be precisely identified.

Table 7-1. Electrical Power Consumption - 1976

Month	House A	House B	House C	House D	Remarks
Jan.	3102 KWH	2243 KWH	1727 KWH	1341 KWH	very cold
Feb.	2333	1861	1533	1118	moderate
March	1695	1711	1073	932	moderate
April	1228	1135	873	503	mild
May	1321	1163	1063	713	mild
June	2520	1664	1633	942	warmer
July	2447	1960	2003	1407	warmer
August	2661	2304	1747	1538	hottest
Sept.	1738	1686	1537	1027	cooler
Oct.	1363	1380	920	1018	cool
Nov.	2299	1484	1233	1018	cold
Dec.	3548 KWH	2396 KWH	2420 KWH	1420 KWH	very cold
	26,155 KWH	20,987 KWH	17,183 KWH	12,776 KWH	

December 1976 averaged 1.5 times colder than Dec. 1975

*Vacation time correction

- House C and D enjoyed excellent natural ventilation, with House D being designed to optimize cross ventilation through the bedrooms and family-room-kitchen area. Houses A and B, each equipped with a front door screen door, are somewhat blocked from the prevailing wind and thus did not enjoy natural ventilation to the degree related to Houses C and D.

- Houses A, C and D all have two occupants whereas House B has five occupants.

- The comparison will be made assuming each house used essentially the same amount of electricity for all purposes other than air conditioning. That is, an equal amount for hot-water heating, cooking, lights, etc. This should be very close to correct for Houses A, C and D.

- Vacation periods for all houses somewhat balance out except for Houses C and D which averaged about 14 days greater than Houses A and B—this is compensated for in the comparison.

Table 7-1 above lists the electrical power (KWH) used by the four houses of the comparison study.

While the energy-saved and dollar-saved figures to follow may not be exact, it is felt that they are within 20% or less of actual. The savings are in close accord with those given under "Energy-Saver Home Examples," Section 9.

To arrive at a more accurate cost comparison for heating and cooling between the four houses, the electrical power (KWH) used by Houses A, B and C are now adjusted to that related to the smallest house (House D). This will make the air conditioning costs for all houses effectively equal. (See table 7-2 below.)

The monthly KWH figures given by Table 7-1 reveal that Houses C and D, each equipped with a heat pump, achieved their highest (greatest) KWH savings over Houses A and B during the winter months. The excellent summer-time savings of Houses C and D over Houses A and B are directly attributable to their double-glazed windows, extra insulation and draft prevention excellence. The figures for the coldest and warmest months of the year are as follows:

Heating Cost—Coldest Month

December - House A 3548 KWH   December - House C 2420 KWH
December - House B +2396 KWH   December - House D +1420 KWH
                    5944 KWH   3840 KWH

House A + House B = 5944/2 = 2972 KWH average
House C + House D = 3840/2 = 1920 KWH average
                Difference = 1052 KWH

1052 KWH's at 4.7 cents per KWH = $49.44 savings for December

The heating cost for Houses A & B averaged 1.6 times that of Houses C & D as averaged. The heat pump thus delivered $1.60 worth of heat per electrical dollar spent.

Table 7-2. Houses Averaged to 1944 Sq. Ft.

House	Sq. Ft.	KWH Used Yearly	KWH Yearly Per Sq Ft	Miltiplied by 1944	KWH Av. Per Month	Monthly Cost @ 4.7¢
A	2040	26,155	12.82	24,823	2077	$97.62
B	2100	20,987	9.99	19,421	1618	$76.05
C	2390	17,813	7.45	14,483	1207	$56.73
D	1944	12,776	6.57	12,776	1065	$50.06

The heating cost for Houses A & B averaged 1.83 times that of Houses C & D as averaged. The heat pump thus delivered $1.83 worth of heat per electrical dollar spent.

Cooling Cost—Warmest Month

August - House A   2661 KWH   August - House C   1797 KWH
August - House B +2304 KWH   August - House D +1538 KWH
                             4965 KWH   3335 KWH

House A + House B = 4965/2 = 2483 KWH average
House C + House D = 3335/2 = 1668 KWH average
                     Difference =   815 KWH

815 KWH's at 4.7 cents per KWH = $38.31 savings for
                                             August

The cooling cost for Houses A & B averaged 1.5 times that of Houses C & D as averaged.

Using the 1944-square feet averaged figures from Table 7-2, the heating and cooling electrical bills of Houses A and B and then Houses C and D can be averaged and used to develop some interesting facts.

Table 7-3. Energy Efficiency vs Energy Bills

House A + B average = $97.62 + $76.05 = $173.62/2 = $86.84 per mo.
House C + D average = $56.73 + $50.06 = $106.78/2 = -53.40 per mo.
                                    Difference = $33.44 per mo.

Monthly heating and cooling costs for A & B averaged 1.62 times the average of C & D. House C & D costs thus averaged to be only 61% that of A & B.

Average yearly savings of C & D over A & B is then $33.44 x 12 = $401.28 per year. For a 30-year period, based on 1978s KWH rate of 4.7¢, the total savings would be $401.28 x 30 = $12,038.40.

And note — these savings are based on 1978's KWH rate average of 4.7 cents. In 1975, here in Austin, Texas, the average yearly KWH rate was 3.83 cents — a difference of 0.87 cents in three years. This is an increase rate of 7.6% per year. What will the KWH rate be in 1979, 1980, etc. Higher, that's for certain — thus, the savings listed above will grow, year after year, as the electrical rates rise.

EXTRA OUTLAY VS. ENERGY SAVINGS

The grand question now is: How much extra capital outlay was required to raise the energy efficiency of House C and D over that of House A and B to realize such excellent energy and dollar savings?

Here is the most wonderful part of the whole energy-saving story—the cost is not high—it is, in fact, very low for the dollar savings gained. The extra cost to raise the energy efficiency of House C can only be estimated, being taken somewhat high at $2,000.00 at 1975 cost levels. For House D, the figure was taken directly from building records and also totals about $2,000.00. These figures cover the extra cost to install a heat pump over a "standard" air conditioner, install double-glazed windows, metal-clad doors, extra insulation and tightly seal the house. In each case, the extra cost is what a contractor would normally charge and thus contains a standard profit margin.

Table 7-4. Pertinent Facts on House D

$2,000.00 extra outlay/$401.28 yearly savings = 4.9 years payback
                                                 time at a 4.7¢ KWH rate

Extra cost per sq. ft. = $2,000.00/1944 = $1.03
Bldg. cost per sq. ft. = $45,000.00/1944 = $23.15 per sq ft
Bldg cost less extra = $45,000.00-$2,000.00 = $43,000.00
Sq. ft. cost at FHA = $43,000.00/1944 = $22.12 per sq ft
Min. Prop. Stds.
Extra cost as a = $23.15 vs $22.12 = 4.7% greater
percentage

It should be noted here that Houses A and B were upgraded by the owners during 1976 to achieve a higher energy efficiency as to heating and cooling as compared to that related to houses built to strict FHA Minimum Property Standards. Thus, the cost comparison between the average of Houses C and D versus that of Houses A and B would have resulted in a higher savings by Houses C and D if Houses A and B had not been upgraded as to energy efficiency. A payback time of less than four years is thus clearly indicated if the comparison had been made against houses built to FHA Minimum Property Standards only.

The extra cost to raise the energy-efficiency level of House D calculates out to about five percent (4.7 actually). This figure can be considered very close and can be used to develop a close estimate of the extra outlay that will be required to raise a house from FHA Minimum Property Standards energy-efficiency to that related to the minimum energy-efficiency level needed today because of the energy crisis.

ENERGY EFFICIENCY UPGRADING

As mentioned above, Houses A and B were upgraded as to energy efficiency during 1976. That is, Houses A and B installed storm windows (in mid year) over their single-glazed windows and improved the caulking and weather-stripping around doors, windows and the house envelope. House A also replaced two wood outer doors with metal-clad units. Both houses also installed a screen door on the front door and used natural ventilation to the maximum degree possible to avoid using the air conditioner.

The 1976 November and December temperatures in the area (Austin, Texas) were markedly cooler than normal while the summer temperatures and humidity levels were about the same for both years. Even so, Houses A & B used considerably less electricity for 1976 as compared to 1975. The facts are given by Table 7-5.

SUMMARY

The dollar savings detailed by Table 7-3 (and those given in Section 9) illustrate the extreme dollar savings that can be realized for a comparatively moderate extra

Table 7-5. Energy Efficiency Upgrading Savings

House A

1975 KWH Usage =	27,572
1976 KWH Usage =	− 24,327
	3,245 KWH
	x 0.047 per KWH
	$152.52

House B

1975 KWH Usage =	25,646
1976 KWH Usage =	− 22,474
	3,172 KWH
	x 0.047
	$149.08

The dollar savings gains are such that the extra outlay (about $500.00 per house) will be paid back in less than 4 years. Thereafter, the savings are total and will be enjoyed for the life of the house. Also, as the KWH rate goes up, the savings increase.

And, the comfort level of both houses was noticeably increased plus the outside noise level was greatly reduced.

outlay to raise the energy-efficiency level of a house. In a pamphlet recently issued by the American Institute of Architects, the following was said:

"In some instances, it may be possible to achieve energy efficiency without additional capital costs. On the whole, however, energy efficient buildings will tend to cost more than traditionally designed and constructed projects . . . about 10 to 20 per cent above usual construction costs."

"It is especially significant that the payback period for capital expenditures for energy efficient buildings might range from 10 to 15 years."

The figures given are somewhat general and cover all types of buildings—offices, factories, schools, homes, etc. The cost figures given by various manufacturers of energy-efficient windows, doors, insulation, etc. generally indicate payback times of from only a few months to perhaps as high as 10 years. The actual energy saved (and thus the dollars saved) will be individual for each house. The actual savings realized is always difficult to establish precisely since one must know exactly what the comparison is made against. That is, do the figures relate to a rather well insulated house, an uninsulated, poorly-built house, etc.

When computing the payback period for a particular energy-saving feature (double-glazed windows versus single-glazed windows, for example), one must consider the future. That is, the cost of electricity here in Austin, Texas rose about 22% between 1975-1978 and will be higher on the average during 1979. In brief, the cost of energy (electricity and gas, mainly) will rise on a year-by-

year basis. Thus, a payback time of 5 years at 1979 energy rates, may be reduced to a total of 3 years by increasing energy costs in the next two or three years.

ENERGY COSTS VS. HOUSE SIZE

The energy costs for Houses A, B, C and D (as factored to 1944 square feet) are listed by Table 7-2 on a monthly-dollar-basis. These figures, divided by 1944, give energy costs for each house on a square-foot basis as follows:

House A - $97.62/1944 = 5.02 cents
House B - $76.05/1944 = 3.91 cents
House C - $56.73/1944 = 2.92 cents
House D - $50.00/1944 = 2.58 cents

These figures can be used to develop a table (Table 7-6) of estimated energy costs for houses of various sized living areas on a monthly basis and for the four levels of energy efficiency demonstrated by Houses A, B, C and D.

Table 7-6. Estimated Energy Costs vs. House Size

Living Area	House A 5.02¢	House B 3.91¢	House C 2.92¢	House D 2.58¢
1200	$ 60.24	$46.92	$35.04	$30.96
1300	$ 65.26	$ 50.83	$37.96	$33.54
1400	$ 70.28	$ 54.74	$40.88	$36.12
*1500	$ 75.30	$ 58.65	$43.80	$38.70
1600	$ 80.32	$ 62.56	$46.72	$41.28
1700	$ 85.34	$ 66.47	$49.64	$43.86
1800	$ 90.36	$ 70.36	$52.56	$46.44
1900	$ 95.38	$ 74.29	$55.48	$49.02
2000	$100.40	$ 78.20	$58.40	$51.60
2500	$125.50	$ 97.75	$73.00	$64.50
3000	$150.60	$117.30	$87.60	$77.40

* Example house

The figures given by Table 7-6 are, of course, only approximates and will differ (even widely) for other climatic areas, different construction standards, different living habits, etc. Yet, the figures are useful and can serve as guidelines. In a practical sense, a larger house will always be less efficient energy-wise because it usually houses a larger family, more children, more windows, etc. Further, large homes usually feature vaulted or cathedral ceilings and thus will have a larger cubic-foot total per square-foot of living space. And, it is the cubic feet that actually count as related to heating and cooling a house.

The figures given by Table 7-6 relate to homes in the Austin, Texas area where mild to moderate winters and moderate to hot summers are normal. The figures given by Table 7-6 can be factored to produce meaningful figures for houses in other climatic areas. This factoring can be accomplished by use of the Degree Days (Heating and Cooling) values obtained from Figures 6-1 and 6-2, Section 6. The Degree Days factors for certain cities are given below by Table 7-7.

Table 7-7. Degree Day Figures - Factored

City	Degree Days Winter	Degree Days Summer	Winter-Summer Totals	Ratio to Austin Figures
Austin, Tx	1800	2850	4650	
Los Angeles	1900	500	2400	2400/4650 = 0.52
Miami, Florida	125	4000	4125	4125/4650 = 0.89
Oklahoma City	3500	2000	5500	5500/4650 = 1.18
Seattle, Wash.	5800	250	6050	6050/4650 = 1.30
Chicago, Ill.	6300	800	7100	7100/4650 = 1.53
Duluth, Minn.	9400	250	9650	9650/4650 = 2.08

The Austin figure, for example, if used for a house in Seattle would have to be multiplied by 1.30. For the Los Angeles area, the figures from Table 7-6 would have to be multiplied by 0.52 to convert them to be approximates for a house in the Los Angeles area. Of course, this figuring can be made only against an all-electric home, with houses using electric-strip heating using House A and B values and with houses using heat pumps taking the House C and D values.

SUMMARY—AUTHOR'S HOUSE

Our house was the first one known in our area (or even in the Austin Tx area as far as I knew) to be built to the "new" standards of energy-use efficiency. Using standard energy-use formulas, I calculated the possible energy load on both a summer and winter basis and was hopeful of achieving the "35% savings" then stated to be possible by an energy-saver home against a home built to the "old" standards, those of FHA Minimum Property Standards.

After the house was completed and had been lived in for six months, I checked the actual energy load versus the predicted load. To my suprise and delight, I found our actual savings to be much higher. Nearer to 50% savings being achieved over other houses of comparable size in our immediate area. Our energy use (all-electric) was so low, in fact, that the electricity supplier (Pedernales Electrical Cooperative) later told me they had checked our meter on several occasions since their computer identified us as having "suspiciously low" energy bills.

What made our house so wonderfully efficient of energy use? To best knowledge, the following accounts for our low energy usage.

- House construction—extra insulation over FHA minimum, double-glazed windows, metal-clad insulating doors, ventilated attic, use of a heat pump, etc *and* with extreme care taken to eliminate any and all potential draft sources. This later point is one that is not generally understood to be so extremely important whereas it can actually make the difference between excellent energy bills and "less than expected" energy bills.

- House design—floor plan and window placement optimized use of natural ventilation. This feature provided cross ventilation in each bedroom and for a full flow of air through the house. On many days when nearby homes were using their air conditioners, cross ventilation alone sufficed to keep our house comfortably cool.

- Conservative outlook—energy conservation was practiced at all times consistent with maintaining a comfortable atmosphere. In brief, we did not "freeze" in the winter nor "swelter" in the summer—we just kept the doors and windows closed or opened as needed. Hot-water usage was studied and reduced by careful use since considerable savings can be so gained. We also reduced the hot water temperature to about 125°F. Also, we planted fast-growing trees to shade the front (North-facing) windows and used a roll-up blind to shade the rear (South-facing) windows in the summer. Lastly, we followed all applicable energy-saving hints detailed in Section 21.

- The floor plan for our home is illustrated by figure 9-1. Though not shown, each bedroom is equipped with two windows to optimize cross ventilation. The house is illustrated on the fly leaf and contains an equal amount of windows at the rear.

Section 8

Comfort Benefits of Energy-Saving Construction

IDEAL COMFORT

Real comfort—ideal comfort—in a home is achieved only when the occupants do not, at any time, feel unduly warm or cold and when they are not bothered by drafts or discomforted by too high or too low a humidity level. Tests have proven that if the house occupants are not physically comfortable in the temperature-draft-humidity sense, correction is almost always wastefully attempted by adjustment of the air-conditioner thermostat.

Ideal home comfort is a condition that must be achieved to answer the physical requirements of the occupants. Basic facts on ideal comfort on a room temperature, draft and humidity basic are as follows:

- We are all "heat-producing machines" in that our bodies internally burn energy to maintain our temperature at a normal of 98.6°F.

- If the body temperature varies from normal due to internal reasons, that person is considered sick. If the skin temperature varies too much for external reasons, that person feels uncomfortably hot or cold.

- A human body feels most comfortable in a temperature-draft-humidity environment where the body heat can be maintained at normal without undue loading of the body's heat producing or cooling functions. For the majority of people this seems to be at a temperature range of between 72° and 75°F.

- The body functions controlling heating and cooling of the body can adjust to wide changes from the ideal level (72-75°F) but only at a slow rate. The time element may be in minutes, hours, or even days dependent upon the degree of temperature change from ideal and upon a person's health, age and outlook.

The above human factors clearly specify that the air-conditioning system must heat or cool *only the occupied space* and *not the occupants* and that the indoor temperature *must be maintained very near the "ideal" temperature* the occupants have been accustomed to for some time.

Basically, this means that if a person moves within a house from the accustomed ideal temperature to a colder area, the body will give up heat to the colder surface (or air) and thus will be discomforted since the body's heat-producing function takes a rather long time to compensate for the change. Similarly, moving from the ideal-temperature area to a warmer area will cause the body's cooling function to adjust the body's heat to the change. Again, the adjustment process is slow and causes bodily discomfort.

For the home occupants to be really comfortable, the following must be maintained:

- Effective temperature level, usually held within the range of 72-75°F.

- Humidity level, higher in winter—lower in summer.

- Air circulation, must be unnoticeable.

- Surface temperature (windows, walls, doors, ceilings and floors), ideally must be held within 5°F or less of effective temperature.

COMFORT CRITERIA

To control the effective (comfort level) temperature range within a home, control of air circulation and humidity level is an absolute must. A home just cannot be efficiently heated or cooled to achieve ideal comfort if the air circulation within the house is excessive. Thus, a drafty house will require that a much higher than normal effective temperature be maintained to achieve even partial bodily comfort within the home. A draft within the house has essentially the same effect upon a body as the wind does outdoors.

We are all familiar with the "chill factor" which takes into account the fact that a body will lose a great deal more heat to moving air than to still air. That is, the skin surface will always be looking at air of the average outdoor temperature if the air touching the skin is constantly replaced. In still air, the body heat can extend away from the skin itself to raise the air temperature slightly a short distance away from the body. Thus, the body will not be called upon to compensate for the rapid heat drain associated with a chill-factor wind. For example, a 25 mph wind may make a 20°F outdoor reading have the same chilling factor as 0°F under calm-air conditions.

Drafts have two very serious effects upon bodily comfort and thus upon the energy-efficiency level of the home. These two effects are:

- makes the house occupants feel uncomfortable which is wastefully compensated for by raising the effective temperature by thermostat setting.

- brings in cold winter air to reduce the effective temperature which, again, is compensated for by thermostat setting on a wasteful basis. Lets cooled air escape from the house in the summer on the same wasteful basis.

Thus, drafts must be reduced to an absolute minimum if true bodily comfort and energy efficiency is to be realized in a home.

A person's reaction to a temperature above or below their accustomed "ideal" temperature is remarkably effected by the humidity level of the surrounding air. In the summer, a higher-level ideal temperature can be tolerated if the humidity level of the air is low (generally 30% or less). Thus, one can tolerate 100°F days in Arizona with its dry air much better than an 85°F day in the humid areas of the East Coast.

Since high humidity makes one feel warmer for a given temperature level, raising the indoor humidity (to 40% or more) can permit ideal bodily comfort in the winter at a lower thermostat setting. Of course, lowering the humidity in the summer will permit the thermostat to be set at a higher setting while still maintaining ideal temperature within the home. A humidifier-dehumidifier is thus recommended for installation in an energy-saver home.

In the past, houses were often built "loose" in that it was felt that the air within the house should change completely every hour or even less. The energy shortage has prompted studies on the need for air change within a home to maintain a "pure" atmosphere. These studies have shown that a house cannot be made "too tight" and that the air change in even a very tight house will ensure a pure atmosphere, in particular if an electronic air cleaner is used. This would be most needed if the home occupants smoke. The air cleaner offers the extra advantage of removing dust and other small particles from the air. A draft-free house with an air cleaner would be practically a dust-free house as well. Thus, installation of an electronic air cleaner is recommended for installation in an energy-saver home.

INSULATE FOR COMFORT AND ECONOMY

The effect of insulation on the inside surface of outer walls, ceilings and floors of a house envelope are graphically illustrated by the following. The study assumes a

House No. 1 - No insulation in walls, ceilings or floor

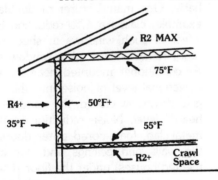

55°F - near floor
75°F - near ceiling
50°F - near wall
180°F

Effective temperature = 180/3 = 60°F

= cold house with a cold floor. Thermostat would have to be set to at least 85°F to achieve an effective 70°F temperature.

House No. 2 - FHA Min. Stds Insulation

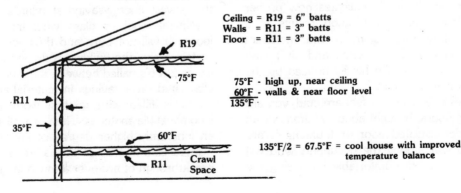

Ceiling = R19 = 6" batts
Walls = R11 = 3" batts
Floor = R11 = 3" batts

75°F - high up, near ceiling
60°F - walls & near floor level
135°F

135°F/2 = 67.5°F = cool house with improved temperature balance

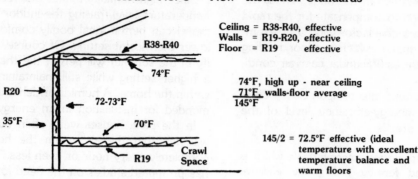

Ceiling = R38-R40, effective
Walls   = R19-R20, effective
Floor   = R19   effective

74°F, high up - near ceiling
71°F, walls-floor average
145°F

145/2 = 72.5°F effective (ideal
temperature with excellent
temperature balance and
warm floors

draft-free house and ideal humidity is maintained.

The above examples clearly show how as the insulation level of a wall, ceiling or floor is raised, the inside-surface temperature rises towards the ideal temperature. This points out that the thermostat need not be set to a higher-than-ideal value to achieve a comfortable average temperature throughout a room and even the whole house if that house is properly insulated and is draft free.

Insulation also prevents or reduces development of "inside-the-house" drafts that are produced by air currents set in motion by interior surface-to-air temperature differences. For example, unless a wall is well insulated any time the outdoor temperature is markedly lower than the effective temperature in the house, the wall temperature may be as much as 20°F or more colder than the "center-of-the-room" temperature.

The heated air from the furnace, when forced out the air ducts, will drift across the room until it approaches the wall. The much colder air near the wall will cool the hot air, causing it to grow heavy and sink to the floor. The cooled air then flows across the floor to the furnace under pull from the furnace fan, is reheated, and the cycle is repeated. A draft is thus developed, whose volume is somewhat proportional to the temperature difference between the wall surface and the air as forced out of the furnace.

People thus often think their walls, windows and doors are permitting outside air to enter to make a draft when the draft is actually being developed inside the house. The wall-to-floor-to-ceiling temperature ratios illustrated by House Example No. 3 clearly indicates how proper energy-saving insulation and construction results in a room (a house) where the maximum and minimum temperatures are very nearly the same and air movement within such a house will be hardly noticed by the occupants.

An old saying states "When your feet are cold, you are cold all over." Cold floors, brought about by drafts or an uninsulated or under-insulated floor or foundation, are sure to cause cold feet among the occupants who will then try to make the room comfortable by raising the

thermostat. Now—the head will be too warm while the feet are just comfortable. This specifies that drafts must be eliminated and the floor or foundation properly insulated as illustrated by Example No. 3. With warm feet, the home occupants can—by wearing sweaters, etc.—tolerate a lower effective temperature. With cold feet, tests have shown putting on a sweater does not make the person feel any warmer as long as the feet are cold. There is no real remedy for a cold floor other than to insulate and to prevent drafts.

INSULATE FOR ACOUSTICAL PRIVACY AND FIRE PROTECTION

Another most excellent benefit realized by a house constructed to energy-saving standards relates to noise reduction on either an outside-to-inside or inside-to-outside basis. One manufacturer of double-glazed windows, for example, claims a 47% reduction in noise transfer. The effect of such windows in shutting off outside noise is really remarkable. With a window open, for example, an air conditioner mounted near the window can input an objectional level of noise into the house. With a double-glazed window closed, the noise level drops to a "barely-heard" level. Noise reduction is also gained by use of metal-clad, foam-cored outer doors and by insulation in the walls and ceilings and (for crawl space or basemented houses) under the floor. The degree of acoustical privacy gained is a most worthwhile benefit and invariably is greatly appreciated by all who build their home to the newest energy-saving standards.

Mineral wool or glass wool insulation (as batts or loose-fill) will not burn and thus act as fire retarders. In certain areas, the building code permits fire blocking (2 x 4's or 2 x 6's nailed between the studs half-way up) to be eliminated (at a savings in material and labor) if the wall cavity is filled with mineral wool, glass wool or any incombustible material. Thus, a well-insulated house has an inherently higher degree of fire protection.

Metal-clad doors also act as fire retarders, resisting the breakthrough of fire over a much longer time period than a wood door (especially as over a hollow-core door). The metal-clad doors also offer a higher level of safety against forced entry through an outer door. A wood door can be bent, drilled, or forced more easily than a metal-clad door. Because of their poor resistance to fire and forced entry, hollow-core doors are outlawed by most building codes for use as an outer door (as well they should be). Actually, a hollow-core door is so flimsy one can easily kick a hole through it. Hollow-core doors, of course, are acceptable for inside-the-house use.

Section 9

The Energy Saver Home

GENERAL

Many things must be considered when preparing to build a house to a high level of energy efficiency. The major items to be considered are:

- House design
- House orientation on lot
- Foundation and floors
- Walls and ceilings
- Outer doors
- Windows and glass patio doors
- Air infiltration
- Ventilation
- Hot-water system(s)
- Heating and cooling system(s)
- Appliances and lighting systems

The above items, except for house design, are covered by the separate sections that follow.

HOUSE DESIGN

Before the development and widespread use of modern air conditioning systems houses were mainly designed on a regional basis to obtain maximum "natural" air conditioning. Each climatic region of the country developed houses whose architectural features tended to reduce the undesired effect of the sun, wind and temperature extremes of the area. Low, rambling ranch-style western homes suited to the hot summers of the South and West were never built in the East while the house styles typical of the colder regions (Northeast and Northwest) were not built in the warmer regions.

The advent of the modern air-conditioning systems made it possible to design a house to realize a high level of bodily comfort on a strictly mechanical basis without regard for "natural" air conditioning gained by house design to suit the climatic conditions of a given locale. In fact, houses were (and are) often designed on the basis the windows would never be opened since to do so would upset the air-conditioning operation. It has been said that one could live most comfortably in a grass hut in Maine during the winter time if one could afford the air-conditioning bill.

The rising cost of energy and the uncertain future of energy sources has now made it mandatory that houses be designed to realize a good level of physical comfort with an absolute minimum expenditure of energy for air-conditioning purposes. House design, in brief, must make a return to use of house positioning on the lot, window shading, cross ventilation, etc. to ease the load on the air-conditioning system.

HOUSE STYLING

There are two extreme schools of thought on how to build an energy-efficient home. These are:

- Improve energy efficiency by making the house smaller, with reduced (less) window and door area and by raising the insulation level somewhat. Vaulted and cathedral ceilings are to be avoided and glass area is reduced to an absolute minimum. The thinking is—with less square feet of outer wall and glass to lose or gain heat through and with less internal cubic feet of space to heat and cool—energy efficiency is assured.

  And so it is but at a cost. Few people want to make such sacrifices, especially as related to window area.

- Improve energy efficiency primarily by increasing insulation to a maximum and by paying extreme attention to reducing or eliminating air infiltration. Vaulted or cathedral ceilings are generally considered only for the family room, with flat ceilings being used throughout the rest of the home. Large window area is "justified" by use of double-glazed windows and (sometimes) adding storm windows on the north or windy side of the house.

A balance between the two schools of thought would seem to be the best choice and will certainly result in a beautiful home with beautiful energy bills.

Here are some thoughts on "ideal" house design from an energy-saving viewpoint:

- In climatic areas where heating is the major concern:

- least amount of walls and windows should face North.

- if front faces North, avoid "U" shaped, "L" shaped and long rambling houses and those with deep entry-ways. These designs tend to trap the wind and thus increase air infiltration.

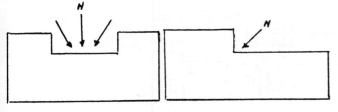

Note

However, use of metal-clad doors with their excellent weatherstripping, double-glazed windows and good draft-prevention techniques can reduce the wind effect.

- if solar energy entering through the windows is planned to assist in house heating, house area most needing heating should face south (within 15° or less).

- if summer-time cooling is no problem, roof could be covered with dark-colored shingles to increase heat build-up in the attic during the winter period.

- In climatic areas where cooling is the major concern:

  - least amount of windows and walls should face South.

  - window shading by roof overhang, shades, porches, trees, etc. will be needed, especially for southern exposure.

  - light-colored walls and roofing should be considered to avoid heat absorption during the summer.

- If solar energy is planned for hot-water or house heating (now or in the future), rear of house should face South (within 15° or less).

- Roof style should permit for an insulated and ventilated attic area to isolate the living area from the roof-top temperature.

- A two-story home is generally slightly less expensive to heat and cool but does have the disadvantage that the lower-floor windows are not provided with roof overhang for sun shading. Awnings, shades, etc. would thus be needed.

ZONED AIR CONDITIONING

Zoned air conditioning is an excellent method of maintaining ideal home comfort with minimum energy costs. Zoning is based upon the real need for air conditioning in the living area only during the "awake" hours and in the bedrooms only during the "sleeping" hours. Thus, if the bedrooms are grouped into one area that can be shut off from the living area during the daytime, separate air conditioners can be used for each area—the living area and the sleeping area. A house having excellent air-

conditioning zoning possibilities is illustrated in Figure 9-1.

Note by Figure 9-1 that a pocket door (a sliding door that disappears into the wall) could be fitted in the hallway to the three bedrooms. When closed, the pocket door would effectively seal off the bedrooms from the remainder of the house. Assuming a house with 2000 square feet of living space and a locale of moderate winters and summers, four tons of air conditioning would suffice. This sizing would also hold for a heat pump. Two units could be used, a 1½ ton unit for the bedroom area and a 2½ ton unit for the remainder of the house. Generally, only one unit at a time would be turned on, resulting in excellent energy savings. Of course, it would be best to insulate the inner walls common to the bedroom area to really isolate the bedrooms from the remainder of the house. Insulation batts, R11 (3-inch thick) are recommended. Note that these should *not* be of the vapor-barrier type. This insulation would have a second benefit, that of noise reduction.

The floor plan illustrated by Figure 9-1 also offers a second air-conditioning zoning possibility as related to heating. That is, if a pocket door was fitted into the doorway from the entry hall into the family room and a second pocket door was fitted into the doorway between the kitchen and the dining room, the entire family room, kitchen and dinette could be shut off from the rest of the house. A free-standing fireplace (an excellent heat source) could be installed in the family room area and would suffice to keep the entire closed-in area warm (all by itself) during all but very cold days (near zero or below). Note that an in-wall fireplace would not be as efficient as the free-standing unit unless it is built to deliver heat on a warm-air basis and not by radiation alone. For additional details, refer to "In-Wall Fireplaces, Section 17."

HOT-WATER ZONING

The house plan illustrated by Figure 9-1 also offers excellent hot-water zoning. That is, if a hot-water tank was installed in the garage directly opposite the sink and dishwasher in the kitchen and the clothes washer in the service area, extremely short runs of hot-water piping would result. A second (but smaller) hot-water tank could be located directly overhead above baths 1 and 2 in the sleeping area or the unit could be mounted on the outer wall and boxed in. The very short hot-water pipe runs offered by this hot-water zoning would result in almost immediate hot water being obtained when called upon. The extreme waste of hot water (and thus energy) and of water associated with long runs of hot-water piping would thus be avoided. For additional details, refer to "Piping Loss," Section 16.

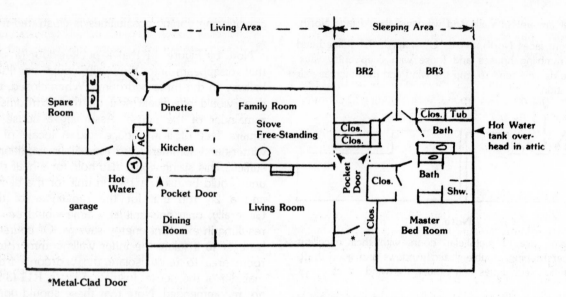

Figure 9-1. Air-Conditioning Zoning

ENERGY-SAVER HOME EXAMPLES

To assist in designing an energy-saver home, four examples of true energy-saving homes are now given. Two groups of homes as designed and constructed by private enterprise, one group (two homes) as developed under Federal direction, and the author's home.

THE ARKANSAS STORY

In Little Rock, Arkansas, some five years ago, a small group of far-sighted pioneers started to build houses to a very high level of energy efficiency. The results were outstanding as to energy efficiency, so much so the figures for heating and cooling costs are almost unbelievable. Yet, the air-conditioning loads on these Arkansas houses were monitored by use of separate meters on the air conditioner (a heat pump).

The houses ranged in size from 1040 to 1200 square feet of living space, with 10 of the houses having separate meters installed for the air conditioner. With a KWH cost ranging from 1.7 to 2.0 cents per KWH, the cost to *heat and cool* the houses ranged from *$60.00 to $100.00 annually.* That's right—per year.

The figures sound incredible yet they are true, proven by the builders and appreciated and enjoyed by those fortunate enough to have purchased one. And, all who live in them report a very high level of living comfort which, in itself, makes this energy-saver design worthwhile.

The whole wonderful story has been assembled into a multi-page report by Owens/Corning Fiberglas which makes fascinating reading. The report—Publication No. 4-BL-6958-B—can be requested from Owens/Corning Fiberglas, Fiberglas Tower, Toledo, Ohio, 43659, price

$2.00. The report gives full details on building techniques and states the houses can actually be built to a very high level of energy efficiency with little or no extra cost over that related to FHA Minimum Property Standards cost. The building techniques, of course, can be used for houses of larger square footage than the 1040 and 1200 square-foot houses discussed in the report.

The Arkansas houses feature the following energy-saving items and construction techniques:

- Outer walls - 2 x 6 stud walls, filled with R19 (6" thick) insulation batts.

- Ceilings - covered with 12" (R38) of insulation batts.

- Window area - approximately 8% of total living-space floor area.

- Windows - double-glazed, insulating.

- Doors, outer - metal-clad, magnetic weatherstripping.

- Foundation - perimeter insulation (2" thick).

- Attic ventilation - powered ventilators on roof in conjunction with eave (soffit) vents.

- Roofing - light-colored asphalt shingles.

- Air conditioner - heat pump, 2-ton, minimum sized—using ducting system run entirely within house.

- Other - humidifier, dehumidifier and electronic dust-precipitator used.

- Draft prevention - extreme care taken to reduce air infiltration to a minimum.

To heat and cool a home, even a moderate-sized one, for a yearly cost of $90.00 to $100.00 at a 2 cent KWH rate is outstanding. Even at a KWH rate of 4 cents, a yearly total of $200.00 maximum is still a remarkable figure. Agreed, the houses are of moderate size and the winter-summer temperatures in Little Rock are rather moderate. Yet, the houses illustrate what can be done.

A point of special interest here is to note that the houses are "ordinary" in appearance, gaining their high energy efficiency by use of well-thought-out building techniques and use of modern insulation along with reduction of air infiltration coupled with use of a heat pump.

MISSION VIEJO HOUSES

In Mission Viejo, California, about 50 miles south of Los Angeles, two Minimum Energy Dwellings (MED) were built to test many new and some old energy-saving materials and building techniques. The project is jointly conducted and financed by the Federal Energy Research and Development Agency, the Southern California Gas Co., and Mission Viejo, a realty development company.

The Mission Viejo houses feature the following energy-saving items and construction techniques:

- Outer walls - 2 x 6 stud walls, filled with R19 (6" thick) insulation batts.

- Ceilings - covered with 10" (R30) insulation batts.

- Window area - less than standard, narrow windows used and fitted into room corners for wall-bounce of light and to provide cross ventilation.

- Windows - double-glazed, wood framed, fitted with adjustable miniature Venetian blinds between panes. Few windows face southwest and side windows are equipped with window wings for shading purposes. All windows shaded with a 3' roof overhang.

- Front door - metal-clad with insulated core. Two outer doors are used, an inner and outer door to a vestibule. This provides a sort of air lock to prevent drafts normally felt when an outer door is opened.

- Garage area door - metal-clad with insulated core, opening into vestibule related to front door.

- Foundation - slab type, with 2" thick insulation panels around perimeter and slab edge.

- Attic ventilation - ridge vents provided across entire top of roof, operating with eave vents.

- Roofing - cement tiles, red—provide six to seven-hour infiltration lag of heat travel through the tile. (Most effective in areas where evening temperatures are markedly below daytime temperatures.)

- Air conditioner - heated and cooled by solar energy, using a "special" unit designed for the homes. Ducts run in attic and are heavily insulated. A clock is provided to setback the thermostat(s) during the sleeping hours.

- Draft prevention - extreme measures taken to reduce air change in house. House is equipped with a "purging" system that operates to turn off the air conditioner (as a heater or cooler) when the outside temperature is "right." Purging system then pumps outside air into house, exhausting house air out via a relief damper in rear wall. Air flow is through air-conditioning ducts.

If the outside air temperature drops below or rises above the "right" temperature, the purging system is cut off and the air conditioner is turned on again.

Entire outside wall is covered with 8-mil plastic sheeting to act as a second vapor barrier (first barrier is provided by insulation batts in walls) and to practically eliminate drafts entering through the house envelope.

- Shading - front-door entry is recessed to shade door while the garden patio is covered with a solid roof plus slats on outside edge to shade glass sliding doors to bedrooms. Shrubs were planted to shade other windows, where possible. A 3-foot roof overhang was also provided to shade windows and outer wall.

- Appliances - compressor (major heat source) is removed from refrigerator and housed in an insulated box. In the winter, the compressor heat is vented into the living area—in the summer, the heat is passed up and out through the roof via a vent.

Gas stove is pilotless while the oven features a fan that swirls the air around in the oven to cut roasting time in half (or less).

- Ventilation - an air vent is not provided in the bathroom— the air is passed over a chemical filter to remove humidity and odor. Though not stated, it seems in order that the kitchen stove-oven may be similarly vented. Such units are now available.

Clothes dryer obtains warm air from outside rather than using house air. Washer and dryer are mounted in a closet behind an airtight door (metal-clad with magnetic weatherstripping) to isolate the heat and humidity developed by units from living area.

The Mission Viejo homes have been occupied for about six months and figures on heating and cooling plus hot-water heating (solar-assisted) indicate the houses will use about 70% less energy than other identical size homes in the same area. An interesting article on the Mission Viejo homes is featured in the Popular Mechanics magazine of July 1977.

AUTHOR'S HOME

The author's home was completed in 1975 and reflects the energy-saving knowledge of the time. Today, late 1979, a much higher level of energy efficiency as to heating and cooling the home can be built into a house. The monthly heating and cooling costs on a four-house comparison are given by Table 7-2, Section 7. The author's home (House D in Table 7-2), as compared to Houses A and B, realized the following energy savings on heating and cooling.

House A - $97.62 per month x 12 = $1,171.44 - $600.72 =
$570.72 greater than House D = 1.95 times
House B - $76.05 per month x 12 = $912.60 - $600.72 =
$311.88 greater than House D = 1.52 times
House C - $56.73 per month x 12 = $680.76 - $600.72 =
$80.04 greater than House D = 1.13 times

The heating and cooling bills for House D versus energy used by House A were such that House D used only 51% of the energy used by House A. For House B figures, House D used 66% of the energy used by House B. Furthermore, both House A and B had been upgraded as to energy efficiency on a heating and cooling basis thus had House D been compared against houses built only to FHA Minimum Property Standards, the savings would have been even greater. The percentage savings of House D over Houses A and B were thus 49% and 34%, respectively. Using the energy-saving materials and building techniques available today (late 1979), a house built to the "new" level of energy efficiency made necessary by the energy shortage would easily save up to 65% on heating and cooling costs over "standard" FHA Minimum Property Standard homes.

BOB SCHMITT HOMES

A highly progressive firm, Bob Schmitt Homes, Inc., of Strongsville, Ohio, has pioneered in the building of energy efficient homes. A bar graph developed by Bob Schmitt Homes, Figure 9-2, graphically shows the excellent energy savings realized by use of increasing levels of insulation, installation of metal-clad doors and double-glazed windows, etc. The bar graph shows four levels of energy efficiency, as follows:

1. *Lowest* - has R11 insulation over ceilings, none in the walls, an insulated slab and with "standard" (little) attention paid to draft prevention. These are the "well-built" houses that have energy bills in the hundreds of dollars per month. Less than FHA Minimum Property Standards. Total BTU drain per year = 105,232,800.

2. *FHA+ Level* - has R11 insulation in walls, R19 over ceilings, an insulated slab, double-glazed windows and somewhat more attention paid to draft prevention. Energy efficiency is slightly better than that related to FHA Minimum Property Standards. A better house than (1) above but is badly out of date as related to the energy crisis. Total BTU drain per year = 71,539,800 or 32% less than house 1.

3. *Higher Level* - has metal-clad outer doors, R11 walls, R25 ceilings, better insulated slab, no patio (glass) door and with extra attention paid to draft prevention. An excellent sample of an energy-saver home and is highly recommended for all areas except those experiencing extreme temperature changes (or where electric-strip heating will be used). Total BTU drain per year = 55,525,300 or 47% less than house 1 and 22.4% less than house 2.

4. *New Level* - has metal-clad outer doors, R18 walls, R25 ceilings, increased slab insulation, double-glazed windows, sealed sill and door-window openings and very special attention paid to draft prevention. An excellent house and it should return excellent energy savings even in areas experiencing very severe temperature changes (even if electric-strip heating is used). Total BTU drain per year = 33,369,100 or 68.3% less than level 1, 53% less than level 2, and 40% less than level 3.

The bar graph BTU figures reveal that a house built to level 4 will, for heating and cooling purposes, use only 31.7% of the energy used by a home built to level 1. When the additional energy saved because of the extreme care taken as to weatherstripping and caulking is taken into account, a total energy savings of *at least 75%* is clearly indicated.

The Bob Schmitt Homes firm also made careful tests and energy-use measurements on two houses identical as to house design, size and construction techniques except for energy-efficiency features. Each house was in the same immediate area and each was occupied by a family of three. House particulars are:

House A
- Insulated to level No. 2 on bar graph.
- Heated by a 160,000 BTUH input gas furnace & cooled by a G.E. condensing unit and coil attached to the furnace.
- 1990 square feet of living space
- Energy used for heating and cooling and all other purposes:

Natural gas = 175,200 cu ft = $521.28 @ $2.975 per MCF av.
Electricity = 15,770 KWH = +$630.80 @ 4¢ per KWH av.
+$1,152.08 = $96.00 per month
= 4.824¢ per sq ft per month

House B
- Insulated to level No. 3 on bar graph.
- Heated and cooled by two 2-ton G.E. heat pumps.
- 1990 square feet of living space.
- Energy used for heating and cooling and all other purposes:

Electricity = 28,045 KWH + $1,121.80 @ 4¢ per KWH average
= $93.48 per month average
= 4.697¢ per sq ft per month

Comparison

House A - insulated to level No. 22 = $1,152.08 per year
House B - insulated to level No. 3 = –$1,121.80 per year
= $30.28 per year

The above illustrates that by raising the energy-efficiency level from Level 2 to Level 3 (as shown on the

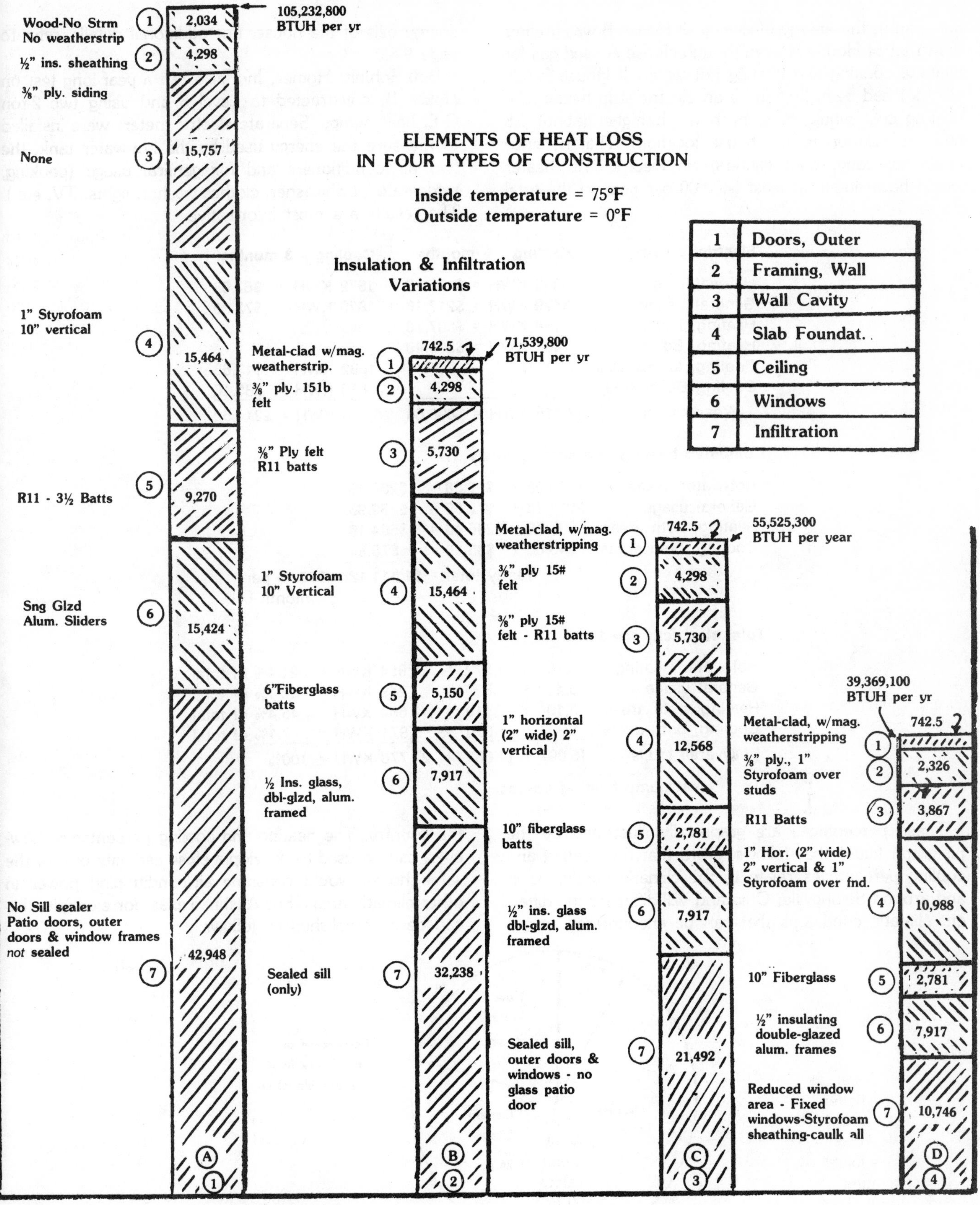

ELEMENTS OF HEAT LOSS
IN FOUR TYPES OF CONSTRUCTION

Inside temperature = 75°F
Outside temperature = 0°F

Insulation & Infiltration
Variations

1	Doors, Outer
2	Framing, Wall
3	Wall Cavity
4	Slab Foundat.
5	Ceiling
6	Windows
7	Infiltration

Column A (1) — 105,232,800 BTUH per yr

Wood-No Strm No weatherstrip — (1) 2,034
½" ins. sheathing — (2) 4,298
⅜" ply. siding
None — (3) 15,757
1" Styrofoam 10" vertical — (4) 15,464
R11 - 3½ Batts — (5) 9,270
Sng Glzd Alum. Sliders — (6) 15,424
No Sill sealer Patio doors, outer doors & window frames *not* sealed — (7) 42,948

(A) (1)

Column B (2) — 71,539,800 BTUH per yr

Metal-clad w/mag. weatherstrip. — (1) 742.5
⅜" ply. 151b felt — (2) 4,298
⅜" Ply felt R11 batts — (3) 5,730
1" Styrofoam 10" Vertical — (4) 15,464
6"Fiberglass batts — (5) 5,150
½ Ins. glass, dbl-glzd, alum. framed — (6) 7,917
Sealed sill (only) — (7) 32,238

(B) (2)

Column C (3) — 55,525,300 BTUH per year

Metal-clad, w/mag. weatherstripping — (1) 742.5
⅜" ply 15# felt — (2) 4,298
⅜" ply 15# felt - R11 batts — (3) 5,730
1" horizontal (2" wide) 2" vertical — (4) 12,568
10" fiberglass batts — (5) 2,781
½" ins. glass dbl-glzd, alum. framed — (6) 7,917
Sealed sill, outer doors & windows - no glass patio door — (7) 21,492

(C) (3)

Column D (4) — 39,369,100 BTUH per yr

Metal-clad, w/mag. weatherstripping — (1) 742.5
⅜" ply., 1" Styrofoam over studs — (2) 2,326
R11 Batts — (3) 3,867
1" Hor. (2" wide) 2" vertical & 1" Styrofoam over fnd. — (4) 10,988
10" Fiberglass — (5) 2,781
½" insulating double-glazed alum. frames — (6) 7,917
Reduced window area - Fixed windows-Styrofoam sheathing-caulk all — (7) 10,746

(D) (4)

Reproduced by permission of Bob Schmitt Homes, Inc.

Figure 9-2. Heat Loss in Four Types of Construction

9-6

bar graph), the energy efficiency of House B was greater than that of House A even though House A used gas for heating, cooking and heating hot water. If House B (all-electric) had been heated by an electric-strip heater, the heating cost would have been much higher (about 1.8 times in relation to the house location). That is, since Ohio has long, cold winters, an electric-strip heater would have added at least $400.00 per year to the total energy bills of the house. For additional details, refer to page 9-8.

Bob Schmitt Homes, Inc. also ran a year-long test on House B, constructed to Level 3 and using two 2-ton G.E. heat pumps. Separate electric meters were installed to measure the energy used by the hot-water tank, the two air conditioners and for general usage (cooking, refrigerator, dishwasher, clothes washer, lights, TV, etc.). The results are most informative.

Electricity User	Heating - 9 months	Cooling - 3 months
Hot-water heating	4382 KWH = $175.28	1572 KWH = $62.88
General Usage	5429 KWH = $217.16	1820 KWH = $72.80
Heating, Living Area	5194 KWH = $207.76	
Heating, Bdrm area	7401 KWH = $296.40	
Cooling, Living area		1092 KWH = $43.68
Cooling Bdrm area		879 KWH = $35.16
Yearly totals	22,415 KWH = $896.60	5,363 KWH = $214.52

Combined heating and cooling totals

Hot-water usage	$175.28 + $62.88 =	$238.16
General usage	$217.16 + $72.80 =	$289.96
*Heating, both areas	$207.76 + $296.40 =	$504.16
Cooling, both areas	$43.68 + $35.16 =	$78.84

Yearly total = $1,111.12 = $92.59 per month

Total electricity used

Hot-water Heating	4,382 +	1,572 =	5,954 KWH =	21.4% of total
General usage	5,429 +	1,820 =	7,249 KWH =	26.1% of total
*Heating, both areas	5,194 +	7,410 =	12,604 KWH =	45.4% of total
Cooling, both areas	1,092 +	879 =	1,971 KWH =	7.1% of total
Overall totals	16,097 +	11,681 =	27,778 KWH =	100%

*Heat pump heating figures

These percentages are graphically illustrated by the pie-graph figure that follows. Note that the heating and cooling percentages relate to the climatic conditions in and around Strongville, Ohio and will differ for the different climatic conditions that can be encountered across the country. The heating and cooling percentages, however, can be used to develop a close estimate of how the same house would consume air-conditioning power in other climatic areas. For Austin, Texas, for example, this can be accomplished as follows:

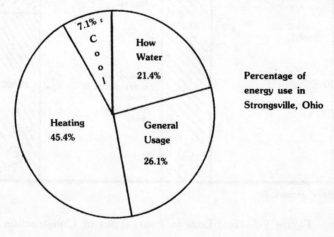

Percentage of energy use in Strongsville, Ohio

Strongsville, Ohio - Degree Days, Cooling = 800
Degree Days, Heating = 5,600
Total = 6,400

Austin, Texas - Degree Days, Cooling = 2,850
Degree Days, Heating = 1,800
Total = 4,650

Ratio, heating = 5,600 to 1800 = 0.32 = 32%
Ratio, cooling = 800 to 2850 = 3.56 = 356%

Austin heating vs Strongsville = 45.4% x 0.32 = 14.5%
Austin cooling vs Strongsville = 7.1% x 3.56 = 25.3%
52.5% versus 39.8%

Thus, a house in Strongsville, Ohio using 52.5% of its total energy for heating and cooling would use only 39.8% if located in Austin, Texas

The figures obtained are only approximate but should be accurate to within a few percent.

Separate metering on the hot-water heater revealed a drain of 5,954 KWH's which, at a 4-cent KWH rate, cost $238.16 per year. This indicates the importance of saving on hot water by careful use, by insulating the tank to save on tank losses, by insulating the pipes and by zoning of hot-water heaters.

The KWH used by the two 2-ton heat pumps indicates the energy savings that can be realized by using a split system (two units) and by being able to shut off the sleeping area from the living area. The sleeping area unit can thus be shut off except for the sleeping hours, being turned on about one hour before bedtime and shut off when the occupants get up. The living unit can then be turned on when the house temperature warms up, remaining on until shortly before bedtime. The net savings in energy usage is considerable and makes a split system worthy of careful consideration.

The electricity used to heat the test home under discussion by means of an electric-strip heater rather than a heat pump can be established rather accurately. Since a heat-pump (in the Strongsville, Ohio area) has an efficiency ratio of 1.8 versus 1 for the electric-strip furnace, we can arrive at the cost by multiplying the heat pump heating figure (from page 9-7) by the heat pump efficiency figure.

Heat pump figure x 1.8 = $504.16 x 1.8 = $907.49
Heat pump figure   -504.16
Electric-strip furnace extra cost per year = $403.33

The cost to heat the house with natural gas can also be developed from the house example. The BTUH's used to heat the house (both areas) as developed by the heat pump can be factored by the heat pump efficiency to arrive at the actual BTUH's that will need to be developed by the gas furnace to achieve the same heating effect.

The heating costs (approximate) for the test house for a heat pump, electric-strip furnace or a gas furnace would be as follows:

Gas furnace = $287.86
Heat pump = $504.16 ($216.30 more than gas)
El.-strip   = $907.49 ($619.63 more than gas)

Heat pump heating KWH's   =   12,604 (obtained from page 9-7)
Factored by heat pump eff.   x 1.8
                                  22,687.2 KWH's
Converted to BTU's   x 3,412 BTU's
Heating total, per year   77,408,726 BTU's

Gas cost = Heating BTU's = 77,408,726 = 96,760 cu. ft. of gas
           1,000 x .8 eff.   800

1,000 BTU's developed from 1 cubic foot of gas, 100% efficiency

96,760 cu. ft. x $2.975 per 1,000 = 96.76 x $2.975 = $287.86

THE QUINTON COMPANY HOMES

The Quinton Company, Beaumont, Texas has built many energy-saver homes in the Beaumont area, building and equipping them as detailed below. The energy bills for a few of their homes are given by Table 9-1. Beaumont, Texas experiences rather mild winter (1500 degree days, average) but the summers are long, hot and humid (4000 degree days, average). The 2-year average monthly bills given by Table 9-1 have been factored to the 1980 KWH average of 4.7¢ per KWH. Even so, note the very low bills for these all-electric homes (with the exception of the 1776-square foot house). Energy bills so low they tend to be disbelieved by many yet they are attainable by any who will build to the same energy-saving standards. These standards now follow.

Air Conditioning and Heating

High efficiency heat pump - EER-7.5 or better at 95°F
COP2.5 or better at 17°F

Rectangular duct system of fiber board with a minimum 4# density run in attic or through furred-down system.

When construction design will permit, locate indoor air handler in closet in air-conditioned space.

Attic Ventilation

Garages and porches and attic-space not above conditioned space should have same ventilation as over conditioned space. Attic should have 1.5 sq. inches of ventilation per sq. ft. of ceiling area. Ridge venting or power venting may be used.

Table 9-1. QUINTON ENERGY-SAVER HOMES

| Square Footage | | | Insulating | | No. of | Air Conditioning | 2-Yr. Avg. |
Living Area	Windows	Doors	Windows	Doors	Occupants	Details	@4.7¢ KWH
1186	67	74	No	No	1	2-ton Heat Pump	$ 31.57
1524	141	56	No	No	5	2½-ton Heat Pump w/10-kw heat strips#	$ 76.01
1776	141	47	No	No	4	2½-ton A/C with 3-ton coil. 80,000 BTU gas furnace.	$ 74.00
1906	204	38	No	No	2	3-ton Heat Pump w/10 KW heat strips#	$ 47.00
2328	145	76	Yes	No	3	3-ton Heat Pump w/10 KW heat strips#	$ 50.76
2416	280	38	Yes	No	5	4-ton Heat Pump w/20 KW heat strips#	$ 90.82
3378	181	88	Yes	No	4	2½-ton A/C w/10 KW heat strips. 2½-ton Heat Pump w/10KW heat strips#	$ 92.80
3445	338*	80	Yes	Yes	5	2 2½-ton Heat Pumps each w/10 KW heat strips#	$121.99

\# Auxiliary heat strips — used only when heat pump efficiency drops too low to maintain selected house-temperature.
* plus 30 sq. ft. of insulated sky lights.

To accommodate 10½ thick (R-30) insulation, air baffles should be installed for each eave-vent opening to allow air passage into the attic and for the insulation to be installed out over the outer plate levels.

Attic Insulation

Open attic area where blown-in insulation can be installed should have R-30 installed. This may be obtained as follows:

Rockwool	10¾ inches	= R-30
Glass fiber	13¾ inches	= R-30
Wood fiber	7½ inches	= R-30

Check amount blown-in in accordance with manufacturer's specification printed on each bag of insulation.

For vaulted ceilings, framing should be able to accommodate a 6″ (R-19) and a 3″ (R11) batt to achieve an R-30 insulation level. If framing cannot accept the two batts, R-19 (6″) batts

can be installed between the ceiling joists and a 1″ thick TG Styrofoam insulating sheathing can be nailed to the bottom of the joists. Note the Styrofoam must be covered with sheet rock (gypsum board) for fire purposes.

Where vaulted ceilings are used and knee walls or attic walls are created, the attic side of these walls should have R-11 fitted between the studs and a 1″ thick TG Styrofoam sheathing nailed on the attic side.

Exterior Wall Framing

All exterior walls enclosing an air-conditioned space shall have R-11 (3″ thick) batts installed between the studs. On the outside, 1″-thick TG Styrofoam (R-5.5) shall be nailed and shall extend up the full height of the stud wall. For areas experiencing high summer-time humidity levels, a vapor barrier of 6-mil polyethylene shall be nailed over the Styrofoam sheathing and shall extend down to partially cover the brick (or stone) ledge. For all other areas not experiencing extremely high humidity levels, the 6-mil polyethylene film shall be nailed to the wall studs on the inside and shall extend down to the floor. The polyethylene film shall be applied before the windows and doors as they are installed. The polyethylene film should overlap at least 24″ at any seams.

Caulking

A polymetric foam (Polycel One or equivalent) shall be used. After all plumbing and electric work is roughed in and all window and exterior doors are installed, caulk as follows:

On interior of house, caulk all sole plates to the concrete slab. (Run a bead along sole plates where they touch the slab floor.)

Caulk all openings made by plumbers or electricians through the upper plates and through the exterior sheathing of the building.

Caulk frames of all windows and outer doors to the building, both on the outside (exterior) and inside (interior).

Caulk any loose joints, breaks, cracks, gaps, etc. in the exterior sheathing.

All caulking **must** be accomplished **before** the insulation batts (R-11 minimum) are installed between the studs.

Ventilation

Fireplaces — install a fresh-air vent/duct system to bring in combustion air for the fire to avoid using internal air. Duct system may run through slab to the outside or be obtained from the attic.

Clothes Dryer — if clothes dryer is located in air-conditioned space, a 4″ vent/duct should be installed form the building outside to the dryer location. This will permit the exhaust air from the dryer to be vented outside. The vent/duct system shall be equipped with a back-draft damper to close off the vent when the dryer is not in use.

Kitchen Vent-a-Hood — should be vented to the outside of building through a duct system using a back-draft damper.

Bathroom Vents — shall be vented into the attic space.

Windows

Where possible, keep window area down. Perferably, windows should be double-glazed thermopane type or, if single-glazed windows are used, insulating (storm) windows should be installed over them.

Outer Doors

All outer doors should be insulating type, preferably steel-clad so that magnetic weatherstripping can be used. All other doors must be tightly weatherstripped.

THE BURNS COMPANY HOMES

The Burns Company of San Antonio, Texas, Buddy Burns, President, builds energy-saver homes that realize ex-

tremely low energy bills. The Burns Company plan their housing subdivisions to obtain the best sun angle for each house, to protect solar privacy to the best degree possible and to stagger houses to provide for excellent natural ventilation for all houses. Their pride in the houses they build is such that they have prepared a checkout that lists the energy-efficiency features of their houses so that this list may be used to check out homes built by other home builders. The checkout list relates to the three main features of a house that determine almost totally it's inherent energy-use efficiency. These main features are:

Basic Design Items - house orientation, type and shape, and windows.

Integral Thermal Protection - insulation and weatherization.

Mechanical Systems - type and efficiency of air conditioning - hot water systems.

The checkout list is both complete and self explanatory and reflects the very advanced energy-saving knowledge and enthusiasm of the Burns Company. Located at the end of this section, this excellent checkout list can be used on both a new-home and existing-home basis. Note the author has made cross reference, wherever possible, to material within this book that relates to the items of the checkout list in case additional detail is felt necessary. The author suggests, most seriously, that if you are planning on building a new home that you use this checkout list to guide your talks with your architect and builder. If you are planning on purchasing an already-built home, use the checkout list as a guide to determine it's inherent energy-use efficiency.

SUMMARY

We have had years of warning — even before the oil embargo of 1973-74 — and yet so little has really been accomplished as related to home building when one considers the entire country. A few companies, led by far-sighted and thoughtful men, are leading the way. They have shown what can be done, that the cost is moderate and will be repaid in a few years and how basically simple it all really is. The companies, the men featured in this book are a "few of the few" and they are all to be highly commended. They are designing and building houses that are true energy savers, that will help with our serious energy problem and that will save their owners energy dollars year after year. They are the "new pioneers", they are leading the way and it is to be seriously hoped that all other home builders learn from these pioneers.

Many other builders advertise they "build energy-saver homes" and talk about the "energy package", the "energy-saver construction", etc. Regretfully, all too often this is merely words used in their advertisements and the homes they build are not energy savers in any true sense. Other builders try to build energy-saver homes and are disappointed with the results saying "I put in the full package of energy-saver materials and equipment, and yet the resulting savings do not warrant the extra capital outlay." The builders who build true energy-saver homes all are knowledgeable and enthusiastic as to building their energy-saver homes and build them right — they put in the whole package.

That is, they exercise two types of quality control — one related to ensuring the house is built to the best standards of home construction and the second, to ensure that the house is properly insulated and weatherized. They know that small gaps, breaks or tears in the insulation blanket can have an energy-loss effect all out of proportion to the size of the gaps, breaks or tears. They realize that "a drafty house is an energy waster and that it will not gain full benefit from any other energy-saving features built into the house." They thus train their men, their subcontractors to install insulation properly to ensure the house envelope is wrapped in an insulation blanket that is complete and provides the necessary thermal barrier. They also train their men, their subcontractors to seal the house, to weatherize it to the new standards. They realize there is no such thing as a "small draft". A "small draft" is like a small hole in a gas tank of a car. In just a few hours, a full tank can leak out, a drop at a time, endlessly, hour after hour.

Nothing can be left to chance, everything must be done properly and all work must be constantly inspected and corrected as needed. Attention to detail is the key — at least for now special care must be taken to ensure that the energy-saving potentials of insulation, insulating doors, multi-glazed glass, heat pumps, zoned hot-water systems, etc. are totally realized. Most care — most attention to detail — clearly relates to weatherization. Stopping the drafts — sealing them off permanently — is so easy, so inexpensive as compared to insulation and multi-glazed windows, etc., and has such a fantastic return of energy savings. Any builder who does not see this clearly will never build houses to realize very low energy bills, regardless of what other energy-saving features he may build into his houses.

The point of special interest to be noted as related to the Arkansas, Mission Viejo, Bob Schmitt, Herman Quinton, "Buddy" Burns, and the author's houses is this — these houses were built by home builders who *believed in the need for energy conservation* and had *studied and worked* to gain construction experience dedicated to building a home to the *very highest level of energy efficiency.* In particular, these builders understood and believed in the need for draft prevention and thus built a "tight" house. This is the point least understood and accepted by the conventional builder — they just don't seem to see how excessive air movement into and out of a house will rob it of heated or cooled air at a rapid and expensive rate.

The Arkansas and Mission Viejo houses were built using 2x6 studs in the outer walls rather than the conventional 2x4's. With 2x6 studs, a wall cavity of about 5½" is provided thus an R19 (6" thick) can be fitted into the wall

cavity. Taking into account the added insulation (R) value related to the inner sheathing (sheetrock, usually) and the outer sheathing, an R20+ wall is realized. Alternately, 2x4 stud walls can be used, providing a 3½" wall cavity to take an R13 insulation. Additional insulation can be fitted in the form of insulation panels to the outside of the wall that can raise the total wall insulation to R17+ while still using a conventional thickness of wall. For additional details, refer to table 11-1, page 11-3.

The Arkansas and Mission Viejo homes and the Level 4 Bob Schmitt homes are about equal in energy efficiency as it relates to house heating and cooling (not taking into account the Mission Viejo home's solar system). The Quinton Company and Burns Company homes are in a class by themselves — super energy savers.

These homes thus substantiate the statements made by the American Institute of Architects that a home "can be built to save up to 80% of the energy used to heat and cool a poorly constructed, uninsulated and loose (drafty) home."

HEAT LOSS-GAIN PERCENTAGES

Many tests have been made by university groups, business firms and the government to determine the percentage of energy transfer (heat loss or gain) through the various parts of the building envelope. The following percentages resulted from a study made on a "standard" 1-story house located in a Northern area. For Southern and Western areas the percentages would differ somewhat.

The energy-transfer percentages given on figure 9-3 are those obtained from measurements made on a house constructed to FHA Minimum Property Standards of insulation and air infiltration prevention. The heat loss-gain percentages for a home built to the new standards of insulation and draft prevention would most likely differ

Sketch from American Society Heating, Refrigeration, Air Conditioning Engineers Handbook of Fundamentals.

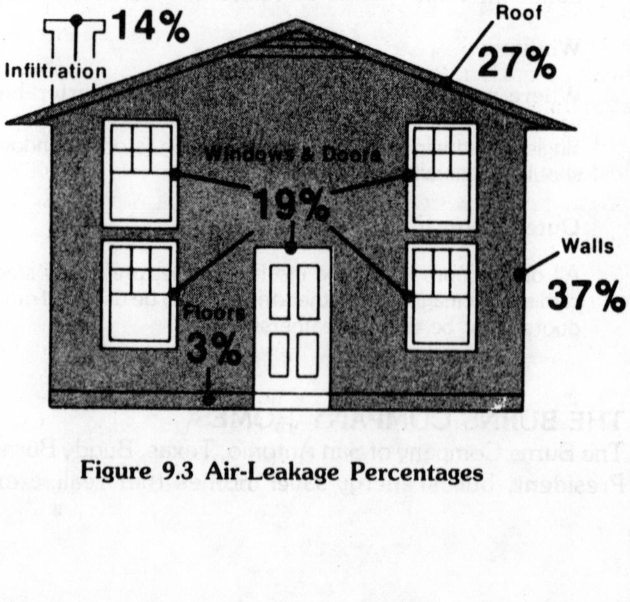

Figure 9.3 Air-Leakage Percentages

from those given. That is, the 19% air exchange listed as occurring through the outer doors and windows should be greatly reduced in a home made tight to the new standards. Also, the heat-loss and gain percentages occurring through the house envelope on a molecular basis might stay somewhat the same as those given by Figure 9-3 while the amounts would be reduced in relation to the energy-efficiency level of the home.

ENERGY-EFFICIENCY LEVEL NEEDED

The total of the energy-saving items and insulation levels listed and detailed in the following sections need not be used in all cases. To build to a particular energy-efficiency level many things must be taken into account. The major of these considerations are:

- Climatic conditions of house locale
- Available fuel and its energy efficiency
- House size and design
- House orientation on lot
- Landscaping
- Construction quality

Recommended energy saving features for various winter and summer conditions are given by Table 9-2. If gas is not available and oil or coal heating is not desired, a heat pump is highly recommended, with this recommendation holding if little or no cooling is needed. An electric-strip heater is just too expensive to run as the previous example showed.

Recommended minimum insulation for ceiling, walls and floor of houses in the various climatic areas of the 48 states are given by Figure 9-4.

Optimum recommended insulation for the attic of houses in the various climatic areas of the 48 states are given by Figure 9-5. The associated tables list suggested attic insulation levels for the five heating and cooling zones given. Note how the R value is raised for the various climatic zones as the cost of gas and electricity increases. Also, the tables show the extreme efficiency of a heat pump, with the tables reflecting the fact that the heat pump is up to 2.5 times as efficient as an electric-strip heater.

The dollar cost related to the amount of insulation installed and the number of energy-saving features incorporated into a house must be weighed (to a certain degree) against the dollar savings resulting from the energy saved. However, the following should be seriously considered when making the decision:

- Energy costs, high today, are certain to rise in the future.
- It is best to build a house now to the energy-efficiency level certain to be mandatory in the near future because energy costs will rise and rise and energy rationing is almost certain to occur, either on a permanent or temporary basis. Upgrading the energy efficiency of a house after it is built is more expensive and less efficient.
- The house can be more readily sold and for a better figure if it has a history of low energy bills.
- With natural gas stated to be in low reserve, natural gas may not be available in the future (10 years or so from now). Thus, it would be best to design the house for an "all-electric" energy efficiency—that is, to a higher insulation and energy-saver level than if gas would always be available.

If the house buying budget cannot stand the extra cost required to raise the energy-efficiency level of the desired house to that required by the energy crisis, it is seriously suggested that the money needed for the extra outlay be made available by reducing the house size slightly or by giving up some expensive decorative feature. It is far better to build a slightly smaller house with a high level of energy efficiency than to build a little larger (or fancier) energy-hog house. Upgrading energy efficiency is always more expensive and less effective.

If the budget for energy-saving items is limited, it might be helpful to know that the following items are considered to the the most needed and will return maximum dollar for dollar invested. These items are listed in what is considered to be the best energy-saving order.

1. Reduced air infiltration, gained by extra care in flashing and caulking all door and window openings and by caulking all possible draft sources—using a very high grade (10-year or better life span) caulking material.

2. "New-standard" levels of insulation in outer walls and over ceilings and under floors.

3. A heating and cooling system of maximum efficiency, sized for the living-area cubic-foot volume and for local climatic conditions—but—not oversized.

4. Double-glazed (insulating) windows, along with reduction in number or size of windows (if possible) and replacement (where possible) of slider windows with fixed windows—and, replacement (where possible) of glass outer doors with wood or metal-clad doors.

5. Metal-clad outer doors, insulating-core type, equipped with magnetic weatherstripping.

6. Insulated foundation or floor, plus sealing of sill (slab foundation) or sole plate (wood foundation).

7. Hot-water system, designed and insulated for maximum energy efficiency.

8. Attic ventilation, based on a high-level of attic insulation being used.

The above items are listed in what is thought to be the best order for energy savings, with cost not being taken into account. When cost is considered, the best "dollar-spent to savings-returned" order is thought to be items 1, 2, 5, 3, 4, 7, 6 and 8.

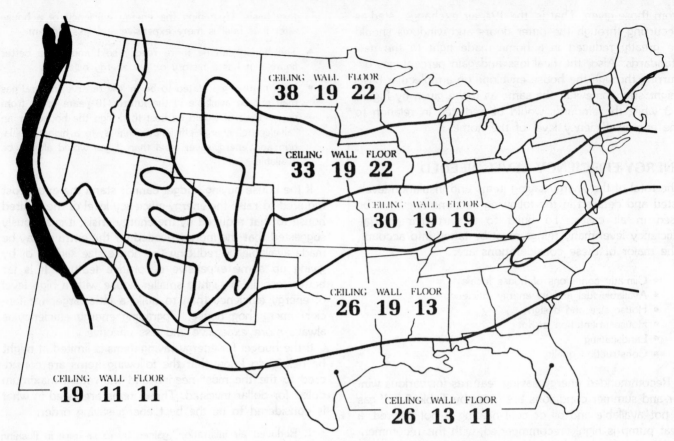

Figure 9-4. Recommended Minimum Insulation Values

Table 9-2. Recommended Energy Saving Features

Features	Winter Conditions				Summer Conditions			
	Severe	Moderate	Mild	Very Mild	Severe	Moderate	Mild	Very Mild
Slab fnd, uninsulated			X	X			X	X
Slab fnd, insulated perimeter		X	X			X	X	
Slab fnd, ins. perimeter & floor	X	X			X	X		
Crawl space, open, uninsulated				X				X
Crawl space, open, ins. floor	X	X	X					
Crawl space, closed, uninsulated			X				X	
Crawl space, closed, ins. perimeter	X	X	X		X	X	X	
Any fnd, lay down vapor barrier	X	X	X	X	X	X	X	X
Walls, insulated to R13			X	X			X	X
Walls, insulated to R18 to R20	X	X			X	X		
Ceiling, insulated to R19 min.			X	X			X	X
Ceiling, insulated to R26 min.		X				X		
Ceiling, insulated to R38 min.	X	X*			X			
Roof, light-colored roofing					X	X	X	
Roof overhang, 36" (std)							X	X
Roof overhang, wide (up to 48")					X	X		
Roof overhang-make into a porch					X	X		
Outer doors, solid-core wood			X	X			X	
Outer doors, insulating type	X	X	X#		X	X	X#	
Windows, single-glazed				X				X
Windows, double-glazed			X	X			X	X
Windows, sng glazed w/storm	X	X			X	X		
Windows, dbl glazed w/storm	X				X			

Features	Winter Conditions				Summer Conditions			
	Severe	Moderate	Mild	Very Mild	Severe	Moderate	Mild	Very Mild
Ventilation, whole house					x	x	x	
Attic, natural gable ventil.							x	x
Attic, powered gable ventil.						x		
Attic, natural chimney ventil.					x	x		
Attic, powered chimney ventil.					x	x		
Air infiltration, max. prevention	x	x	x	x	x	x	x	x
Heat pump, no gas or oil avail.	x	x	x		x	x	x	
High-efficiency cooler - EER8 min.					x	x		
Gas or oil-fired furnace, little cooling needed	x	x	x	x				

*If electric-strip heating is used.   #Optional

Winter heating

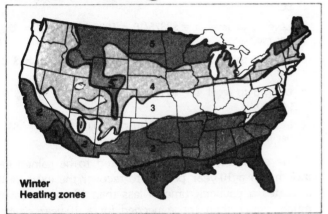

Winter Heating zones

Attic insulation for winter heating only								
Heating cost				Recommended insulation				
Gas (therm)	Oil (gallon)	Electric Resistance (kWh)	Electric heat pump (kWh)	Zone 1	Zone 2	Zone 3	Zone 4	Zone 5
9¢	13¢	—	1¢	R-19	R-19	R-19	R-19	R-19
12¢	17¢	—	1.3¢	R-19	R-19	R-19	R-19	R-30
15¢	21¢	—	1.7¢	R-19	R-19	R-19	R-30	R-30
18¢	25¢	1¢	2¢	R-19	R-19	R-19	R-30	R-30
24¢	34¢	1.3¢	2.6¢	R-19	R-19	R-30	R-33	R-38
30¢	42¢	1.6¢	3.3¢	R-19	R-19	R-30	R-33	R-38
36¢	50¢	2¢	4¢	R-19	R-30	R-33	R-38	R-44
54¢	75¢	3¢	6¢	R-19	R-30	R-38	R-49	R-49
72¢	$1.00	4¢	8¢	R-19	R-38	R-44	R-49	R-60
90¢	$1.25	5¢	10¢	R-19	R-38	R-49	R-57	R-66

Summer cooling

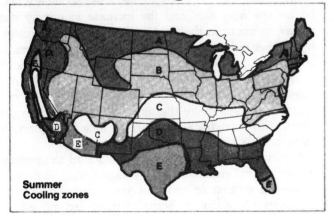

Summer Cooling zones

Optimum attic insulation for summer cooling plus heating						
Air conditioning cost		Recommended insulation				
Electric (kWh)	Gas (therm)	Zone A	Zone B	Zone C	Zone D	Zone E
1.5¢	9¢	*	*	R-19	R-19	R-19
2¢	12¢	*	*	R-30	R-19	R-19
2.5¢	15¢	*	R-33	R-30	R-19	R-19
3¢	18¢	*	R-38	R-33	R-30	R-30
4¢	24¢	*	R-44	R-38	R-30	R-30
5¢	30¢	*	R-44	R-44	R-38	R-33
6¢	36¢	*	R-49	R-44	R-38	R-38

✳ Heating criteria prevails

Figure 9-5. Optimum Suggested Attic Insulation

THE COST

To best experience and estimates, the extra cost to raise the energy-efficiency level of a house to that required by the climatic conditions of an area and the high price of fuel is somewhat difficult to determine. The major points to be considered are:

- Climatic conditions.
- House size and design.
- Uncertainty of fuel prices and availability.
- Fuel costs in house area and type of heating system used.
- Possibility of future rationing.

The need for insulation, double-glazed windows, metal-clad doors and all the other energy-saving features can range all the way from little to maximum, mainly in relation to the climatic conditions at the house locale. The bar graph, Figure 9-2, illustrates heat loss or gain as related to four levels of energy-efficiency construction. These four levels are:

1. Little insulation and energy-saving features—adequate only for areas enjoying very mild winters and/or summers.

2. FHA Minimum Property Standards, plus somewhat higher insulation and energy-saving features—adequate only for areas experiencing mild winter and summers. If electric-strip heating must be used, energy-efficiency level 3 should be used.

3. Higher level of insulation and energy-saving features—adequate for all areas experiencing moderate summers and winters. If electric-strip heating must be used, use level 4 instead.

4. Tops in insulation and energy efficiency and highly recommended for all areas having severe winters or summers.

These four levels of energy-efficiency can be used as a guide as to how much insulation and what energy-saving features should be incorporated into a house on a practical basis. If a house is to be built featuring large areas of glass and/or with high cubic-foot living space resulting from vaulted ceilings, the next higher level of energy efficiency should be considered. Also, if electric-strip heating must be used, the next higher level should be considered.

The extra cost required to raise the energy efficiency of a house to the required level can range between 5 and 10% above the "uninsulated" price somewhat as follows:

- Consider a 1500 square-foot house costing $30.00 per square foot (not counting lot cost):

- To raise house from level 1 to level 2 = about 5% of $30.00
  = $1.50 per square foot
  = $2250.00 maximum

- To raise house from level 1 to level 3 = about 7.5% of $30.00
  = $2.25 per square foot
  = $3375.00 maximum

- To raise house from level 1 to level 4 = about 10% of $30.00
  = $3.00 per square foot
  = $4500.00 maximum

While it is sometimes suggested that a payback period of 5 years would justify the extra cost, a little thought will make it clear that a payback period of even 10 years will make the extra outlay worthwhile. Again, who can foresee the future and what savings may be realized five years from now, 10 years from now, etc. For a 10-year payback time, the following energy savings would have to be realized:

- Level 1 to level 2 = $2250/10 = $225.00 per yr. = $18.75 per mo.

- Level 1 to level 3 = $3375/10 = $332.00 per yr. = $28.13 per mo.

- Level 2 to level 3 = $1125/10 = $112.50 per yr. = $ 9.38 per mo.

- Level 3 to level 4 = $1125/10 = $112.50 per yr.= $ 9.38 per mo.

- Level 1 to level 4 = $4500/10 = $450.00 per yr. = $37.50 per mo.

The small energy savings required to be gained each month (on a 10-year period) to recover the extra outlay indicates a payback time of less than 10 years. Savings much higher than those needed for a 10-year payback period are clearly practical and achievable.

Moreover, the extra costs considered above are felt to be on the *high* side and the increase in energy costs certain to occur in the future will most certainly result in higher per-month savings. When all other factors are considered (home comfort, less worries about rationing or over-peak problems, and how the house will be more readily saleable) a payback period even in excess of 10 years would still make the extra outlay a good bargain. Then, with a payback period of as little as 5 years, the extra cost is certainly an outstanding bargain.

For an existing home, the cost required to upgrade a house as to insulation and energy-saving features is somewhat difficult to arrive at since many factors must be taken into account. Some of these factors are:

- Present energy-efficiency level of house.

- Efficiency level planned, with this being directly related to climatic conditions in the house locale and the type of fuel used for heating and the heating equipment (gas or oil-fired furnace, electric-strip heater or heat-pump heating).

- Labor costs in house area and amount of skilled labor or contractor work required.

- Amount of upgrading accomplished on a do-it-yourself basis.

To raise the energy efficiency of a house from level 1 to level 4 could run as high as $3.00 to $3.50 per square foot if all work is accomplished by contractors. Fortunately, a great deal of the upgrading can be done as do-it-yourself projects or by hired handymen since much of the work does not require a high skill level.

For additional cost details, refer to "Energy Saving Upgrading," Section 23.

SUMMARY—ENERGY-SAVER HOME DESIGN

The main features of a well-designed, energy-saver home are graphically illustrated by figure 9-6. This figure was developed by the Texas A & M University, College Station, Texas and is used to key the summary that follows:

1. Exterior siding—wood, brick or stone. Refer to page 11-3 and 11-4 Section 11.

2. Tongue-and-groove insulated sheathing to provide added protection against heat flow and air infiltration. Refer to figure 11-1, page 11-2, Section 11.

3. Conventional 2" x 4" studs for wall framing—may also be 2" x 6". For details, refer to figure 11-1, page 11-2, Section 11.

4. Insulating batts fitted into wall cavity. For possible R values, refer to table 11-2, page 11-4, Section 11.

5. Sealer between slab and plate to prevent air infiltration. Refer to page 11-1, Section 11 and page 14-2, Section 14.

6. Eave (soffit) vents to allow air entry into attic for ventilation purposes. Refer to figure 15-3, page 15-3 (for gable vents) and figure 15-2 (for eave vents), Section 15.

7. Baffles installed between ceiling joists to prevent insulation (in batts, loose-fill or blown-in form) from blocking eave (soffit) events, if used. Refer to figure 15-2, page 15-2, Section 15.

8. Ridge venting, to allow attic air to escape on a "hot-air" chimney basis. For details, refer to figure 15-4, page 15-4. Section 15.

9. Ceiling insulation · blown-in, loose-fill or batts. For possible R values, refer to table 11-5, page 11-8, Section 11.

10. Metal-clad insulating-type exterior door with magnetic weatherstripping. For details, refer to pages 12-2 and 12-3, Section 12.

11. Double-glazed insulating glass window. For details, refer to table 13-1, page 13-3, Section 13.

12. Heat exchanger to preheat hot water (in summer). For details, refer to page 16-5 and 16-6, Section 16.

13. Energy-efficient heat pump. For details, refer to page 19-6, Section 19.

14. Energy-conserving hot-water heater, equipped with extra shell insulation installed on outside. For details, refer to Tank Loss, page 16-3, Section 16.

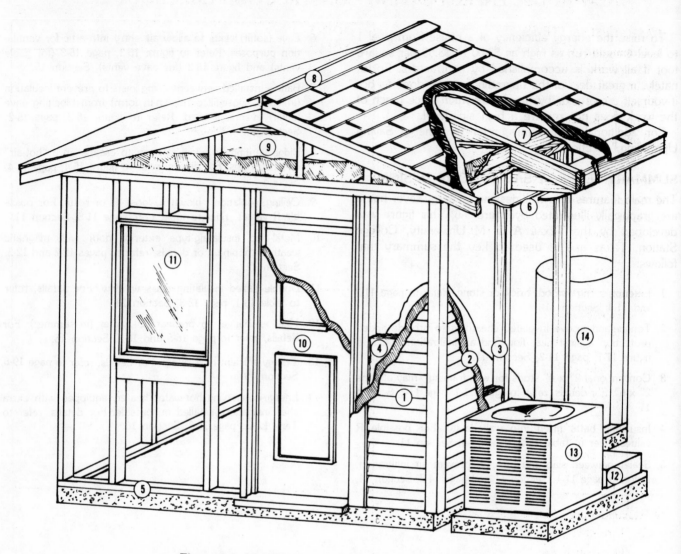

Figure 9-6. Main Features—Energy-Saver Home Design

NEW-HOUSE ENERGY-SAVING CONSTRUCTION CHECKOUT LIST

BASIC DESIGN ITEMS	POINT VALUE	FOR DETAILS, REFER TO:
1. Orientation (Wall Exposure)		
Long Axis Facing 5°–15°	60	
Long Axis Facing 350°–5° 25° Range @ North	50	
Long Axis Facing 185°–195°	45	Review "House Orientation," page 20-1.
Long Axis Facing 170°–185° 25° Range @ South	40	See Figure 20-5
Long Axis Facing generally West (250°–310°)	−30	
Long Axis Facing generally East (80°–140°)	−50	
2. Solar Conversion Feasibility		
Sun Rights Protected (Min. 45′ open)	25	
Adequate roof (s.f.) faced 160°–200°	*	Refer to Table 20-1
Roof pitch of South roof plane 7½/12 min.	*	
Additional Roof Framing	*	
3. Type and Shape		
A. Basic style		
1. Two story	40	
2. Split level	20	
3. One story	0	Review "House Styling," page 9-1
B. Shape		
1. Rectangular (approx. 2:3 dimension)	20	
2. L Shape	10	
3. U Shape	0	
4. H Shape	−20	
4. Maximum Use of Minimum Glass		
A. Percent of glass area to floor area		
Less than 10%	40	
10% to less than 12%	24	
12% to less than 15%	0	Review "Windows and Glass Patio Doors—
15% to less than 20%	−24	General" page 13-1
Greater than 20%	−40	
B. Shading of Glass		
100% shaded	48	
Less than 100%, more than 90%	32	
Less than 90%, more than 75%	16	Review "Window Shading," page 13-7
Less than 75%, more than 60%	0	
Less than 60%, more than 40%	−32	
Less than 40%	−48	
INTEGRAL THERMAL PROTECTION		
1. Shell Insulation		
A. Outside walls		
R-22 insulation installed	15	
R-19 insulation installed	10	Review "Insulation and Vapor Barriers,"
R-13 insulation installed	3	Section 5.
OVE corner system	3	
Wiring run at 48″ height or at plate	3	
R-11 insulation installed	0	

*no value to heat gain or loss calculations.

NEW-HOUSE ENERGY-SAVING CONSTRUCTION CHECKOUT LIST

	POINT VALUE	FOR DETAILS, REFER TO:
B. Ceilings over conditioned areas		
R-30 insulation installed	15	
R-26 insulation installed	10	
R-22 insulation installed	5	See Figure 5-3
R-19 insulation installed	0	Refer to Table 5-2
C. Fenestration		
Storm windows on 100% glass area	12	Refer to "Storm Window Details," page 13-1.
80% to less than 100%	10	
60% to less than 80%	8	Refer to "Energy Efficient Outer Doors," page 12-2.
40% to less than 60%	6	
Less than 40%	0	
D. Exterior Doors		
Insulated metal	3	
Wood	0	
E. Light Shade of Roofing	3	
2. **Infiltration of Unconditioned Air**		
A. Soleplates sealed at slab	12	
B. Soleplates sealed at sub floor	12	
C. No plumbing drain/vents in ext. walls	12	
D. Mechanical chases/knockouts sealed	12	
E. Ext. doors and windows weatherstripped	3	
F. Ext. doors and windows caulked	6	See Figures 14-1 and 14-2
G. Attic scuttle weatherstripped	3	Refer to Table 14-2
H. Polyethylene film installed on ext. walls	8	
I. Subfloor joints glued PL400	3	
J. Duct end plates taped to ceiling or subfloor	3	
K. No ceiling lights on rough-in boxes	3	
L. No ext. wall outlets on 2nd floor	3	
M. No recessed light/mech. equipment in ceiling	5	
N. 100% stucco exterior	10	
3. **Exfiltration of Conditioned Air**		
A. All electric: No combustion venting required	25	
B. Fireplace with:		
Damper, combustion air intake and glass screen	20	
Damper, combustion air intake	10	
Locking damper	0	Review "Fireplaces," Section 17
Standard damper	−15	See "Attic Ventilation," page 15-1
C. Attic Ventilation		
Soffit vents 48" o.c. or continuous	3	
Ductboard baffles at vent locations	6	
Continuous ridge vent at 6/12 or less roof pitch	3	
Turtle vents 48" o.c. 12" below ridge on 7/12 or over roof pitch (Locate out of sight)	3	
D. Ventless Range Hood	3	
E. Bathroom Venting (where required)		
4" fresh air intake 8" off floor	3	

NEW-HOUSE ENERGY-SAVING CONSTRUCTION CHECKOUT LIST

	POINT VALUE	FOR DETAILS, REFER TO:
Weatherstrip door @ bath	3	
F. Inside utility room Double reverse 4″ vents	6	
Weatherstrip door	3	
MECHANICAL SYSTEMS		
1. **Air Handler or Heating Unit Location**		
Centrally located	8	
Conditioned Space	8	
Unconditioned Space	3	
Attic Space	0	
2. **Duct System**		
One level for 2 stories (cavity between floors)	8	Review "Ducting and Vents," page 19-3
Conditioned Space	8	
2 return air grills (filter grills)	3	
Unconditioned Space	2	
Attic Space: R-7 Insulating; sealed joints	0	
3. **Cooling Efficiencies at 95° Outdoor Temperature, 78° Indoor Temperature**		
9.5 EER or greater	13	
9.0 to 9.5 EER	10	
8.5 to 9.0 EER	8	
8.0 to 8.5 EER	5	
7.5 to 8.0 EER	3	
7.0 to 7.5 EER	0	
6.9 EER or less	−15	
4. **Heating Efficiencies at 47° Outdoor Temperature, 68° Indoor Temperature**		
3.5 SPF or greater	12	
3.0 to 3.5 SPF	10	Review "Basic Facts—Cooling Systems," page 19-2
2.5 to 3.0 SPF	8	
2.0 to 2.5 SPF	6	
1.0 to 2.0 SPF	4	
1.0 SPF or less	0	
5. **Water Heating System/Hot Water conservation**		
Heat recovery equipment	8	
Located within 20′ of kitchen/utility areas	2	Review "Heating Water With A Heat Exchanger," Page 16-4
Water lines insulated	3	
3 GPM flow restriction at faucets and shower heads	2	
TOTAL		

Section 10

Foundations and Floors

GENERAL

Four types of foundation-floor combinations are in common use today. these are:

- Crawl space-wood floor
- Concrete slab-concrete floor
- Basement space-wood floor
- Composite

The type of foundation-floor combination selected for a given house has generally been, up to now, based upon satisfying one or more of the following factors:

- Cost
- Soil stability
- Ground-water problems
- Floor comfort

With the advent of higher energy prices and the extreme need for energy conservation, an almost new factor has been added to foundation construction — energy efficiency must be considered. Thus, all foundations must be insulated to the degree required by the climatic conditions of the building area. In general, home builders in the colder areas of the country insulate foundations since years of experience has shown that this is necessary if the home is to achieve a reasonable comfort balance in the winter. However, in the warmer areas of the country, insulating a foundation (particularly a slab) is met with immediate rejection. The author has found that this single subject insulating a slab foundation - has caused more reaction from the home builders than any other subject except perhaps that related to air infiltration. It is clear that home builders and their foundation subcontractors must all, regardless of geographic location, become knowledgeable of and be willing to insulate foundations (slab, crawl space or basement types).

The discussions to follow on the various types of foundations will highlight the energy efficiency of each type.

CONCRETE-SLAB FOUNDATION

The concrete-slab foundation, figure 10-1, is generally the most economical to build since the slab top is the basic floor and thus first-floor framing and covering is not required. The slab foundation is most often used in areas that experience ground-water or soil-stability problems. The slab foundation is also widely used where cost is a deciding factor.

If properly insulated and a well-installed vapor barrier of heavy plastic film is used, a slab can be considered as an excellent foundation-floor combination as to energy-use and construction-cost efficiency. The slab has two major drawbacks:

1. Being made of concrete, the floor is rigid and does not have the natural "give" of wood or its warmth.

2. The sewer pipes and (sometimes) the hot and cold water pipes are run under the concrete floor and thus are inaccessible for repairs, if needed. If repairs are needed, the floor must be opened with a jack hammer at great expense and trouble. In fact, if water-pipe trouble occurs (blockage or leakage), it is customary to rerun the pipes through the attic, entirely replacing the under-slab piping.

Concrete has a very low R value and thus is an excellent conductor of heat. Thus, a slab foundation should be insulated to reduce to an acceptable degree the flow of heat out of the house in the winter and, in the warmer areas, to reduce the flow of heat into the house in the summer. A slab foundation can be insulated in two ways: (1) with perimeter-mounted insulation as illustrated by Figure 10-1 and (2) by installing rigid-foam insulation panels under the entire floor related to the living area of the house.

Perimeter insulation is the easiest to accomplish and the least expensive of the two methods. The preferred insulation is in the form of rigid-foam boards, from ¾" to 2" thick dependent upon climatic conditions at the building site. Suggested thickness for Styrofoam SM insulation is given by Figure 10-7. Perimeter insulation is very effective and acts primarily to reduce the heat flow into or out of the house through the slab walls and floor. Perimeter insula-

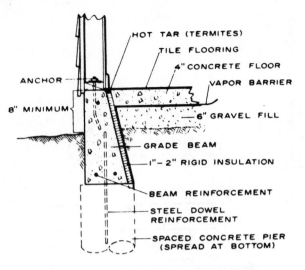

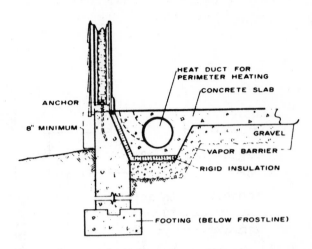

Reinforced grade beam for concrete slab. Beam spans between concrete piers located below frostline.

Full foundation wall for cold climates. Perimeter heat duct insulated to reduce heat loss.

Figure 10-1. Concrete-Slab Foundation

tion is rather easily installed when the slab footings are poured first, followed by the floor. As illustrated by figure 10-1, the rigid foam insulation is simply laid against the finished foundation wall. The insulation panel must extend from just below the frost line up to about ½″ below the top of the slab floor when it is poured. The fill is then spread between the slab walls, compacted, and the vapor barrier is laid. The slab floor is then poured, usually being 4″ thick.

In many parts of the country, particularly in the warmer areas, a concrete slab is poured as a single operation. The method is illustrated by Figure 10-2. A wood wall is built to form the outer edge of the slab. Paper sacks filled with finegrained fill material are then stacked up to form the second wall of the footing. The area between the paper sacks of the four walls of the foundation is then filled with fine-grained fill material, usually not compacted. To insulate the perimeter, the rigid-foam insulation panels are placed alongside the paper sacks and held in place with tiebacks into the top of the top sack. The reinforcement steel is then fitted into the top of the fill to form the slab top (flooring). Some cutting of the rigid-foam panels may be required and some of the reinforcement steel may pass through the panels. In either case, care should be taken to minimize the hole or cut area. The concrete is then poured in the normal manner — in a single pour into the footing and wall area first, building up until the slab top can be poured and leveled. The rigid-foam panels will not be compressed by the concrete to any appreciable degree and the panel material will not take up water. The insulation value thus is not lessened by the concrete pressure or water in the concrete.

An alternate method to install perimeter insulation for a single-pour slab foundation is illustrated by figure 10-3.

Note the rigid-foam insulation is attached to the outside of the finished foundation by means of a mastic (manufacturer-recommended special adhesive). To protect the rigid-foam panels from damage, the panels must be covered with asbestos board or coated over with stucco (cement). The flashing illustrated in figure 10-3 is a termite shield, installed on top the foundation setback related to the outer sheathing (brick in the illustration).

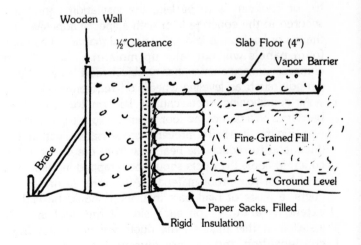

Figure 10-2. Single-Pour Concrete Slab Foundation

Rigid-foam insulation panels may also be laid on top the vapor barrier over the full area related to the floor of the air-conditioned portion of the finished house. This method is more expensive both as to material and installation costs but is somewhat more effective than perimeter insulation. If cost is a factor, perimeter insulation is recommended.

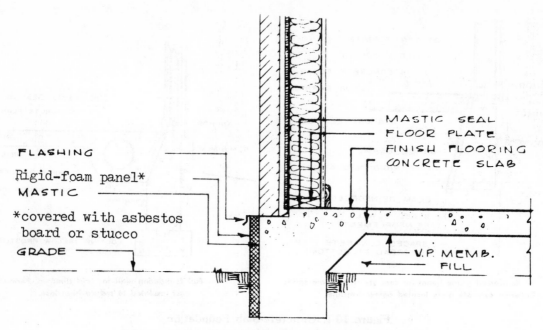

Figure 10-3. Exterior-Installed Peripheral Insulation

Labels in figure:
FLASHING
Rigid-foam panel*
MASTIC
*covered with asbestos board or stucco
GRADE
MASTIC SEAL
FLOOR PLATE
FINISH FLOORING
CONCRETE SLAB
V.P. MEMB.
FILL

Ceramic-type tile and linoleum can be very cold to touch in the winter if laid directly on top of a concrete floor. A warmer tile or linoleum covered floor results if the area directly beneath the related floor area is covered with rigid-foam insulation panels. To accomplish this, the concrete floor is poured such that it will be lower than the other floor-top surfaces by the amount related to the combined thickness of the insulation panels and the tile. When the tile or linoleum is to be laid, the insulation panels are secured to the concrete floor with a special adhesive and the tile or linoleum is laid in the normal manner. The rigid-foam panels will not take up moisture and will not compress unless a small, heavy object rests on it for long periods (such as leveling wheels on refrigerators).

Air-conditioning ducts can be laid on top the vapor barrier to be a part of the floor when the floor top is poured (see Figure 10-1). To prevent condensation within the ducts and to reduce the heat flow from the ducts to the concrete floor, the ducts should be wrapped in insulation (and be of rust-proof material). Also, directly under the ducts, a piece of rigid-foam insulation should be laid — extending about 3″ on each side of the duct area. If installed in this manner, the ducts will not suffer from condensation and will not give up their heat to the concrete in the winter nor take up heat from the concrete in the summer.

A wood floor can be built on top the concrete top of the slab if desired. This floor framing is usually made of 2 x 4's, machine-nailed to the slab top. Insulation batts (R11 usually) can be laid between the 2 x 4's before the top cover (usually plywood sheets) is nailed down. If such a floor is used, the water pipes (if not run through the attic) should be fitted into the wood flooring. Such a floor is somewhat expensive but it does result in a warmer, more resilient floor plus the floor is well insulated. However, in colder climates, permiter insulation would still be cost and comfort effective.

Carpet laid on a concrete floor should be laid on top of a good quality pad, preferably a fiberous one which has a higher combination (carpet and pad) insulation value (R2.08) than a foam-pad combination (R1.23). Linoleum or tile, if not laid on insulation panels, should be laid on top particle boards to gain a warmer and more resilient floor.

Like all foundations, care must be taken to keep the flow of humidity up from the ground from passing into the house. This is particularly important now that houses are being built much tighter than in the past, now having a very low air-change rate. A good vapor barrier, usually consisting of a heavy plastic film, must be installed to good practices. The film should be overlapped at least 6″ at each seam and at the perimeter should be laid part way up the perimeter insulation. It is of utmost importance that any tears or breaks in the plastic film be repaired before the concrete is poured; otherwise water vapor from under the entire plastic film will "travel" to the break and enter the house. In brief, the vapor barrier under a slab foundation must not be taken lightly and must be complete under the entire area related to the air-conditioned portion of the finished house.

CRAWL-SPACE FOUNDATION

The crawl-space foundation, figure 10-4, consists of a concrete wall sitting on top a concrete footing. The footing (up to 30″ wide) provides stability to the wall which is

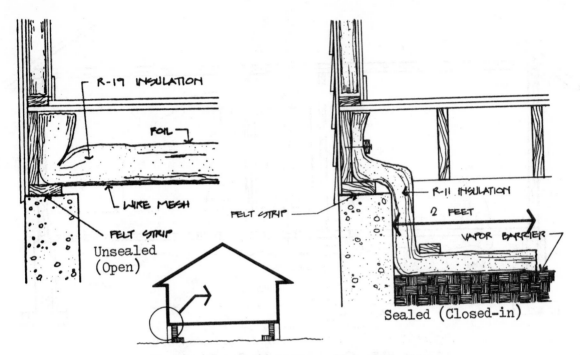

Figure 10-4. Crawl-Space Foundation

usually about 14″ wide (wide enough to hold the plate and any masonry (brick or stone) used as outer cover).

The footings and walls extend all around the full perimeter of the air-conditioned portion of the house except for the garage area which is customarily poured as a slab. In certain cases, a sunken living room will have a concrete floor. A minimum of about 28″ of clearance must exist between the ground level and the lowest point of the flooring (usually the beams holding the floor joists) to allow relatively easy access to the under-floor area. It is recommended that the ground under the flooring be cleared of rocks and other material that would otherwise make it difficult to crawl under the house. Of course, no cellulosic material (wood or paper) should be left under the house even if buried in the dirt. To do so would invite termites.

The main advantages of a crawl-space foundation are:

- Permits air-conditioning ducts to be placed under the floor. Also, the entire under-floor area (if suitably insulated and sealed) can be used as a ducting system (a plenum).

- Should a solar system be used at some future time to heat (and cool) the house, large-volume storage space must be provided to contain the liquid (most likely water) that will store the accumulated heat for use during the "no-sunshine" hours. The underfloor area provided by a crawl-space foundation could be used to contain a large storage tank when needed.

- Wood floors, with the natural give of wood, provide a floor that is "easy on the feet" and is warm.

- Permits easy access to all plumbing and for checkout of possible termite invasion.

A crawl-space foundation, by any analysis, is inherently more energy efficient than a slab foundation. That is, the slab foundation is a solid mass laying directing on the ground and with a concrete floor. Even if well insulated, the slab will still be less efficient energy-wise than the crawl-space foundation since its floor literally sits on air. A crawl-space foundation generally costs somewhat more than a slab foundation but actual dollar comparisons are difficult to make because:

- The floor must be made of expensive beams and floor joists, topped with a subfloor and final floor covering. This represents a material and labor cost extra to a degree over a slab.

- Few "corners can be cut" in the building of a crawl-space whereas many economies (resulting in a poor foundation) can be made when building a slab. Thus, a crawl-space cost comparison should always be made against a comparable-quality slab foundation.

- The energy-efficiency features of a crawl-space foundation plus its extra comfort features tends to suggest its use where ground water or soil stability is not a problem.

If the crawl space is used as a plenum, the foundation walls must be insulated and the entire underfloor area tightly sealed to prevent escape of the conditioned air. Use of the underfloor area as a plenum is usually efficient only for heating and makes for a warm floor.

If the crawl space is not used as a plenum, it *must* be ventilated to prevent humidity build up. The foundation walls or outer floor joists must be vented on a basis of

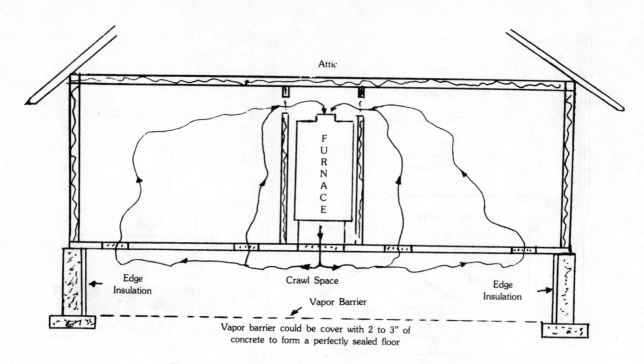

Attic

Edge Insulation

Crawl Space

Edge Insulation

Vapor Barrier

Vapor barrier could be cover with 2 to 3" of
concrete to form a perfectly sealed floor

Figure 10-5.   Crawl Space Air-Conditioning Plenum

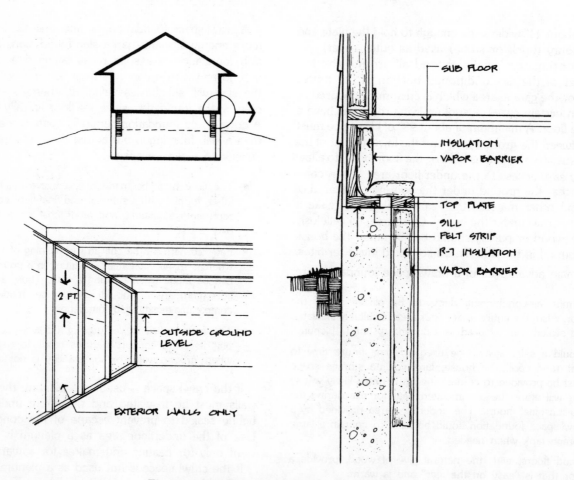

SUB FLOOR

INSULATION

VAPOR BARRIER

TOP PLATE

SILL

FELT STRIP

R-7 INSULATION

VAPOR BARRIER

2 FT.

OUTSIDE GROUND LEVEL

EXTERIOR WALLS ONLY

Figure 10-6. Basement-Space Foundation

1:150 or one square foot of vent area for each 150 square feet of crawl space. Vents should be provided on all four sides of the foundation to provide positive cross ventilation and thus to ensure that no area acts to trap and hold humid air. A vapor barrier must be installed to keep down the moisture rising from the ground. If desired, concrete (2" to 3" thick) can be poured on top the vapor barrier to form a perfectly sealed floor against humidity and insect invasion.

When used as a plenum chamber, Figure 10-5, a down-flow furnace is used to keep the air in the plenum under slight pressure. The heated air then flows through the plenum and up into the house interior through floor-mounted vents which may be installed anyplace desired. Air return to the furnace can be through return vents in the ceiling or high in the walls and a ducting system either installed in the attic or inside the house. Alternately, if the furnace is centrally located in the house in a closet, vents in the closet wall (by themselves) can provide an acceptable air-return system. The combustion air required by the furnace must not be drawn from the plenum or from inside the house as this will waste heated air.

The plenum system can realize a cost savings since underfloor ducts are not required while a warm floor is assured. Savings as high as $300.00 have been quoted in newspaper ads. Tests made by the University of Florida show that the temperature difference between the floor level and a height of five feet averaged less than two and one-half degrees for both heating and cooling. For further information, write for the Plenwood System Manual—Underfloor Plenum, Western Wood Products Assoc., Yeon Bldg., Portland, Oregon, 97204—Dept. SP-3, price 25¢. For additional information on plenum systems, refer to Section 19, "Heating and Cooling Systems," page 19-6.

BASEMENT-SPACE FOUNDATION

This foundation, Figure 10-6, is identical in construction to a crawl-space foundation with the exception that the foundation walls are tall enough to permit erect access to the underfloor area. The foundation walls, being mostly below ground level, should be waterproofed. Ideally, the floor should be a concrete pad up to 4" thick laid on a properly installed vapor barrier. If the underfloor area is to be air conditioned to any degree, perimeter insulation should be installed as illustrated by Figure 10-6. Again, if the basement area is to be air conditioned, the entire underfloor area must be sealed to prevent loss of air-conditioned air. If windows are used in the basement walls, they should be insulating (double-glazed) types. Outer

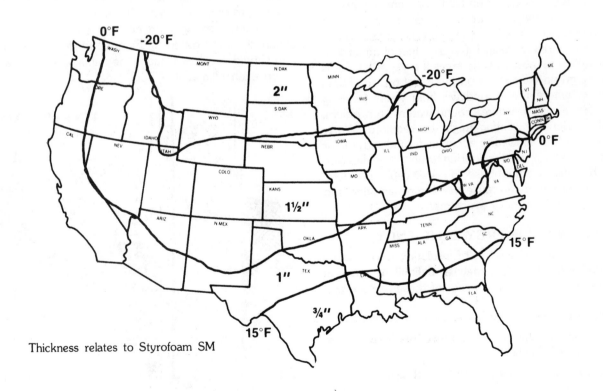

Thickness relates to Styrofoam SM

Figure 10-7. Recommended Thickness— Foundation Perimeter

doors ideally should be of the metal-clad type using magnetic weather-stripping. If a furnace is to be installed in an air-conditioned basement, the unit should be installed in an air-tight closet and the needed combustion air should be drawn from outside the house. If the basement area is not to be air conditioned, adequate venting must be provided even if a vapor barrier is used on the floor. The venting ratio should be the same as detailed for a crawl space — one square foot of vent for each 150 square feet of basement floor area.

For additional details on insulating a basement, refer to "Underfloor Insulation," page 23-16, Section 23.

COMPOSITE FOUNDATION

A particular house design may require foundations of the slab, crawl space and basement type. For example, almost all garage floors are poured as a slab. In other cases, a sunken living room may be featured, with the floor being dropped to ground level as a slab foundation. Again, part of the house may have a deepened under-floor area to provide a basement section.

UNDERHOUSE VENTILATION

Underhouse ventilation, already briefly covered, is a most serious matter and care must be taken to ensure a sufficient air flow under the house to prevent build up of moisture in any crawl space or in a basement area that is not air conditioned. A rather standard ratio of one square foot of venting area for each 150 square feet of underfloor area will suffice in most climatic areas if a vapor barrier is used on the ground. If a vapor barrier is not provided or in those areas where the ground will hold water for long periods after a rain or where ground water is a problem, additional underfloor venting might be required. Water vapor must not be allowed to accumulate under the floor since it can pass through the flooring (even if provided with a vapor barrier) into the house to cause vapor problem. Also, the water vapor can cause wood to rot and floors to buckle —both very serious problems.

INSULATION VS. ENERGY EFFICIENCY

The energy saved as a result of insulating a foundation and/or under the floor is somewhat difficult to arrive at for a variety of reasons. The major of these reasons are:

- Type of foundation (slab, crawl space or basement).
- Square feet of foundation wall above frost level and exposed to the weather.
- Thickness of insulation and resultant R value.
- Climatic conditions at the house locale.
- Cost of heating fuel (gas, oil, coal or electricity)

The cost for insulating the perimeter of a slab is really not very high. The rigid panels require very minor effort to be placed into the slab before the concrete is poured. The cost thus relates mainly to the cost of the panels. The rigid panels may be formed from polystyrene, Styrofoam or TF400. The R value of these varies somewhat

- Polystyrene = R4.35
- Styrofoam SM = R5.41
- TF400 = R8

Recommended minimum thickness for slab perimeter insulation is given by Figure 10-7 for Styrofoam SM. The thickness suggested would also hold when polystyrene and TF-400 is used, except TF400 might be reduced to ¾". The cost for foam insulation boards as related to a 1500-square foot house might be:

Foundation walls = 50' long x 30' wide @ 2' average height
= 50 + 30 x 2 x 2' = 320 sq. ft.
1" thick insulation = 20¢ per sq. ft. = 320 x .20 = $64.00 maximum

In areas experiencing extremely cold winters, 2" thickness is recommended thus the cost would be about $128.00. In such cold areas, a "top cap" of ½" to 1" foam-panel sheets is also recommended to cover the entire top of the slab before the concrete is poured. For a 1500-square foot house, the cost would be about 1500 x 20¢ (maximum) = $300.00 maximum for 1" sheets. Also, where heating (and cooling) ducts are laid in the concrete, as illustrated by Figure 10-8, foam panel insulation should be placed under the ducts, extending at least 3" on each side of the duct pipe.

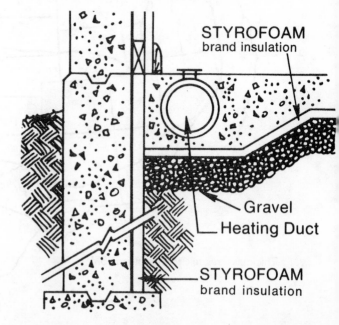

Figure 10-8. Insulated Slab with Heating Ducts

Recommended minimum perimeter thickness for crawl-space perimeter insulation is also given by Figure 10-7. Perimeter insulation is used, as previously discussed, only when the crawl space is completely sealed off. Installation is somewhat more costly than that related to slab perimeter installation since the insulation panels must be cemented to the walls or nailed to furring strips. If the insulation panels are made of flammable material, the panels must be covered with a non-flammable material for fire safety. This covering is usually cement-asbestos board (about ¼" thick minimum) or sheet rock (½" thick minimum). The insulation panels may be installed on either the inside or outside of the foundation walls.

If the crawl space is to be ventilated, perimeter insulation should not be used. Instead, insulation batts (3" minimum - 6" maximum) should be installed between the floor joists. Material and installation costs for 6" batts might run as high as 25¢ per square foot. For a home with 1500 square-feet of living space the cost might be:

1500 sq. ft. x 0.8 x .25 = $300.00
0.8 = floor joists account for 20%
of total floor area.

The cost of insulating the foundation of a 1500 square-foot house could thus run from a low of about $64.00 (slab perimeter) to about $300.00 (open crawl space). The BTU savings theoretically possible to be gained by insulating 320 square feet of foundation wall (either as related to a slab or crawl-space foundation) is as follows:

Assume: Fnd wall = 12" thick at R0.08 per inch = R.096 = U1.04
Fnd wall covered w/1½" insulated panels = R7.5 = U0.13

Uninsulated	= U x Sq Ft x Hrs x Degrees Days, Austin, Tex.		
	= 1.04 x 320 x 24 x 1800	= 14,376.960	BTU's per winter
	= 1.04 x 320 x 24 x 2850	= 22,763,520	BTU's per summer
	Total	= 37,140,480	BTU's per year
Insulated	= 0.13 x 320 x 24 x 1800	= 1,797,120	BTU's per winter
	= 0.13 x 320 x 24 x 2850	= 2,845,440	BTU's per summer
	Total	= 4,642,560	BTU's per year
Difference	= 37,140,480 - 4,642,560	= 32,497,920	BTU's per year

The calculated value, however, is considered to be high for several reasons. That is, the actual heat loss or gain as related to the actual living space of the house through the foundation walls is modified by carpets and padding on the floor, the floor itself (either concrete or wood), the fill material (slab only) and the stabilizing effect of the earth temperature under the foundation. Thus, even approximate figures as to energy and dollars saved can be based only on practical experience which indicates worthwhile dollar savings. Savings appear high enough to make even maximum dollar outlay ($300.00 for an open crawl-space foundation) worthwhile and repayable in perhaps five years (minimum) and 10 years (maximum).

The insulation is most effective in the summer as it reduces heat flow into the house as developed by the sun's rays striking the foundation wall. In the winter, the insulation tends to keep the house heat from traveling out through the foundation walls. Generally speaking, a foundation must be insulated if a comfortable climate is to be maintained in a home since cold floors result in cold feet.

Section 11

WALLS AND CEILINGS

GENERAL

The exterior walls, in conjunction with the windows and exterior doors, act together with the ceilings to form the house "envelope". This envelope stands between the air-conditioned comfortable interior and the outside climate which might be uncomfortably hot or cold. At present, the FHA Minimum Property Standards (MPS) for insulation call for R11 walls and R19 ceilings. These values are demonstrably too low in relation to the high energy costs of today and the projected even higher energy costs of the future thus the FHA (and other government agencies related to home building) are planning to raise the minimum insulation levels for walls and ceilings.

To qualify as an energy-saver home exterior walls insulated to R11 can only be used in areas experiencing very mild winters and/or summers. In all other areas, walls insulated to R19 are now commonly used and even higher R values are considered necessary in areas of extreme climatic changes. Ceiling insulation for an energy-saver home will range from R19 (mild-climate area) to R40 in extreme-climate areas. In these areas, if electric-strip heating is used, even higher R value ceilings are warranted. Recommended minimum insulation values for walls, ceilings, and floors throughout the 48 contiguous States are given by Figure 9-4, page 9-13. Optimum suggested attic floor (ceiling) insulation levels for the five climatic areas of the country are given by Figure 9-5, page 9-14. These values are, however, considered to be somewhat on the high side in line with the new knowledge that it is not cost-effective to insulate above R levels that have proved to be cost practical.

ACHIEVING RECOMMENDED R VALUES

Recommended R values for walls and ceilings can be achieved as follows:

Walls
R-19
- 6" batt/blanket (6" stud wall only)
- 3½" batt/blanket + 1" foam board (R5 or better)
- 3" cellulose loose fill + 1" foam board (R5 or better)

R-11
- 3" batt/blanket
- 3" cellulose loose fill

Ceilings
R-19
- 7½" to 9" wool or glass loose fill
- 5" cellulose loose fill
- 6" batt/blanket

R-26
- 8¼" batt/blanket
- 2 layers 3½" batt/blanket (R13 type)
- 12" mineral fiber loose fill*
- 7" cellulose loose fill

R-30
- 9" batt/blanket
- 5½" batt/blanket topped by a 3½" batt/blanket
- 11½" to 13½" mineral fiber loose fill*
- 8" cellulose loose fill

R-33
- 5½" batt/blanket topped with 5½" mineral fiber loose fill*
- 12½" to 15" mineral fiber loose fill*
- 9" cellulose loose fill

R-38
- 12" batt/blanket*
- 2 layers 6" fiberglas or 5½" mineral wool batt/blanket
- 14½" to 17½" mineral fiber loose fill*
- 10" cellulose loose fill

*Mineral wool value — for fiberglas, increase by 10%

EFFECTIVE INSULATION

A house envelope is often referred to as having "R19 walls" or "R26 ceilings." These figures actually relate to the insulation value of the insulation used and is not entirely correct. That is, the wood used to frame the walls and ceilings and to box in doors and windows, vents, disappearing stairways, etc., take up some of the total area and thus reduce the wall or ceiling cavity into which the insulation will be installed. For a wall containing doors and/or windows, the area related to each will have a lower insulation level than that of the insulated wall. For a ceiling containing air-conditioning vents, light-fixture boxes, whole-house fans, disappearing staircases, etc., the area related to each will have a lower insulation level than that of the insulated ceiling (attic floor). The effective (actual) insulation level of a particular wall or ceiling is then the total of the insulation installed factored downward to take into account the lower-value insulation areas.

THERMAL ENVELOPE

The well-insulated walls, ceiling and floor form a thermal envelope about the house. This envelope **must** be

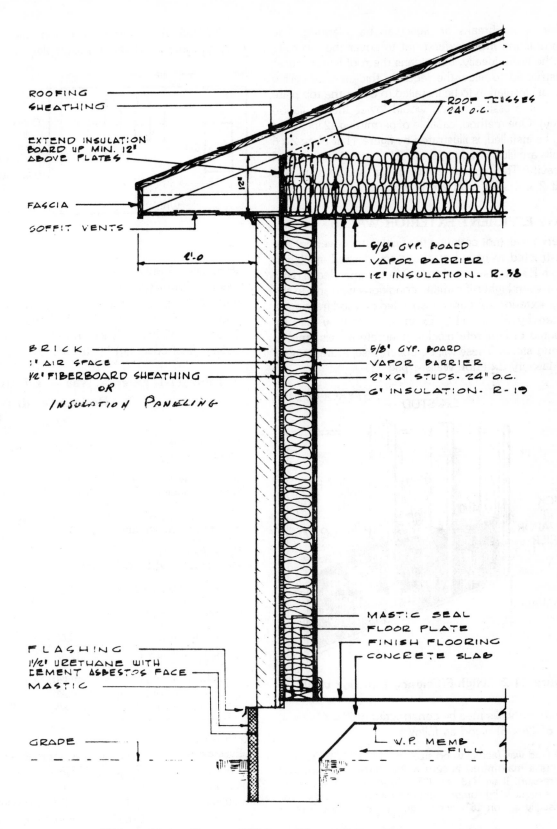

ROOFING

SHEATHING

EXTEND INSULATION
BOARD UP MIN. 12"
ABOVE PLATES

FASCIA

SOFFIT VENTS

ROOF TRUSSES
24' O.C.

12"

1'.0

5/8" GYP. BOARD
VAPOR BARRIER
12" INSULATION. R-38

BRICK
1" AIR SPACE
1/2" FIBERBOARD SHEATHING
OR
INSULATION PANELING

5/8" GYP. BOARD
VAPOR BARRIER
2"x6" STUDS. 24" O.C.
6" INSULATION. R-19

MASTIC SEAL
FLOOR PLATE
FINISH FLOORING
CONCRETE SLAB

FLASHING
1 1/2" URETHANE WITH
CEMENT ASBESTOS FACE
MASTIC

GRADE

W.P. MEMB
FILL

Figure 11-1.   Energy Efficient Thermal Envelope

complete — no breaks or gaps can be tolerated. The ceiling insulation **must** extend out to cover the top plate (top of the wall). Ideally, this means the roof trusses must be constructed to allow the required thickness of ceiling (attic floor) insulation to be installed to cover the top plate without compression (which would lower the insulation efficiency). One method, capable of permitting 12 inches of batts to be installed, is illustrated by figure 11-1. Note 2 x 6 stud walls are illustrated to permit R19 batts to be installed in the cavity. The requirement to cover the top plate also exists if 2 x 4 stud walls are used.

ENERGY-EFFICIENT EXTERIOR WALLS

An exterior wall (not counting the final outer covering) can be constructed to have just about any desired insulation level from R3 (no insulation) to R19 (recommended in most areas) or even higher if climatic conditions warrant. In the majority, exterior walls are constructed of wood framing as illustrated by Figure 11-2. Exterior walls may also be constructed of concrete blocks, concrete panels, special bricks and stone. These will be covered separately under "Solid-Masonry Exterior Walls--, page 11-6 .

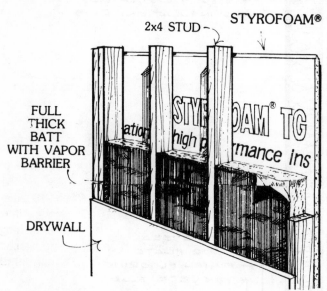

FULL THICK BATT WITH VAPOR BARRIER

2x4 STUD

STYROFOAM®

DRYWALL

Figure 11-2. High-Efficiency Exterior Wall

Wood exterior walls may be constructed of 2" x 4" (2 x 4) or 2" x 6" (2 x 6) wood as follows:

- 2 x 4 stud wall (actual wood size = 1½" x 3½"). This wall can (as a maximum) accept a 3½" batt (R11) without compression. If an R13 batt (3⅝" thick) is used, insulation value is reduced by compression to about R12.68. 2 x 4 studs are usually set on 16" centers, giving a cavity width of 15 inches.

- 2 x 6 stud wall (actual wood size = 1½" x 5½"). This wall can (as a maximum) accept a 6" batt (R19) with slight compression, resulting in an effective insulation level of R18.5. 2 x 6 studs are usually set on 24" centers, giving a cavity width of 23 inches.

To illustrate the effective insulation value of an exterior wall, consider the following example:

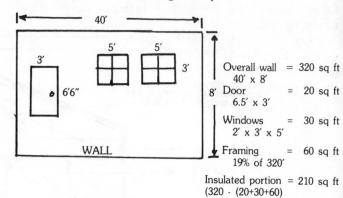

WALL

Overall wall = 320 sq ft
40' x 8'
Door = 20 sq ft
6.5' x 3'
Windows = 30 sq ft
2' x 3' x 5'
Framing = 60 sq ft
19% of 320'

Insulated portion = 210 sq ft
(320 - (20+30+60))

Windows — dbl-glzed = R1.5
Door — Insulating steel = R15
R13 (3⅝") batts — effective R = R12.68
Outer sheathing — ¾" thick Hi-R panels = R6.00
Gypsum wall board (sheet rock) = R0-45
Siding (final covering) ⅝" thick redwood = R0.93

Table 11-1. Exterior Wall — Effective R Value

	Resistance (R) Path Through	
	Framing	Wall Cavity
Outside Surface 15 mph wind	0.17	0.17
Siding, redwood ⅝" x 8", lapped	0.93	0.93
Hi-R sheathing, ⅝" +40° mean temperature	6.00	6.00
Batts, friction-fit 3⅝" compressed to 3½"		12.68
Fir or pine framing 2x4s	4.35	
Gypsum wallboard, ½"	0.45	0.45
Inside surface (still air)	0.68	0.68
Total resistance (R)	12.58	20.91

Adjustment for framing = 60/320 = 19%
for door = 20/320 = 6%
for windows = 30/320 = 9%
Batt-insulated portion = 210/320 = 66%

Effective R $= \dfrac{.19}{12.58} + \dfrac{.81}{20.91} = 0.015 + 0.0387 = 0.0537$

$= \dfrac{1}{0.0537}$ = R18 effective insulation value

An insulating door, with about an R15 value, has nearly the same insulation value as the remainder of the wall and thus does not lower the effective R value much. The windows, at R1.5, can thus be seen as a "nearly-open passageway" for cold into or out of the house even though double-glazed insulating types are used.

These estimated effective-insulation percentage figures would calculate out the same regardless if batts, rock wool, glass-fiber, cellulosic or foam insulation is used between the stud pairs that form the wall cavity. Note, however, that if rigid-foam insulation panels are nailed over the wood framing, the wood is covered and thus there is no effective reduction of the insulation value of the rigid-foam panels. This also holds for ceilings where the insulation (either batts, blankets or blown-in type) covers the ceiling joists.

A few examples of how a wood-framed wall may be constructed to various insulation levels are given by Table 11-2.

Table 11-2. Outer Wall Insulation Combinations

	2 x 4 Walls				2 x 6 Walls			
Inside air film	0.68	0.68	0.68	0.68	0.68	0.68	0.68	0.68
5/8" sheet rock	0.56	0.56	0.56	0.56	0.56	0.56	0.56	0.56
3" batts — R11 No compression*		11.00						
3 5/8" batts — R13 Comp. to R12.68*			12.68	12.68				
6" batts — R19 Comp. to R18.50*					18.50	18.50	18.50	18.50
3/4" wood sheath	0.95				0.95			
1/2" fiber board		1.32						
1" Styrofoam panels						5.41		
3/4" TF-400 or Hi-R foam panels			6.00				6.00	
1" TF-400 or Hi-R foam panels				8.00				8.00
Empty wall cavity	1.00							
Outside air film	0.17	0.17	0.17	0.17	0.17	0.17	0.17	0.17
Effective R values	3.36	13.73	20.09	22.09	20.59	25.32	25.91	27.91

The values given relate to solid walls thus no insulation correction is needed for doors and windows. Also note the insulation reduction related to wood framing was, for simplicity sake, not taken into account. The 2x4-wall values are reduced by about 13% and the 2x6-wall values by about 10% if wood framing is taken into account. Note also the wall cavities can be filled with foamed-in insulation during the construction phase (before the walls are covered inside) and with foamed-in or blown-in insulation after the walls are covered inside. Table 11-3 gives the effective R values detailed by Table 11-2 but adjusted for wall cavities filled with foamed-in or blown-in insulation instead of batts.

The vertical pieces (studs) of a wood-framed wall are nailed to the base piece (known as the sole or plate). It is of utmost importance that the sole-plate be sealed to the floor since recent tests have shown that (on the average) 25% of all undesired air infiltration occurs under the sole-plate. For a slab foundation, the sole-plate can be laid in a freshly-spread bed of mortar and the nuts on the foundation bolts tightened to draw the sole-plate into the new mortar. This is very important since a concrete floor is always uneven.

For a wood floor, the sole-plate can be laid in a freshly-spread heavy bed on long-lifed caulking material and the nuts on the foundation bolts tightened to draw the sole-plate down into the caulking material. In addition, it is highly recommended that a bead of long-lifed caulking material (Polycel One or equivalent) be spread up against the sole-plate and the floor surface (wood or concrete) to make a final positive seal.

RIGID-FOAM OUTER SHEATHING

Rigid-foam panels are now being used in increasing volume as the outer sheathing on exterior walls and, in certain cases, on the inside of the walls as well. The use of this sheathing is highly recommended over the conventional fiberboard which has an average value of R2.64 per inch of thickness. This compares to Styrofoam TG with a R5.41 value (200% better), and to TF-400 and Hi-R panels with an R8 value (300% better). The cost of rigid-foam panels is about twice that of the conventional fiberboard sheathing. Installation of the rigid-foam panels is somewhat easier than that related to fiberboard since the rigid-foam panels

Table 11-3. Wall Insulation Foamed-In/Blown-In

	2 x 4 Walls			2 x 6 Walls			
Table 11-2 eff. R values	13.73	20.09	22.09	20.59	25.32	25.91	27.91
Less cavity insulation	-11.00	-12.68	-12.68	-18.50	-18.50	-18.50	-18.50
"Empty"cavity value	*16.73	7.41	9.41	2.09	6.82	7.41	9.41

"Full" cavity values

• Foam = R4 per inch							
2x4's = 3.5 x 4 = R14*	*16.73	21.41	27.41				
2x6's = 5.5 x 4 = R22				24.09	28.82	29.41	31.41
• Cellulosic = R3.7 per inch							
2x4's = 3.5 x 3.7 = R13	15.73	20.41	22.41				
2x6's = 5.5 x 3.7 = R20				22.09	26.82	27.41	29.41
• Rock wool = R2.8 per inch							
2x4's = 3.5 x 2.8 = R10	12.73	17.41	19.41				
2x6's = 5.5 x 2.8 = R15.4				17.49	22.22	22.81	24.81
• Glas fiber = R2.2 per in.							
2x4's = 3.5 x 2.2 = R7.7	10.43	15.11	17.11				
2x6's = 5.5 x 2.2 = R12.1				14.19	18.92	19.51	21.51

*Example: R2.73 + R14 = R16.73

may be easily cut with a knife, whereas fiberboard must be sawed. Nailing of the rigid-foam panels is no more difficult than that related to fiberboard sheathing.

If properly installed, nailed carefully and with all cracks, breaks, holes, etc. repaired, the rigid-panel sheathing both increases the insulation efficiency of the wall and acts to reduce air infiltration. The two benefits make the use of rigid-foam panels a must. The panels can be obtained in 2-foot or 4-foot widths and in 8 foot lengths, with special lengths available. Taking a cost of about $7.00 per 4 x 8 panel of rigid-foam versus a $3.50 per 4 x 8 panel fiberboard cost and a 48' x 8' solid wall, the cost difference would be — 12 panels needed = $84.00 versus $42.00 or a difference of $42.00. Clearly, the extra insulation and air-infiltration benefits warrant the extra cost.

All rigid-foam panels are essentially vapor barriers in that vapor will pass through them, if at all, at a very low rate. This means that an effective vapor barrier is placed in front of the inside-the-house vapor barrier that must be used to keep water vapor out of the insulation in the wall cavity. In general, a vapor barrier should not be placed in front of another vapor barrier if insulation exists between the two vapor barriers. Tests made on Styrofoam TF rigid-foam panels have positively proven that water condensation in the wall cavity does **not** occur since the Sytryofoam panel will pass through to the outside the very low level of water vapor that passes through the inside-the-house vapor barrier. Venting of the Styrofoam panels is thus not required. However, the TF-400 and Hi-R rigid-foam panels (and others) are covered on both sides with an aluminum foil which acts as a most positive vapor barrier. Tests have shown that venting by means of manufacturer-provided plastic venting strips must be used in areas where the average January temperature is below 35°F. In areas where the average January temperature is about 35°F, venting is not required. This is illustrated by Figure 11-3.

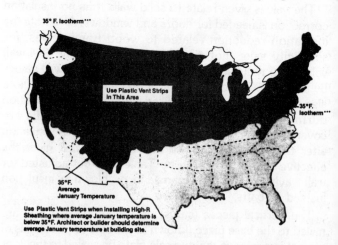

Figure 11-3. Venting-Required Areas

Since all rigid-foam panel insulation act as a vapor barrier of the insulation in the wall (or ceiling) cavity, a vapor barrier must be provided immediately under the interior sheathing (gypum wallboard, paneling, etc.) to prevent water vapor entering the cavity to be trapped here and soak into the insulation. A 6-mil polyethylene vapor barrier is recommended if vapor-barrier batts are not used. Rigid-foam panel insulation may also be installed on the inside of walls or ceilings. The use of rigid-foam panels does not do away with the need for interior wall covering such as gypsum wallboard (sheet rock) etc. since the panels will burn. If wood-veneer paneling is used, it must not be applied directly to the foam panels. Gypsum wallboard (½" thick) must first be nailed over the foam panels to provide a fire-retardant covering.

The many ways rigid-foam insulation panels may be used in house construction are detailed in manufacturer's literature. To obtain any desired literature, refer to "Insulation, Rigid-Foam Panels" in the Bibliography.

SOLID-MASONRY EXTERIOR WALLS

Entire exterior walls or portions thereof may also be constructed of concrete blocks, concrete panels, stone or special bricks. These walls are all, by themselves, inherently low in insulation efficiency and must be specially constructed to achieve the insulation levels now considered mandatory. Each wall type is now considered separately.

Concrete Block Wall. Concrete blocks, by themselves, have an R value of between R1.1 and R2 though the hollow-core effect can raise the value ot about R3 maximum. To raise the R value, rigid-foam panels can be nailed to the outside or inside of the block wall by means of furring strips (1 x 2" wood strips secured to the blocks by adhesive or gun-fired nails). If rigid-foam panels are attached to only one side, and if R8 panels are used, a total R of about R11 can result. If R8 panels are attached on both sides of the block wall, the R value can be raised to about R19 (an adequate value by today's standards). In some cases, the air space within the concrete blocks is filled with foamed-in material, raising the R value to between R10 and R15 depending upon the type of foam used and the size of the air gap in the blocks. Note that if rigid-foam panels are used, they must be covered with a fire-retardant material such as gypsum wallboard (interior walls) or asbestos board, stucco, etc. (exterior walls).

Concrete Panel Wall. Exterior (and interior) walls can be precast as concrete panels and erected by special means. Such walls are seldom used in home construction but are rather widely used in commercial construction. The panels could be cast with rigid-foam insulation within the panel much like a concrete floor using top-cover insulation. Alternately, rigid-foam panels can be attached to the walls in the same manner as detailed for a concrete-block wall.

Brick Wall. Special bricks, up to 6" thick, are sometimes used in home construction and are rather widely used in commercial construction. The bricks have a very low R value, usually about R0.2 per inch of thickness. This is completely inadequate even in areas of extremely mild winters and/or summers. For a 6-inch thick brick, this would give an R1.2 value which, plus the inner and outer air film, would give a total R value of about R2. The insulation value of a brick wall can be raised by attaching rigid-foam panels to the inside or outside of the wall as detailed for the concrete-block wall. At best, using an R8 (1" thick) rigid-foam panel on the inside, an R10 wall will result and if an R8 panel is attached inside and outside, an R value of about R18 will be gained. The R18 wall should be considered if electric-strip heating is to be used.

Stone Wall. Stone, like brick and concrete, has a very low R value (about R0.15 per inch of thickness). An entire exterior wall is seldom made solely from stone since such a wall is a great energy waster. However, many exterior walls contain a fireplace made of solid stone. Table 11-4 illustrates the energy efficiency of a stone-wall fireplace versus a well insulated (R19) wall.

Table 11-4. Stone Wall Insulation Ratio

Total wall = 8' high x 25'	=	200 sq ft
Fireplace portion, stone	=	–64 sq ft
R19 wall portion	=	136 sq ft
Stone = 14" thick = 14 x R0.15 = U0.476		
Degree Days, Heating	= 800	Austin, Tx
Degree Days, Cooling	= 2850	Austin, Tx

Energy Drain Comparison

BTU Loss = U x Sq Ft x Hrs x Degree Days

Stone Wall

Cooling = 0.476 x 64 x 24 x 2850 =	2,083,738	BTU's per yr
Heating = 0.476 x 64 x 24 x 1800 =	+1,316,045	BTU's per yr
	3,399,783	BTU's per yr

R19 Wall

Cooling = 0.526 x 136 x 24 x 1800 =	309,036	BTU's per yr
Heating = 0.526 x 136 x 24 x 1850 =	+489,306	BTU's per yr
	798,342	BTU's per yr

Stone wall portion consumes	3,399,783	
R3 portion consumes	+ 798,342	
Wall total	4,198,125	
Size ratio - stone wall =	64/200 =	32% of wall
- R-19 wall =	136/200 =	68% of wall
		100%
BTU ratio = stone wall =	3,399,783/4,198,125 =	81%
= R19 wall	798,342/4,198,125 =	19%
		100%

This study indicates how 32% of the total wall can use 81% of the total energy needed to heat and cool the area inside the wall. And, that 68% of the wall (being well insulated) uses only 19% of the air-conditioning energy. While the dollar difference to heat and cool the stone portion versus the R19 portion may be only $25.00 or so per year, the comfort difference is considerable. In particular, the cold wall associated with a masonry wall during the winter time can make the entire room feel most uncomfortable. As a result, the thermostat is usually set higher and thus the actual energy waste is higher than that caluclated.

A stone wall (and a concrete wall, etc.) is thicker than a 2x4 or 2x6 wall and thus has more mass. The solid mass of a masonry wall (stone, concrete, etc.) can delay the travel of heat through it. That is, if the wall is cool in the morning, the summer sun will heat the wall up during the day as the outside temperatures rise. This heat build up will pass through the stone mass towards the cooler interior. If the outdoor temperature does not rise too high in relation to the thickness of the stone wall, and the nighttime temperature drops rather sharply from the daytime peak, the heat may not travel all the way through the stone before the heat flow will be reversed. However, if the nighttime temperature only drops a few degrees (10°F or less) from the daytime peak, the wall will gradually heat up until it is heated all the way through. After that, the heat transfer through the mass will be relatively independent of the mass effect. Thus, a solid-masonry wall really does not have the insulation effect commonly attributed to it unless the temperature differences, daytime to nightime, are somewhat broad. For this reason, solid-masonry walls should be insulated to the new minimum standards for the related climatic area.

The values given by Table 11-4 hold equally well for a fireplace wall built of a double row of facing (regular) bricks, separated by a 1" air space.

If an exterior wall is desired to be constructed such that the masonry (usually stone or brick) is visible from inside, the extreme BTU loss associated with masonry can be reduced by erecting the masonry wall against a well-insulated wall (insulated to the local standards). That is, a stud wall can be erected and insulated, equipped with a vapor barrier on the inside, and then covered on both sides with the desired masonry (stone or brick). The extra cost for the stud wall and insulation would be moderate in comparison to the energy dollars saved and the increse in comfort would be well worth the extra outlay by itself. For additional details, refer to "Energy Loss Through Fireplace Wall," page 17-5, Section 17.

INTERIOR WALLS

The interior walls surrounding any area that might be completely shut off from heating and cooling (a spare bedroom for example) for an extended time period should be insulated with R11 batts, non-vapor barrier type. This is required because when an area is shut off from the air-

conditioned portion of the house, if it's walls are no insulated, heat will pass through them from the air conditioned side at a somewhat rapid rate. This wil continue until the temperature of the closed-off are reaches that of the air-conditioned part of the house. Also if the closed-off area contains forced-air or return-air vent a closable-type should be used; otherwise, closing off th area will not really seal it away from the air-conditionec portion of the house. If a closed-off area is insulated anc the vents are closed, the area will present a very small loac to the air-conditioning system when the room is not in use This can result in an appreciable yearly energy savings

OUTER COVERING — EXTERIOR WALLS

To reduce heat buildup in the walls during the summer time, light-colored wall covering or paint will act to reflec more of the sun's rays and thus keep the wall cooler. This is particularly important if the wall insulation is below ar R15 value. Remember, stone, brick or stucco (concrete are very poor insulators while aluminum siding (by itself, can be considered to have an insulation factor of about zero. Wood outer walls have a useful insulation rating (R1.25 per inch thickness average).

When stone or brick is used as the final cover on ar exterior wall, the stone or brick should be installed to leave a 1" air space between it and the wall. This will add about R1.01 to the insulation rating of the wall, a worthwhile addition.

INNER COVERING — EXTERIOR WALLS

Gypsum wallboard (sheet rock) is customarily used to cover the inner surface of outer walls (and both sides of interior walls) of a house. This covering has a moderate R value (R0.56 for a ⅝" thickness). If the wallboard is textur-ed by a spray process (tape and float), a small additional R value is gained.

If rigid-foam panels are nailed to the studs on the inside, these panels must be covered with a fire retardant material such as gypsum wallboard. Wood paneling will not do since it is not fire retardant. The rigid-foam panels are soft and will dent or hole easily thus a second reason they must be covered.

If the wall cavity is filled with insulation, a vapor barrier should be provided. If desired, the gypsum wallboard can be painted with a special "seal and prime" paint that acts as an acceptable vapor barrier. Alternately, a plastic film, 4 to 6 mils thick, can be nailed to the studs to act as a vapor barrier.

ENERGY-EFFICIENT CEILINGS

An uninsulated ceiling has a greater effect upon the energy drain and comfort of a home than that related to an uninsulated wall. The ceiling must be insulated to a level hat effectively isolates the air-conditioned interior from the attic temperature.

Ceilings are usually constructed of 2 x 6 lumber (or larger), with the ceiling joists set of 24" centers. Since ceilings do not have window and door openings or fire blocking, the overall insulation value is lowered mainly as related to the wood area. This is felt to reduce the calculated insulation value by a maximum of about 10 percent. The ceiling area related to air-conditioning ducts and light-fixture boxes is relatively minor on the average and is thus generally not considered. A disappearing staircase, having an area of about 9 square feet, should be insulated and weatherstripped. For details, refer to "Attic Insulation — Disappearing Staircase", page 23-28, Section 23.

A few examples of how a ceiling (attic floor) may be constructed to several levels of insulation efficiency (using 2 x 6 ceiling joists) are given by Table 11-5.

Table 11-5. Ceiling Insulation Combinations

Inside air film	0.61	0.61	0.61	0.61	0.61	0.61	0.61	0.61
⅝" gypsum board	0.56	0.56	0.56	0.56	0.56	0.56	0.56	0.56
No cavity insulation								
6" batts, no compression		19.00						
6" batts + 3" glass fiber = R18.5 + R6.6			25.10					
6" batts + 3" rock wood = R18.5 +R8.4				26.90				
6" batts + 3" cellulose = R18.5 + R11					29.50			
Two layers of 6" batts = R18.5 + R19						37.50	37.50	37.50
1" Styrofoam panels							5.41	
1" Hi-R/TF400 panels								8.00
Attic Air	1.03	1.03	1.03	1.03	1.03	1.03	1.03	1.03
Effective R totals	2.20	21.20	27.30	29.10	31.70	39.70	45.11	47.70

The values given relate to a solid ceiling thus no insulation correction is needed. Also note the insulation reduction related to wood framing was, for simplicity sake, not taken into account. The effective values must then be reduced by 10% to account for the wood framing (probably by 8% if 2x8's are used for ceiling joists). The 6"-thick (R19) batts, fitting into the 5½"-deep cavity between the 2x6 joists, will stand up above the joists by about ½". Slight compression may occur when loose-fill or batt insulation is laid on top the batts between the joists, reducing this insulation value to about R18.5. For details on a roof truss design that will permit up to 13 inches of batts to be installed over the top plate without compression, refer to Figure 11-1.

The recommended minimum insulation values for ceilings are given by Figure 9-4, page 9-13. However, these values are considered minimum only when oil or gas heating is used or if a heat pump is used. If electric-strip heating must be used in any area experiencing even relatively mild winters, the next higher level or ceiling insulation should be considered.

VAULTED AND CATHEDRAL CEILINGS

Vaulted and cathedral ceilings, not having any attic space, present a special problem as to insulation. The ceiling rafters for vaulted and cathedral ceilings are usually made from 2x8 or 2x10 lumber while 2x6 lumber is sometimes used. The batts fitted between the ceiling rafters must not fill the entire depth of the cavity since ventilation must be provided between the top of the batts and the roof. This to ensure that any vapor that might pass through or be developed in the cavity is carried off and does not get trapped and, by so doing, builds up to water saturate the insulation with a consequent severe loss of insulation efficiency. Thus, if 2x6 raters are used, 6" (R19) batts must not be used since the 5½" cavity will not accept the 6" thick batt and still leave an air space. At best, a 3½", 3⅝" or 4" thick batt may be used. For 2x8 rafters, the cavity depth (7½") will take up to a 7" (R24) batt while a 2x10 rafter will provide a cavity depth of 9½" and could take two layers of batts as long as at least a ½" air clearance is provided between the roof and the insulation. Note if two layers of batts are used, the layer next to the roof must not be equipped with a vapor barrier. If it has one, it should be slashed to make it a non-vapor barrier type.

The need to provide ventilation over the batts in the cavity is best answered by use of the top-ridge venting system operating in conjunction with ample eave (soffit) vents. For details, see Figure 15-4, page 15-3.

The insulation level of a cathedral or vaulted ceiling can be raised above the R level of the batts between the rafters by nailing rigid-foam insulation panels to the rafters. The panels can be either nailed on the top (roof side) or on the inside of the rafters. If aluminum-foil backed panels are used on the inside, they will serve as the vapor barrier and the batts fitted between the rafters must then be the non-vapor barrier type. If foil-backed panels are nailed to the roof side of the rafters, since a ventilation space is provided, the fact that the foil-back panels act as a vapor barrier can be disregarded.

Vaulted or cathedral ceilings featuring exposed rafters (beams) cannot be insulated between the rafters. Instead, rigid-foam panels, up to 2″ thick, can be nailed on top the finished ceiling as illustrated by Figure 11-4. It is generally though that a vapor barrier should first be laid down on top the ceiling planks before the rigid-foam paneling is nailed down. If foil-backed panels are used, they will operate as a vapor barrier themselves.

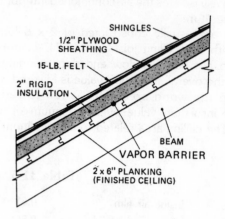

Figure 11-4. Exposed Ceiling Insulation Details.

A flat roof featuring exposed ceiling planking and beams can be insulated in the same manner except that instead of shingles being used, the roof covering would be tar and gravel laid on top of felt paper (usually up to four layers).

Section 12

Outer Doors

GENERAL

Outer doors are a critical component in achieving a very high order of energy efficiency in a home. In fact, a poorly fitting outer door, operating with defective or missing weatherstripping, can be one of the worst energy wasters in the entire house. A recent report by the U.S. Department of Housing and Urban Development (HUD) stated that:

"Almost 70% of a typical single-family dwelling heating and cooling load is traceable to outer doors (and windows)."

Careful thought and consideration is thus indicated in the selection of outer doors because of the role they play in:

- the overall energy efficiency of the home
- personal safety as to fire and burglar protection

Two types of energy losses can occur as related to outer doors — heat transmission and infiltration — as illustrated by figure 12-1.

Figure 12-1. Energy Losses Through Outer Doors

1—HEAT TRANSMISSION
heat passing through materials

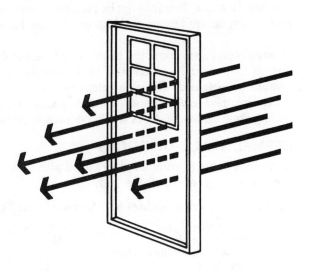

2—INFILTRATION
air passing through cracks
under and around doors.

DOOR FACTS

Outer doors, excluding garage doors, have a much greater impact upon energy efficiency and personal comfort in a home than is generally thought. When considering an outer door, the following facts should be kept in mind:

1. Door should not warp or bend in relation to temperature and/or humidity changes since to do so will break the weatherstripping seal and thus permit a high level of air infiltration.

2. Door should have a positive-seal weatherstripping since even the best of doors cannot compensate for poor, ill-fitting weatherstripping.

3. Door should have a good insulation value.

4. Door should exhibit a high resistance to fire and forced entry.

5. Glass inserts in door, if used, should be kept down in size and be double-glazed type. French doors (doors with many small glass panes) should be avoided. If possible, a single front door should be used rather than a double-door entry. If side lights (glass panels) are used on either or both sides of the front door, these should be of minimum size and double-glazed for energy efficiency.

6. Most-used outer doors (including glass patio doors) should be equipped with automatic door closers (at small expense to ensure doors are not left open needlessly.

ENERGY-EFFICIENT OUTER DOORS

The door that most perfectly answers requirements 1 through 4 above is the metal-clad, foam-core door, using magnetic weatherstripping of the same type used on refrigerators. These doors are extremely sturdy and cannot warp or bend nor will the surface crack or peel. The doors are also considerably more fireproof and burglar proof than a wood door, in particular as related to a hollow-core door. (A large hole can actually be easily punched or kicked into a hollow-core door).

And—of extreme importance—the doors have an insulating factor of up to six times that of a wood door. A thermal break is built into the door covering to prevent transfer of cold through the metal thus condensation will not form on the interior portion.

Once installed, metal-clad doors will remain weathertight and intact on an indefinite basis, something that cannot be said for even the best of wood doors. The doors may be obtained with a pleasing variety of face design and with double-glazed glass being available and highly recommended. The doors may be painted or antiqued as desired and cannot be told from a wood door. The metal-clad door is a real energy saver and their cost—for initial installation—is very competitive with comparable-quality wood doors.

The steel insulating door is such a perfect answer to outer door requirements under today's need for energy conservation that it is felt its use cannot be over-emphasized. The door saves energy two ways:

- Insulating doors have a thermal resistance value of up to R15, or as much as 6½ times better than solid wood doors, and nearly four times better than an entry door made of wood and covered by a storm door. A six-city test conducted by the Georgia University of Technology showed that insulating steel doors cut heat losses by as much as 85% compared to other doors. Summer-time savings are also indicated.

- The magnetic weatherstripping used on steel-covered insulating doors is magnetically held against the door facing so tightly that tests have shown the air infiltration rate to be 60 per cent lower than a tight-fitting wood door and 20 per cent lower than for a combination tight-fitting wood door covered with a storm door.

Recent research has clearly pinpointed air infiltration (drafts) as having a greater effect upon energy waste than even insulation. Thus, the energy saved by the almost perfect draft seal made by magnetic weatherstripping will be even greater than that saved by the high insulation value of the door.

- Note that some metal-clad doors are constructed of aluminum and thus magnetic weatherstripping cannot be used (aluminum has no magnetic attraction capabilities). Since the magnetic weatherstripping is of utmost importance in reducing drafts, use of aluminum-clad outer doors is not recommended.

To review — if a really high level of energy efficiency is to be built into a house on a year-in-and-year-out basis, steel insulating doors must be used. The best of wood doors can never be made weathertight on an indefinite basis since the wood must contract and expand (and thus bend) in relation to temperature and/or humidity changes. Thus, the weatherstripping around even a tight-fitting wood door can never be 100 percent efficient. The action of the magnetic weatherstripping on steel insulating doors must be seen to be appreciated. If the door is closed slowly towards the magnetic weatherstripping, when the door is within about ½" of the weatherstripping, the magnetic pull will close the door by itself. This means that if a steel insulating door is buffetted by high winds or the wood jamb contracts or expands, the magnetic weatherstripping will still hold to the door to form a perfect seal at all times.

A steel insulating door (as tests have shown) is so energy efficient and exhibits such excellent draft prevention capabilities a storm door may not be required even in areas experiencing severe winters and high winds. See Table 12-1.

If any doubt exists about the beauty of a steel insulating door, it is seriously suggested that manufacturer's literature be obtained. The many attractive doors offered will certainly please. Alternately, a visit to a local company handling steel insulating doors would be most informative.

THERMAL VALUE OF DOORS

The thermal value of common doors used with or without storm doors is given by Table 12-1.

Table 12-1. Thermal Values of Common Door Types

Door Type	R-Value
Hollow-Core Wood	R-1.0
Hollow-Core w/Storm Door	R-1.5
Solid Wood	R-2.3
Solid Core w/Storm Door	R-3.5
Metal w/Urethane Core	R-13.5*
*Some run as high as R-15	

AUTOMATIC DOOR CLOSERS

Few people seem to be aware that each time an outer door is opened, a large opening (3' wide and 6'8" high) is made in the house. In the winter, the heavy cold air flows into the house when the door is opened, pushing out expensively heated air. In summer, the reverse happens. A trip out to the mail box and back — with the door open — can exhaust a large part of the expensively conditioned air from the house. Remember, your air conditioner is sized to heat and cool your house, not the entire neighborhood.

Peachtree Door, Inc. of Norcross, Ga. commissioned a six-city study by the Georgia Institute of Technology on their steel insulating doors. The calculations were made for doors operating in the average temperatures of each city over a 50-year period. With an outside temperature of zero and an inside temperature of 72°F, an average of 18,000 BTUs are lost for each minute an exterior door remains open. For electric heat, one KW will develop 3412 BTUs of heat. This figure, divided into 18,000, reveals a total of 5.3 KWs are need to restore the heat lost per minute through an open door. Taking an average of 3.5¢ per KWH, the open door thus costs about 18.5¢ per minute.

Open exterior doors are thus great wasters of energy. With children in the house, the exterior doors will be opened and closed many times a day. And, all too often, the door is not closed or is closed only partially. This condition can be remedied by the installation of automatic door closers. For hinged doors, one excellent door closer is a unit that looks like a slightly larger hinge. This is fitted to the door between the top and bottom hinges and acts to positively close the door. It can be adjusted for a "soft" close. Once installed, it operates noiselessly and smoothly closes the door. Automatic door closers are also available for glass patio sliding doors and are highly recommended.

WOOD VERSUS INSULATING DOOR SAVINGS

The cost difference between steel insulating doors and wood doors is somewhat difficult to arrive at since wood doors come in such a variety of carvings and other trim. Steel insulating doors may also be fitted out with a variety of trim (but not carvings, of course). Trim is less expensive to mount on a steel-faced door so the cost difference between steel and wood doors as related to trim is not really a cost factor.

Basic cost comparison can actually be made only on a plain-door basis. A recent price check indicated a top-quality solid-ash wood door ran about 25 percent less than the same size steel insulating door. The doors, prehung in that they need merely be placed in the door opening and nailed, were priced as follows:

Basic, steel insulating door, in frame, complete w/weatherstripping	= $105.00
Basic, solid-ash wood door, in frame, no weatherstripping	$ 80.00
Difference	$ 25.00

The difference is really somewhat less since the wood door is not equipped with weatherstripping. This will add about $9.00 to the wood door cost, thus the net difference is about $16.00. Hardly enough cost difference to warrant a justification.

The study made by the Georgia Institute of Technology calculated the annual heat loss through various type doors to be as follows:

Conventional wood door —
used 4,095,600 BTUs per year
Wood door w/storm door —
used 2,400,195 BTUs per year
Steel foam-core door —
used 624,579 BTUs per year

The steel insulating door thus used 75 per cent less energy than a wood door covered with a storm door and 85 per cent less than for a conventional wood door alone. For electric heating energy cost, at a 3.5¢ KWH rate, are:

Wood door alone	$\dfrac{4{,}095{,}600 \times .035}{3412} = \$42.01$
Wood w/storm	$\dfrac{2{,}400{,}295 \times .035}{3412} = \$24.63$
Steel insulating	$\dfrac{624{,}579 \times .035}{3412} = \$ 6.41$

The yearly savings against a wood door is thus $42.01 — $6.41 = $35.60. Clearly, steel insulating doors are well worthwhile and will have a most excellent payback period (less than one year).

WOOD DOORS — WEATHERSTRIPPING

The very best of weatherstripping should be used on wood doors to compensate for the slight bending and warping that occurs with even high-quality wood doors in response to temperature-humidity changes.

The potential for air infiltration and exfiltration around the door edges is considerable. For example, if a 1/12th

inch gap existed completely around a door (6'-8" x 3'), the gap area totals 19.33 square inches. This is equivalent to a 4x5 inch hole in the door. Clearly, such a hole will cause a large air flow into or out of the house thus all outer doors should be carefully weatherstripped.

For details on weatherstripping of wood doors, refer to "Outer Doors", page 23-18, Section 23.

SUMMARY

When considering exterior doors, the following should be kept in mind:

- Exterior doors can be very great energy wasters.
- Steel-clad, insulating doors are clearly the most energy efficient, cost only about 25% more than a comparable-quality wood door, and are highly recommended.

- Steel-clad insulating doors are manufactured to use either magnetic weatherstripping or other types. Since air infiltration is now known to be the worst energy waster, the best door weatherstripping material (magnetic) should be used. Insulating doors not using magnetic weatherstripping are not recommended.
- The extra cost of an insulating door over a wood door should be repaid within a year. Three steel-clad insulating doors (an average per house) should not add much more than $100.00 to the house cost over wood doors of comparable quality and trim.
- Wood doors must be equipped with top-quality weatherstripping and this weatherstripping should be check for tightness at least twice a year.
- The door frame, as fitted into the door opening, should be carefully caulked to eliminate drafts. Any open spaces within the door framing should be filled with insulation (preferably of the expandable-foam type).

Section 13

WINDOWS AND GLASS PATIO DOORS

GENERAL

Windows and glass doors are the soul of a home, they bring the outdoors to our immediate sight, keep us in touch with the weather and all, brighten and lighten the interior and add balanced beauty to a house. Yet, most regretfully, in an otherwise well insulated house, the windows and glass doors can act to lower the energy-use efficiency of a house. Happily, this need not be so.

A recent report by the Dept. of Energy stated:

"Contrary to popular belief, houses with large windows may not consume more energy than houses with small windows. Properly designed, located and used windows can actually reduce heating and air conditioning costs; poorly designed, located and used windows will increase these costs."

"In the winter a window can catch the sun's warmth while providing a barrier to heating system losses. In the spring and summer it can be opened to take advantage of mild temperatures and breezes to provide natural conditioning of indoor air. In the summer it can flush the house with cool night air, then insulate against daytime heat. During all seasons daylighting can serve as a free source of illumination."

A house, to be truly energy efficient, need not be built with a minimum of windows. Large size windows and a large overall window area, however, can be justified **only** if the house is built to a fairly high level of energy efficiency. This includes orienting the house to the best sun angle to either optimize winter-time gain from the sun or to minimize summer-time sun entering the house, using windows that may be opened for ventilation purposes and shading or screening windows as needed. The author's home of 1944 square feet living area features large windows, totalling 310 square feet or 16% of the living-space area. The excellent energy efficiency of the home clearly shows that large expanses of glass can be used if the house is designed, built and oriented to optimize energy savings. However, consider the following:

A report issued by the Housing and Urban Development said in part:

"Almost 70% of a typical single-family dwelling heating and cooling load is traceable to windows (and outer doors)."

This statement, in contrast to the excellent energy efficiency gained by many homes with large expanse of windows, clearly indicates the extreme importance of selecting high-quality windows and glass patio doors. The windows must also have a very low air-infiltration rate through the moving sections and they must be installed to reduce air infiltration through the window frame to an absolute minimum. These windows will limit the energy loss through the glass and frame to a very acceptable level.

Heat flow into and out of a house through the windows is due to:

- **Conduction** — the molecular flow of heat through the glass itself and the frame (either metal or wood). This flow is always from the warmest side towards the coolest side and is in direct proportion to the admittance (U) factor of the glass and frame material. Conduction is affected by the air currents or breezes flowing by the window, with the heat-flow rate increasing if the air movement speeds up.

- **Infiltration** — through the moving parts of operating windows and around the window frame and window opening. This can be reduced to a very low value by selecting windows with a low air-leakage rate and by properly sealing the window into the window opening.

- **Radiation** — The sun's rays, passing through the glass, can be a heat gain in the winter and a cooling loss in the summer. House orientation and window screening or shading must be considered on either of two conditions:

  1. Heat gain in the winter is of prime importance and cooling loss in the summer is of secondary importance.

  2. Cooling loss in the summer is of prime importance and heat gain in the winter is of secondary importance.

WINDOW FACTS

All windows fall into one of the following three general types:

1. Single glazed   2. Double glazed   3. Triple glazed

The term "single glazed" identifies a window of one-pane construction whereas "double glazed" states the window consists of two lites (panes) as illustrated by figure 13-1.

There are two major types of double-glazed windows. One—where the window is made of two lites (panes) sealed to an aluminum spacer (¼" wide, usually). A dessicant is sealed between the two panes to keep down interpane moisture. The second type also consists of two panes but these are fused together at the edges to make the two panes as one with an air space (¼" usually) being maintained. This closed area is evacuated to reduce the air content to a very low value. This reduces the chance of discoloration between panes. This type is generally called "insulating" glass and is considered superior to double-glazed units in that there is less chance of air leakage into the between-panes area.

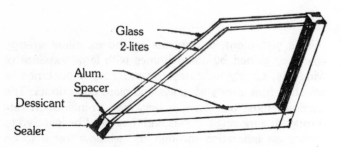

Figure 13-1. Double-glazed Window Details

Double-glazed windows can cost up to twice the cost of the single-pane windows of comparable quaility. Insulating windows are usually mounted in wood frames and can cost up to 4 and even 5 times that of comparable sized single-glazed windows. In this book, the term double-glazed will be used to identify both types. An *effective* double-glazed unit can be made by installing a storm window over a single-glazed unit. For details, refer to "Storm Windows," immediately below.

Triple-glazed windows are of two general types. One—where a storm window is installed over a double-glazed unit. The second type consists of a double-glazed unit mounted in a frame specially designed to permit installation (and removal) of a third pane of glass about 1" out from the double-glazed unit. The general energy efficiency of both types is about equal. The main benefit of the second type is appearance since the third pane does not appear as an "add-on" unit. This is not such an important point now since the new "fitted" storm windows are equally as attractive.

STORM WINDOW DETAILS

Modern storm windows are made of glass panes mounted in a special frame, usually aluminum. The windows are of the "self-storing" type in that they need not be taken down at winter's end for storage since they are also *most definitely* energy savers against the summer heat. The windows are attractive and appear as part of the window,

not having the "add-on" look of the old style units.

Storm windows are actually improperly named. Their very name—storm window—implies they are of use only when a storm is blowing and thus they are of use only in the winter. Oddly enough, most people still tend to see storm windows as for winter-time use only. This is entirely incorrect. That is, the air space between the multi-panes of double-glazed, triple-glazed, or single-glazed with-storm-window units acts to reduce the molecular flow of heat from the warmer side to the colder side. In the winter, the colder side is clearly outside the house and the heat flow is from the house out to the outside. In the summer, things are reversed thus the heat tries to flow from the warmer outside towards the colder (air conditioned) inside. Thus, multi-glazed windows are clearly effective on both a winter and summer basis.

Storm windows are designed to fit outside the existing (prime) window and may be of three types: half-hung (lower part opens vertically), slider (one pane slides horizontally) and picture window (a non-opener). Storm windows are generally made of the same weight glass as the window they are to cover and thus they have at least the same safety factor as the prime window.

Storm windows that can be opened (half-hung or slider type) must have their two panes constructed to be equal in size to those of the prime window. This will position the center-bar of the prime and storm windows at the same height. In general, if the fixed and moving parts of a storm window are of equal size (the center-bar is in the middle of the window height), both the sliding and fixed part of the storm window can be removed from inside the house. A real benefit for second-floor installations. However, if the two parts are of unequal size, usually only the lower half of the storm window can be removed from inside the house. However, in this case, panes of most storm windows can be removed from outside the house without removing the frame from the prime window. Note that a storm window that opens will come equipped with a screen and that the screen of the prime window is not needed and cannot be installed since it will block movement of the storm window.

Storm windows, if properly installed, seldom need to be dismantled for cleaning within the inter-pane space. For further details on storm window installation, see "Storm Window Installation," page 23-24, Section 23.

ENERGY-SAVING FACTS

Here are some interesting facts on energy saving made possible by use of various types of windows:

- Comparing a single-glazed window having an R0.88 value against a well-insulated wall having an R20 value, the R ratio is R20/R0.88 = 22.72 or about 23 to 1. Thus, one square foot of single-glazed window will pass up to 23 times the energy that would pass through one square foot of an R20 wall. To put it another way, 23 square feet of

R20 wall will have a heat (energy) flow equal to that passed through only one square foot of a single-glazed window. For an R11 wall, as a further example, the ratio would be R11/R0.88 or about 13 to 1.

- For a double-glazed window and an R20 wall, the ratio is R20/R1.54 or about 13 to 1.

- Storm windows properly installed over a single-glazed window can raise the window R value to a possible 1.8. The square-foot ratio is then R20/R1.8 or about 11 to 1— a little better than for double-glazed windows.

  - Storm windows properly installed over a double-glazed window can raise the window R value to a possible 2.56. The R ratio is then R20/R2.56, giving a square-foot ratio of 7.8 or about 8 to 1.

Note

The R values given above for storm-window combinations are optimum and can be achieved only if the storm windows are properly installed. For installation details, refer to "Storm-Window Installation," Section 23.

The energy-saving ratios of windows against outer walls of various R values are given by Table 13-1.

Table 13-1. Energy Savings vs. Multi-Glazing

Window Type	Ins. Values R	U*	Effic. Ratio to Sng-Glzd	Loss Ratio - 1 sq ft Window to Ins. Wall R10	R15	R20
Sng-glazed	0.88	1.14		11.5	17.0	23.0
Dbl-glazed	1.54	0.65	75% better	6.5	9.7	13.0
Sng w/Strm	1.80	0.56	104% better	5.5	8.3	11.0
Dbl w/Strm	2.56	0.39	190% better	4.0	6.0	8.0

*See Table 5-1, Section 5 for winter-summer values

COMFORT BENEFTIS OF MULTI-GLAZING

The comfort benefits of multi-glazing are considerable and—by themselves—would actually make the extra cost over single-glazed glass worthwhile. These comfort benefits are illustrated by Figure 13-2.

The above manufacturer's information indicates the reduction in sunlight (glare) and solar radiation resulting from multi glazing. Note in particular the sound reduction, 40% or more. This benefit has to be felt to be fully appreciated. A noise, objectionably loud when the window (or glass door) is open, drops to a "hardly heard" level when the window (or door) is closed. This feature is especially important for bedrooms and can make the difference between a restless night and restful sleep.

The air temperature immediately near the inside of a window (or glass door) will be at some ratio to the outside temperature dependent upon the type of glazing used. For a single-glazed unit on a very cold or warm day, the air temperature near the glass can be most uncomfortable. The temperature difference—inside to

outside—is reduced in direct proportion to the air spaces. That is, the temperature difference is the greatest for single-glazed windows, considerably less for double-glazed, while that for single-glazed units covered with storm windows is about equal to that related to double-glazed units. Triple-glazed windows are available and should have a temperature difference ratio somewhat better than that related to double-glazed units covered with storm windows.

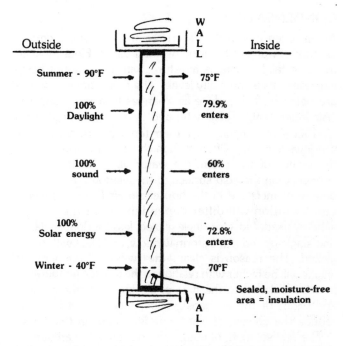

Figure 13-2. Comfort Benefits of Multi-Glazing

The space between window glass of multi-glazed windows is not the same for all manufactured units. The air-gap spacing varies from about ¼" (minimum) to about ½" (maximum), with a slight increase in energy-saving efficiency being gained by use of the ½" gapped units. With the wider space between window glass, some multi-glazed units are now being offered with a built-in Venetian blind. This blind can be operated with a small crank and can be positioned anywhere between fully-closed and fully-opened—an excellent sun shade. These windows, however, are currently offered only in narrow units (about two feet wide).

In general, the public (and even some "experts") tend to consider multi-glazed and storm windows to be effective only during the winter. In particular, storm windows are all too often thought to be of use only during the winter and that they "won't be of any use during the summer time". This is completely incorrect. Storm windows and multi-glazed windows are cost-justified for use in any area that experiences any climate other than that related to extremely mild winters and/or summers.

The point to remember about multi-glazed and storm windows is this—the units resist the flow of heat, into the house in the summer and out of the house in the winter. This heat flow is calculated on a "no-sun" basis and thus relates only to the energy-saving efficiency of the total window on both a summer and winter basis. For additional details, refer to "Single-Glazed vs. Multi-Glazed Energy Savings," page 13-5.

CONDENSATION

All air, even that of the desert regions, contains a certain amount of water in the form of water vapor. Household air most certainly contains moisture, with the amount being expressed as a "humidity level." The more modern homes are being built to reduce air changes to a minimum (see "Air Infiltration," Section 14) and thus they can contain a high level of humidity. If the air temperature against the windows is greatly different than the air temperature near the center of the room, the water vapor in the air will condense on the cold surface of the windows. For a given degree of moisture in the household air (humidity level), condensation will differ dependent upon the type of window used. Most for single-glazed, less for double-glazed and single-glazed wth a storm window, and least with triple-glazed. The reason is clear—the "window" temperature inside will be higher with relation to the outside temperature in direct relation to the type of glazing used (the number and width of the air gaps). Thus, multi-glazed windows reduce the chance of water condensation on the glass.

The real solution, of course, is to reduce the amount of water developed in the home by careful use of controlled ventilation to remove the water-vapor laden air in the kitchen and bathroom areas. Recommended levels of humidity for a house with an indoor temperature of 70°F in relation to various levels of outdoor winter-time temperatures are given by Table 13-2.

Table 13-2. Humidity Levels vs. Outdoor Temperature

Outside Air Temperature	Recommended Relative Humidity
-20°F or below	not more than 15%
-20°F to -10°F	not more than 20%
-10°F to 0°F	not more than 25%
0°F to 10°F	not more than 30%
10°F to 20°F	not more than 35%
20°F to 40°F	not more than 40%

THERMAL-BREAK WINDOWS

Today, most window frames are manufactured from aluminum while, to a smaller degree, others are made from wood. Aluminum-framed windows are generally less expensive than wood-framed windows, have a longer frame life and need less maintenance. Unfortunately, the aluminum frames can pass heat at a fantastic rate, this being about 1,770 times faster than through wood. That is, a 1″ thick piece of soft pine has an R value of about R1.25 while a 1″ thick piece of aluminum has an R value of R0.0007. An aluminum frame will thus measure on the inside almost the same temperature as that outdoors. This means that aluminum frames can cause the water vapor in the air to condense on the aluminum when the window glass itself does not show signs of condensation. Wood window frames will pass less heat in or out of the house and will show less signs of condensation than a "regular" aluminum-framed window.

Fortunately, aluminum windows constructed with a "thermal break" are available. That is, the aluminum frames are constructed in two sections, bonded together with a plastic insert that effectively separates the two metal pieces. This plastic insert raises the effective R value of the aluminum frames to be equal to or better than that related to wood-frame windows. These windows are somewhat more expensive than the "regular" aluminum-framed windows but their cost is considerably less (on the average) than that related to wood-framed windows. Thermal-break windows are highly recommended if aluminum-framed windows are desired. Thermal-break aluminum-framed glass patio doors are also available and are also highly recommended for the same reasons.

DESIGN CONSIDERATION FOR WINDOWS

Window size and placement is all too often being determined by architectural styling, the need for daylight illumination, a desire to enjoy a view, for ventilation purposes, and building-code requirement. Not too much attention is given to window size and placement based on the need for energy conservation. In the past days of inexpensive energy, heat loss or gain through the windows was not a costly thing since the energy needed to compensate for this was so cheap. With the advent of the energy crisis, windows are now being examined from an energy-saving viewpoint. The easy answer—eliminate windows and/or reduce window area—is not *really the right answer* in all cases.

When one views a large home with large expanse of glass, many automatically think "the heating and cooling bills of that house must be very high." In actual fact, that need not be the case. Windows must not be considered only heat wasters since they can make meaningful contributions to house heating in the winter. Their comfort effect upon the home in the winter is considerable by virtue of the solar energy (heat) they pass into the house and hold. A recent pamphlet issued by the Federal Energy Administration states:

"A sealed double glass unit (in the Boston, Mass. area) with a U of 0.55 will lose during January about 380 BTU per square foot per day more than a wall having a U of 0.10 (R10), but it will transmit (into the house) from solar radiation an average of 520 BTU per square foot per day, for a net improvement of 140 BTU per square foot per day over the performance of the wall. During November the difference is greater, the index of superiority of the double-glazed windows being on the order of 270 BTU per square foot per day."

The above statement indicates that windows can be energy gainers if properly oriented to the sun's winter path, with southern-facing windows developing the highest solar gain. In areas where winter heating is the main problem (and summer cooling needs are minor), glass area need not be considered to be energy wasters. But, double-glazed glass must be used to hold the gained heat in and—of course—air infiltration around the window frames must be reduced to near zero during the installation phase.

Where solar energy entering through the glass contributes to the heat required by a house, that heat must be distributed throughout the house to be really useful. This can be accomplished by setting the heater unit into the "FAN ONLY ON" mode to move the hot air from in front of the sun-lit windows and distribute it through the duct system to the entire house. Of course, drapes or shades on unsunlit windows and glass doors should be drawn to hold the heat in the house.

In areas where summer cooling is more important than winter heating, large areas of glass (especially if facing south) can be *justified only if*:

- The house is built to realize a very high level of energy efficiency.

- Double-glazed or single-glazed units with storm windows are used throughout the house.

- All windows in the sun's path are shaded to the best degree possible in the summer. Shades and drapes should be drawn when the sun is on the related glass (window or patio door). Awnings, roof overhang and porches must be designed into the house to shade the windows from outside.

- Deciduous trees should be planted to shade the glass (southern-exposure particularly). The trees in summer, being in leaf, will shade the glass while in the winter (with the limbs bare), the sun can enter the house as a heat gain.

ENERGY-EFFICIENT WINDOWS

The large amount of heat transferred through windows into and out of the house by conduction and radiation must be taken into account along with air infiltration through the window frame if a house is to achieve a high level of energy efficiency. The very large heat loss or gain through the windows can be reduced to acceptable levels as follows:

- The house plans should be studied to determine if:

    (1) Any window can be eliminated.

    (2) Any window can be reduced in size.

    (3) Any window that opens can be changed to a fixed window.

CAUTION

Local building codes must be checked to determine the minimum allowable window area (usually 10% of the outer wall area) and if each room must have a window that can be opened to provide a fire exit.

- All windows should be double-glazed of good quality or single-glazed units covered with storm windows. While such windows are somewhat expensive today, the cost of energy in the near future will make them mandatory in a year or two.

- In areas of extreme temperature ranges (particularly very cold and/or windy winters), storm windows mounted over double-glazed windows might be considered. This is of particular importance with relation to north-facing windows and/or those facing a high prevailing wind.

- All opening windows should be equipped with high-quality weatherstripping material and be capable of being tightly closed. This thought also holds for patio doors with their large area. It is suggested that all windows purchased conform to the following standards of weatherstripping (as marked on the window with a tag).

AAMA Standard 302.8   ANSI Standard A134.1

- Extreme care must be taken to prevent drafts (air infiltration) around the window frame when installed. For draft-prevention details, refer to "Exterior Windows," Section 14, page 14-7.

- Each window that presents a sun-entry problem should be shaded by either roof overhang, porches, trees, shrubs, etc.

- Where possible, window shades of good quality should be used. Also, a thermal-barrier lining may be sewn into the drapes of large windows to act as a partial barrier to heat transfer into and out of the house. For additional details, refer to "Window Shading," page 13-5.

- Where windows must face the sun unshaded, consideration might be given to installing a reflective material on the glass. For details, refer to "Solar-Energy Reflectors", page 13-6.

SINGLE-GLAZED VS. DOUBLE-GLAZED ENERGY SAVINGS

Double-glazed windows are somewhat more expensive than single-glazed units of the same quality and are about equal in price to single-glazed units covered with storm windows. The square-foot cost for single or double-glazed units varies according to size and type and as to quality.

An important point should be noted here—single-glazed windows are a highly competitive product in the building market thus the cost and quality of single-glazed windows of the same size can vary greatly. An inexpensive (poor quality) window might cost about half that of a good quality window of the same size. The comparison to follow is made against single and double glazed windows of identical (good) quality. Also, the prices given relate to aluminum-framed units since wood-framed units are quite a bit more expensive.

A fairly realistic square-foot cost of windows, aluminum framed, of good quality might be:

Single-glazed = $2.30 per sq ft (except picture windows)
Double-glazed = $5.40 per sq ft (except picture windows)

For cost and energy-saving comparisons, assume a house as follows:

House living space = 50′ long x 30′ wide = 1500 sq ft
Outer wall area 50′ + 30′ x 2 x 8′ = 1280 sq ft
Glass area = 1500 sq ft x 12.75% = 192 sq ft

Dbl-glazed, est. = 192 x $5.40 = $1036.80
Sng-glazed, est. = 192 x $2.30 = - 441.60
Cost difference = $595.20

The winter-summer savings using double-glazed windows instead of single-glazed units as installed in an all-electric home in Austin, Texas are as follows:

BTU load = U x Area x Degree Days x 24 hrs = BTU Load

Winter, sng-glazed = 1.13*x 192 x 1800 x 24 = 9,372,672 BTU's

Winter, dbl-glazed = 0.65*x 192 x 1800 x 24 = 5,391,360 BTU's
BTU difference = 3,981,312 BTU's
- - - - - - - - - - - - - - - - - -
Summer, sng-glazed = 1.06*x 192 x 2850 x 24 =13,920,768 BTU's

Summer, dgl-glazed = 0.61*x 192 x 2850 x 24 = 8,011,008 BTU's
BTU difference = 5,909,760 BTU's

Winter - cost difference = $\frac{3,981,312}{3412}$ = 1167 KWH @ 4¢ = $46.68

Summer - cost difference = $\frac{5,909,760}{EER x 1000}$ = 809 KWH @ 4¢ = $32.36
EER = 7.3   Saved = $79.04

Extra-cost difference - at 4¢ per KWH = $595.20/$79.04 = 7.5 yrs

*Per Table 5-1, - at 6¢ per KWH = $595.20/118.56 = 5.0 yrs
Section 5   - at 8¢ per KWH = $595.20/158.08 = 3.8 yrs

For the same house with gas heating and electric cooling, the savings would be:

$\frac{3,981,321}{10,000 \times 0.8}$ = 498 mcf at 3¢ = $14.94   Gas = 3¢ per mcf
                                                  Elec. =4¢ per KWH

Summer savings = $32.36
Total saved = $47.30 per year

Payback time = $595.20/$47.30 = 12.6 years. Higher gas rate would result in a faster payback period.

For electric heat pump heating and cooling, the savings would be:

$\frac{3,981,312}{3412 \times SPF}$ = $\frac{3,981,312}{3412 \times 2.25}$ = 519 KWH pr yr @ 4¢ = $20.76
+ summer savings = $32.36
Total savings = $53.12

Payback time = $545.20/$53.12 = 11 years. Higher electric rate would result in a shorter payback period

It should be noted that the savings detailed relate to "no-sun" conditions since only the ability of the window to resist the molecular flow of heat was considered in the calculations. The ability of multi-glazed windows to restrict the flow of solar energy into the house is an added benefit. Two other worthwhile benefits are: (1) less air infiltration and (2) improved sound insulation.

Agreed, the payback periods indicated (except for electric heating and cooling) do not seem to indicate multi-glazed windows are "worthwhile." Yet, they most certainly are worthwhile and will have a better payback period than that indicated by the above calculations. When the solar-shading and air-leakage effects are taken into account, the payback periods can just be about halved. Another point, the tests relate to the relatively mild climate of Austin, Texas. For Duluth, Minn., for example, the dollar savings developed for Austin must be multiplied by 2.08 to compensate for the climatic differences in winter and summer. Climate factoring for other areas is given by Table 7-7, page 7-5, Section 7. The Austin, Texas savings as related to Duluth, Minn. would thus be $79.04 x 2.08 = $164.40 for an all-electric home, $98.38 gas heating and electric cooling and $110.40 for heat-pump heating and cooling.

Installation of storm windows, according to a study detailed in the January 1976 issue of Mechanics Illustrated, resulted in a 24 percent reduction in the heating bill. These savings would also relate to using double-glazed windows instead of single-glazed units. The same test, by the way, showed that insulating the walls saved 15 percent, insulating the floors saved 8 percent and increasing the ceiling (attic) from 3-½ inches to 9 inches saved another 5 percent. Recall that installing storm windows alone saved 24 percent, a much better dollar spent-to-dollar earned investment.

The Architectural Aluminum Manufacturers Association (AAMA) made some tests on the replacement of single-glazed glass (windows and doors) with double-glazed insulating glass units in a "standard" house. The data was verified by the National Association of Homebuilders Research Foundation. The test results, developed when energy prices were still relatively inexpensive, take into account only the loss of heat directly through the glass.

Table 13-3. Savings—Single Glazed vs. Double-Glazed

City	Electricity	Fuel Oil	Natural Gas
Minneapolis, Minn.	$76.00	$68.00	$32.00
Chicago, Ill	$50.00	$54.00	$26.00
Rochester, N.Y.	$48.00	$55.00	$37.00
Richmond, Va.	$26.00	$31.00	$22.00

Practical experience has shown that energy-efficient windows must be installed or retrofitted if a house is to achieve a high order of energy savings. The cost of energy-efficient windows at today's prices must be compared against what they will cost next year, five years from now, etc. And, the price of energy, certain to rise to no one knows what heights, must be taken into account. In brief, buy energy-efficient windows and glass doors today to ensure reasonable energy bills now and in the future.

IDENTIFYING QUALITY WINDOWS AND GLASS DOORS

The Architectural Aluminum Manufacturers Association (AAMA) has prepared technical specifications to encourage producers to maintain high quality standards. If a window bears the AAMA Certification Program label, it is in conformance with th ANSI/AAMA 302.9 quality standards as to air and water leakage and structural integrity. A thermalized (thermal-break) window manufactured to AAMA Thermalized Standards will bear a label to this effect. These labels identify a top-quality window in all respects. A quality window is also identified if tagged ANSI Standard A134.1.

WINDOW SHADING

Tests have proven that it is seven times better to keep the sun's rays from entering the house than to try to counter the heat gain after it has been developed. Back in the old "hardship" days before modern air conditioning became practical, houses were kept cool in the summer by careful use of window shading and air ventilation. In warm areas, the houses were built with wide roof overhangs or porches to keep the sun off the windows. Windows not shaded by roof overhang or porches and awnings were all equipped with shades and/or drapes. And, as soon as a house was built, trees or large shrubs were planted to shade the windows.

The importance of window shading is illustrated by the following table:

The values given are BTU's per hour per square foot, representing air conditioning loads due to solar energy—averages for August 1, 5:30 AM to 6:30 PM—for a location of 30° and 40° North latitude.

Table 13-4 gives the solar gain into the house for August 1 built within a given latitude range. The values will differ for the same latitude on a day-by-day basis and

Table 13-4. Air-Conditioning Load Due to Solar Energy

Type of Glass	Type of Shading	N	NW & NE	E & W	SW & SE	S
Sng-glz	None	19	52	77	66	36
Dbl-glz	None	17	44	66	57	31
Sng-glz	Draperies	11	28	44	36	19
Dbl-glz	Venetian Blinds	10	25	40	33	18
Sng-glz	Roller Shades	14	36	57	48	25
Sng-glz	Awnings	16	17	18	17	16
Dbl-glz	Awnings	11	12	12	12	11

Above in BTU's per sq ft

for any given day will differ for different latitudes. This information can be obtained from local sources particularly the U.S. Weather Bureau. As mentioned, exterior sun shading is the most efficient since it acts to stop or reduce the solar energy from entering the house through the glass. Inside shading with drapes, blinds and roller shades is less effective but is still well worthwhile. A recent pamphlet issued by the Federal Energy Commission included the following table:

Table 13-5. Efficiency of Shading Device

Device	Reduction in Solar Heat
White opaque roller shade	50%
White lined draperies	33%
Venetian blinds (slat @40° slant)	18%
Venetian blinds (closed)	29%
White translucent roller shade	44%

Note: White-colored shading is most efficient since white reflects heat.

For maximum efficiency, a roller shade or venetian blind should be mounted inside the window frame as illustrated by figure 13-5. If installed on the wall, air convection can set up air currents between shade and window to circulate the heated air developed in the window cavity throughout the house.

A recent study by the Illinois Institute of Technology indicates that window shades may save up to 15% of the heating and cooling costs. The study revealed that a drawn roller shade (mounted within the frame) can prevent from 24 to 31% of the heat loss through the glass in the winter. In the summer, a sunlit window with a drawn roller shade will admit only about 50% of the heat that would enter through an unshaded window. Again, the roller shade was mounted within the window frame.

The study also revealed that for a house with a 15% window area, the use of ordinary (roller) window shades reduced total house heat loss by approximately 8% in the winter. In summer, the reduction in energy required for total house cooling was more than 20 percent. The study also concluded that even if a home is not air conditioned,

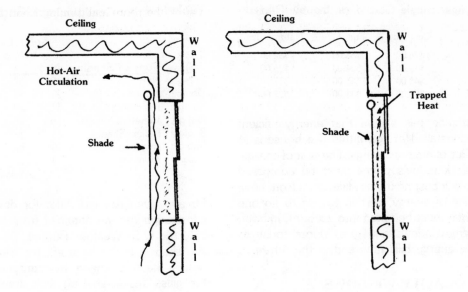

Figure 13-3. Roller Shade Installation Details

the inside temperatures can be appreciably lowered by proper use of window shades.

Thermal-barrier lining sewn into drapes (facing the window) can act to block solar radiation into the house and to reduce the sun fading unlined drapes would experience.

Wooden shutters have been used for centuries to prevent the sun's rays from entering the house in the summer and the house heat from exiting in the winter. These shutters are relatively efficient but are not practical in that the window has to be opened to operate them. Shutters, made of plastic slats, are available that can be mounted outside and yet be raised or lowered from inside the house. Each slat is an extruded double wall with a dead air space which effectively acts as a sound and energy barrier. Once closed, the shutters can be locked from inside, making it impossible to raise them from outside. These shutters, known as "rolling shutters", can be fitted into the soffit (new construction) or just under the soffitt (existing home) and blend well with the house design. They are manufactured in standard sizes to fit 85% of all windows and glass patio doors. The shutters can also be used on screened porches, serving counters, and service areas.

An insulating solid shutter, home made, is now sometimes being used primarily in the winter on bedroom windows that face into the north winds. These shutters are cut from rigid-foam panels (such as Styrofoam) to fit tightly within the window frame on the inside. Two hand-holds are usually glued on to permit the unit to be fitted into the window at night. Usually made from 1" thick panels, the shutters sharply increase both the insulation value and act

to reduce drafts. The shutters can also be used in the summer time, being placed in those windows that cannot be shielded from the sun. When so used, the shutters act to reduce the solar heat from entering the room. Wall paper is sometimes glued on one or both sides to make them more attractive if left up during the daytime. Their cost is low and their effectiveness makes them well worthwhile.

SOLAR-ENERGY REFLECTORS

Practically speaking, it is much better (up to 7 times) to stop solar heat (sunshine) from entering the house through the windows than to counter the effect after it enters. To keep solar heat from entering through the windows, various types of reflective film and screen materials have been developed. These materials act to "bounce" the solar energy back from the window. The film material, generally about 3 mils thick, is made of a plastic film upon which a reflective film has been coated. Screen material is somewhat thicker but is of somewhat general construction.

The film material is rather easily installed on all except picture windows where experience in handling a large piece of material may be needed. Film material is almost always installed on the inside of the glass where it is protected from the elements. The material can be cleaned but the instructions given by the manufacturer must be carefully followed.

Film material *must not* be used on the inside of double-glazed windows or on tinted glass, plexiglass or windows with compound curves. The reason for double-glazed windows is that the heat bounced back off the film, if used, would act to raise the heat level in the air space between panes. This could actually cause either or both glass panes to crack. For tinted glass and plexiglass, the heat bounced back could alter the tinting color and discolor the plexiglass material. As related to glass with compound curves, the material may not adhere to the glass.

One manufacturer — Therm-O-Lux — advertise that their solar reflecting films can be used on the inside surface of multi-glazed windows (including those covered with a storm window) without danger heat buildup will crack the glass.

Screen material is mounted on the outside of the glass or in front of the glass and can be used in front of storm windows or double-glazed windows. The material may also be fitted as a screen, replacing the existing insect screen.

The screen material has one drawback—it can severely restrict the flow of air and thus should not be used if natural air ventilation is used to cool a house. Also, it should be noted that some very exaggerated claims of energy savings are made for screens (somewhat less for film). Further, the price of screens, in particular, are often quoted at a price greater than that for a good quality storm window. Since the energy-saving potential of a. storm window is inherently greater than that of the screens, unless the screens are less expensive—storm windows are recommended.

The reflector material should not be used if the windows are expected to introduce solar heat into the house during the winter. The reflector materials do have one drawback—they act as mirrors from the outside and can be annoying to across-the-street neighbors. The film material is generally available in silver, smoke, bronze or gold colors. Reflector screens are generally available in gold, copper, chrome, white, red and blue colors. Since screen material can be mounted on the outside of the glass, special types are available for use in areas having atmospheres containing high levels of sodium chloride or toxic chemicals.

Also, it should be noted that some very exaggerated claims of energy savngs have been made for both film and screen material. Further, the price for screens, in particular, are often quoted at a much inflated price — sometimes being ever more expensive than a good quality storm window as installed. It is thus suggested that film or screen material be purchased from or be installed by a trustworthy company. The film and screen material, acting as a mirror, can be rather annoying to across-the-street neighbors when the sun shines on it. Also, film material gives day-time privacy in that one can see out of the house but not back into the house. However, at night time, the conditions is reversed so this should be kept in mind. And, as a last thought — the use of film or screen material will darken the room and give an off-color (usually silver-grey) look to the outdoors.

Claims by manufacturers, generally substantiated by users, are:

- Reduces heat gain within the house through windows by up to 2/3rds—by preventing up to 75% of the solar heat from entering the house.

- As a result, cooling costs can be reduced by up to 1/3.

- Reduces glare (indoors) by up to 70%.

- In the winter time, tends to prevent passage of radiant heat out of the house.

- Reduces ultra-violet ray penetration—thus protecting carpets, drapes, furniture, etc. from sun fading and damage.

- Provides privacy and security (you can look out—no one can look in—during the day time. At night time, conditions are reversed for some films.)

- Makes windows shatter resistant.

- Aids in reducing sound penetration.

SUMMARY - WINDOWS

A summary on windows is warranted because they are so important to the energy-efficiency level of a home.

- Single-glazed windows—use is justifiable only in areas experiencing very mild winters and/or summers. If electric heating is required, double-glazed units are recommended.

- Double-glazed windows—should definitely be considered in any area experiencing anything other than mild winters and/or summers. In particular, are definitely indicated if electric heating of any type is used.

- Storm windows—an excellent "add-on" feature for existing homes for any area experiencing anything other than mild winters and/or summers or where electric heating is required. In areas experiencing very severe winter and/or summer conditions, storm windows over double-glazed units are recommended. For a new house, storm windows over single-glazed windows are not recommended since it is less costly and better to install double-glazed windows.

- Reflective films and screens—an excellent feature for reducing amount of solar energy entering house during summer. Of minor help in keeping radiant energy from escaping from inside house. Should not be used if windows are expected to introduce solar heat during winter. Cost, particularly for screens, should be compared against cost of storm windows since storm windows are more efficient on an overall basis.

- Tinted glass—reflective type glass available in bronze, smoke or silver tints. This special glass acts to reflect the solar rays in the same manner detailed for films and screens. Should not be used if windows are expected to introduce solar heat during winter. Cannot be considered a replacement for double-glazed or storm windows.

Section 14

AIR INFILTRATION

GENERAL

"Air infiltration" is the flow of outdoor air into a house. Since this air flow acts to raise the air pressure within the house, the air flowing into the house will be balanced by an equal flow of air out of the house (ex-filtration). However, for simplicity, the term "infiltration" will be used to indicate movement of air into or out of a house. Since, as we shall see, it is most important to reduce infiltration to an absolute minimum, all possible draft sources must be sealed off. For simplicity of term, this will be called "weatherization".

Traditionally, houses are built to have an infiltration rate such that the house air will be completely replaced "at least twice an hour" with outdoor air. In fact, an air-infiltration rate of four air-changes per hour is not considered excessive by many builders. The thinking is — "The air within the house must be "freshened" with outdoor air on a regular basis if the house is to remain free of smoke or odor and to move out any water vapor developed in the kitchen or bathrooms".

The energy problem and the ever-increasing cost of energy has caused all phases of house construction to be re-evaluated. For example, when the author built his home, all "experts" of the time (1974) stated a house must have two air changes per hour — at least — if it is not to be overcome with odor and humidity. The author concluded that this rule was completely wrong and built his home as tight (draft free) as possible, saying "If it should get heavy with odor or humidity, I can always open a window." Energy-saving calculations made from the house plans indicated the author's home should save about 35% on it's energy bills as compared to a "standard" house — one built to FHA Minimum Property Standards. After living in his house for six months, the author found his energy bills indicated an actual savings of 55 percent. The extra 20% savings was clearly gained by the almost total elimination of drafts made possible by caulking and sealing the house to standards just now being reached by a few builders. Humidity is controlled at the source by use of area ventilation in the kitchen and bathrooms. And, except for kitchen "accidents" and for large parties, the air (even with

the house closed up for heating or cooling) has remained sweet and pure at all times without the need for an open window. The air-change rate of the house is considered to be one-half change per hour or less. Regretfully, all too many houses are being built that exhibit an air-change rate as high as four changes per hour.

Ongoing research by Texas Power and Light Company reveals that an "average" 1500 square-foot home in a 15-mph wind "leaks" more than 600,000 cubic feet of air a day — enough to fill three Goodyear blimps. Clearly, it is wrong to heat or cool air at a considerable expense and then to let it escape from the house at a high rate. With an air change every two hours (considered normal by outdated standards), the entire air within a house will be replaced 48 times a day. Immediately, one can see that this is most wasteful of energy since the heating or cooling system must constantly turn on and off to condition the new air flowing into the house, with this air flow pushing out previously conditioned air.

A five-year study by the Dept. of Energy (DOE) revealed that "insulation is not what it's cracked up to be". The study revealed that cracks and holes in the wall sheathing and improper house design, for example, are much more important factors in loss of heat and energy in buildings than lack of adequate insulation. The study also revealed that adding insulation is not particularly effective in decreasing air flow (into or out of a house). A similar study by Applied Science and Engineering indicates "the current faith in insulation may be based on erroneous assumptions, and the home owners pouring money into the burgeoning insulation business won't see the savings they are promised." The study also revealed the air-infiltration rate of an uninsulated house is nearly the same as that of an insulated house. This is indicated by Figure 14-1 and reveals that the percentage of heat lost through air infiltration in an uninsulated house is nearly the same as that of an insulated house. Insulation thus has little effect upon air infiltration but air infiltration has a very great effect upon insulation — greatly lowering it's effective efficiency.

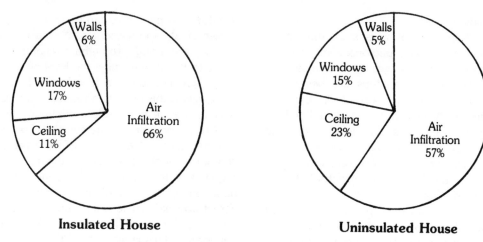

Figure 14-1. Heat Loss Percentages

The energy problem has caused a complete re-evaluation of what constitutes an "energy saver" house. Studies made by various government agencies and private firms reveal the potential for energy saving in a home breaks down somewhat as follows:

Table 14.1. Potential for Energy Saving

House Orientation	=	16.67%
House Design	=	21.33%
Thermal (Insulation) Protection	=	12.00%
Reducing Air Infiltration	=	33.33%
Appliances and Equipment	=	16.67%

The table has been proven to be both practical and accurate. Note that air leakage (infiltration), if prevented, will save nearly three times as much energy as if the thermal efficiency (insulation) had been increased over normal. The table clearly shows that the old, outdated concept that "a house must have an air-change rate of from two to four times per hour if it is to be livable" is **entirely incorrect**. It **must** be replaced by the new and proven concept — "make the house as tight as you can without worry that it will be too tight — it won't be." Cooking and bathroom odors can be handled with area ventilation and water vapor held to acceptable levels by installation of a properly installed vapor barrier. If smoke or odor should get heavy at times, an open window will soon clear it out. If water vapor is a problem, a dehumidifier can be used. If the occupants smoke, a dust precipitator can be used.

Finally — the author has talked with many people who desired to have a true energy-saver home built and to building contractors who wanted to build houses that could truly qualify as energy savers. Yet, even though they built many houses to high standards of energy-use efficiency, the houses just did not perform as calculated. To the author's knowledge, in all cases the poor performance was directly traceable to lack of understanding and even lack of concern over air infiltration. In general, weatherization was not performed to the standards now known to be mandatory if a house is to actually exhibit a high order of energy-use efficiency.

The very seriousness of weatherization (draft prevention) and the lack of understanding displayed by many building contractors indicates a real need for education. Building contractors perform quality control inspection on each house they build as a matter of course, based on experience gained over the years. This quality control relates to checking that walls are straight and plumb, floors are level, suitably braced and properly covered, that water piping and electric wires run through the walls have been properly installed, etc. A building contractor can thus deliver each new house with pride to the owners, confident that the house is well built in all ways. However, today it is quite clear that a **second type of quality control must** be exercised by a builder — that related to seeing that the house is tightly sealed to the best practices of the new concept of weatherization. And, as new and more effective materials and techniques are developed to improve weatherization, a progressive builder must stay abreast of the field. This new type of quality control, being so recent and related to a new concept, will have to be carefully performed by the builder until it becomes "second nature."

What it really sums up to is this:

> "A house must be made as tight as possible. A house can never be made energy efficient, regardless of the amount of insulation installed, if insulating windows and doors are used, etc., if it has an air-change rate much in excess of one per hour."

The need for quality control as to weatherization is so important it is recommended that it be stressed in the building contract. In fact, the building contract should "spell out" exactly what the building contractor must do. A list of recommended weatherization features and materials is given in Section 23, page 23-2. This list may be helpful in drawing up the building contract.

The importance of weatherization is such that many people having a new home built personally inspect the house during the construction stages to determine for themselves if the draft-prevention steps are being performed as outlined in the building contract. An extreme step but well worthwhile. A point here — it would be best to perform the weatherization inspections after building hours. If it must be accomplished when workmen are present, do not discuss any possible problem with them, deal only directly with the building contractor. He will appreciate your thoughtfulness.

The discussion on air infiltration points and related weatherization that follows applies equally to new-home construction and existing-home retrofitting. Of course, it will be immediately evident that the perfect time to correct air infiltration is during the time the house is being built. However, very meaningful reduction in air infiltration can be made in an existing house with a little extra effort. Existing-home upgrading related to air infiltration prevention will be covered under Section 23, Energy-Saving Upgrading.

A SUPER TIGHT HOUSE

Just recently, an article in the Wall Street Journal discussed a super-tight house built by the National Association of Home Builders in Mt. Airy, Maryland. Extreme measures were taken to reduce the air flow into or out of the house to an absolute minimum. In fact, the air infiltration rate is considered to be one air change every 10 hours. Note the "standard" air-change rate is thought by most builders to be 2 per hour or 48 per day while the NAHB house has a rate of 2.5 per day—about one-twentieth that of "standard" house.

Making a house this tight does, however, result in problems. The air-change rate is so low that the minute amounts of vapor and gases emitting from the household furniture, carpets, etc. can be measured. The amounts of "objectional vapors and gases" measured are infinitesimal yet they are thought to be harmful and further tests will be made to try to determine the level of such vapor or gases that might constitute a true health hazard.

However, this condition relates to a house designed and built to exhibit an absolute minimum air infiltration rate. This rate—one air change every 10 hours, will NEVER be reached even if a house is weatherized to the best standards of the day. Extraordinary measures would be required to reduce the air infiltration rate to 2.5 every 24 hours or 1/20th that of the "standard" house. The Wall Street Journal article will no doubt be used to prove that reducing the air infiltration rate from "normal" can be dangerous. This is not true in the least and many homes, built to exhibit an air change rate of one-half change per hour, prove that the household air will remain pure and healthy with this low air-change rate.

AIR INFILTRATION POINTS

The points related to air infiltration (and exfiltration) into a house have been rather precisely established by many tests performed by government and private agencies. One of the most complete and useful of these tests was made by Texas Power and Light Company, a most progressive electric power company. Tests on 50 houses in the Dallas-Fort Worth area pinpointed the draft points in the test houses. These are detailed on an average basis by Table 14-2. The piegraph, Figure 14-2, illustrates the averages and is most informative. Key points for controlling air infiltration through the house framing are illustrated by Figure 14-3.

The averages given by the piegraph invariably surprise builders and home owners. The piegraph shows the most serious draft points are:

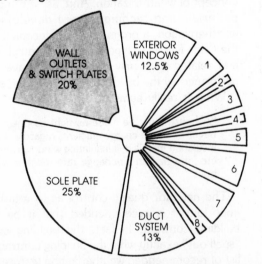

5%	RECESSED SPOT LIGHTS	1
1.5%	BATH VENT	2
4.5%	EXTERIOR DOORS	3
2%	SLIDING GLASS DOOR	4
3%	DRYER VENT	5
5.5%	FIREPLACE	6
6%	VENT A HOOD	7
2%	OTHER	8

WALL OUTLETS & SWITCH PLATES 20%

EXTERIOR WINDOWS 12.5%

SOLE PLATE 25%

DUCT SYSTEM 13%

Figure 14-2. Air-Leakage Test Results

Table 14-2. Air-Leakage Test Data

ITEM TESTED	AVERAGE	% of TOTAL	NO. of ITEMS	CFM	% of TOTAL
Size of home	1,728 sq.ft.				
Total leakage	2,424 CFM			2,424	100
Leakage/sq. ft.	1.41				
Air change @ .10	1.49				
Duct system	317 CFM	13.07	1 ea.	317	13.1
Vent-a-hood (unclamped)	146 CFM	6.02	1 ea.	146	6.0
Fireplace (closed)	137 CFM	5.65	1 ea.	137	5.6
Dryer vent	78 CFM	3.22	1 ea.	78	3.2
Sliding glass door	48 CFM	1.98	1 ea.	48	2.0
Exterior door	35 CFM	1.44	3 ea.	105	4.3
Bath vent	34 CFM	1.40	1 ea.	34	1.4
Recessed spot	30 CFM	1.24	4 ea.	120	5.0
Exterior window	25 CFM	1.03	12 ea.	300	12.4
Wall outlet & switches	8 CFM	0.33	60 ea.	480	19.8
Soleplate (linear crack ft.)	3.6 CFM	0.15	170 ea.	611	25.2
Other				48	2.0

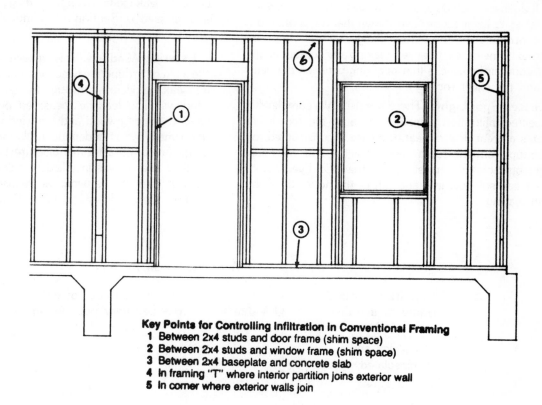

Key Points for Controlling Infiltration in Conventional Framing
1 Between 2x4 studs and door frame (shim space)
2 Between 2x4 studs and window frame (shim space)
3 Between 2x4 baseplate and concrete slab
4 In framing "T" where interior partition joins exterior wall
5 In corner where exterior walls join

Figure 14-2. Air-Leakage Test Results

Soleplate. The worst leakage (25%) occurs under the soleplate. (For those unfamiliar with construction terms, the soleplate is the first piece of framing lumber (a 2 x 4 or 2 x 6) put down on the foundation as a base for the studs. (See item 3, Figure 14-3.) The *Sole Plate* is also often called the sole, the plate, the baseplate or the sill. The air flow under the soleplate is generally greater when a concrete floor is used.

Wall Outlets & Switches. The air flow into and out of a house through the wall plugs (convenience outlets) and switches must be felt to be believed. Note that, on the average, it accounts for 20% of the air infiltration total. The air flow results because of air entering through holes drilled in the topplate (item 6, Figure 14-3) to permit electric cables and water pipes to be run within the wall cavity made by adjacent stud pairs. Cracks and holes in the outer sheathing will also allow air to flow into or out of a house through the wall outlets and switches. For wall outlets, the air flow is both out around the plastic-cover plate edges and around the outlet. The air can also flow out of the outlet itself through the holes provided for the electric plug to be inserted.

Duct System. This leakage, 13% of the total, represents only the leakage between the vents mounted in the wall, ceiling or floor and the duct material plus around the vent itself. It does not include any air leakage related to the duct material itself. Inspections have shown that ducts often do not sit properly on the mating flanges of the vents, in certain extreme cases not even making any contact at all. The second air leakage is that occuring between the vent itself and the sheet rock.

Recessed Spot Lights. These are usually a completely unsuspected infiltration point but, because the spot light generates a great deal of heat, the case is constructed to vent air up from the room past the light. This will cool the light but acts to exhaust air into the attic. Even if not used, air can still flow into and out of the house through the light casing.

Fireplace. This figure, 6%, is the yearly total related to "average" dampers. That is, dampers that seat fairly well but still cannot entirely stop air leakage. Of course, if a damper is not provided or is left open, the air leakage rate will be much higher.

Vent-a-hood. On the average, a vented hood such as used over ranges accounts for 6% of the air leakage. This leakage relates both to a small continuous leakage past the damper and past the hood itself where it fits against the furred-down ceiling and the wall.

Exterior Doors. This leakage, 4%, is that occuring through the crack between the door and the door frame (item 1, Figure 14-3) unless a perfect seal has been made. For an average outer door (6'8" x 3'), the crack distance around the door totals 232". If a 1/12th inch gap existed around the entire door, the gap area would total 19.3 square inches. This is the equivalent of a 4" x 5" hole in the door. A second air infiltration point can be that related to the air flowing into or out of a house between the wood framing and the door casing (item 1, Figure 14-3).

Sliding Glass Door. The sliding-glass door (one) in each test house account for 2% (as an average) of the air leakage. This leakage is that between the door frame and the wood material used to box in the door (item 1, Figure 14-3). Air leakage between the sliding part of the glass door is discussed in Section 13, Windows and Glass Patio Doors.

Exterior Windows. This leakage, 13%, represents only the leakage around the window frame and does not include any leakage occuring through the double units of opening windows. The leakage measured occured between the window framing wood and the window frame itself. Test performed by an independent laboratory for Coplana Corp. (a foam sealant manufacturer) on a premium brand window after it was installed revealed the following: (Air leakage through the windows themselves is discussed in Section 13, Windows and Glass Patio Doors.)

Table 14-3. Wind-Seal Test Results

Condition around frame of installed window	U Value	Estimated cost of energy loss per year per 100 sq. ft. of window *
Unsealed and uninsulated	3.12	$104.85
Insulated*	1.80	$60.48
Sealed	0.66	$22.18

*Fiberglas stuffed between window and frame material
#Cost based on 5,000 degree days and gas at 2.8¢ per perm

Dryer and Bath Vents. The dryer vent (3%) and the bath vent (1%) air leakage relates to the air leakage past the damper and around the vent itself where it fits into the wall or ceiling.

Others. Other possible air infiltration points are now discussed.

Kitchen cabinets, both as hung on the wall or mounted on the floor, can be literally flooded with unwanted air flow. Kitchen cabinets hung on the wall are usually dropped down by from 6" to 12" below the standard ceiling height (8') for ease of access. A box is usually built from framing material and covered with sheetrock, with the box being as wide as the cabinets and as long as the total of cabinets. This is usually called "furred-down". All too often, the fur-down may not have sheet rock at the back; thus the space between all studs so exposed is open to air flow. Any openings in the wall cabinets related to electrical or plumbing penetrations or cracks and gaps in the back-wall of the cabinets will then allow air to flow into or out of the house at a most serious rate. This also holds for sink cabinets, particularly where the water pipes are brought down from the attic through the stud space.

Other exterior (perimeter) points for air infiltration are illustrated by Figure 14-4. Note that some of these have already been discussed. The potential for air infiltration through the remaining points is self evident.

Figure 14-4. Perimeter Air Infiltration Points

WEATHERIZATION

The weatherization details to follow relate mainly to a home under construction. The material, however, will be informative as to existing-house upgrading. Full details on weatherization of an existing house will be found under "Draft Elimination," Section 23, Energy-Saving Upgrading.

Probably the most effective new product available today for caulking all sorts of cracks and filling of small holes is a single component urethane foam material that expands slightly as it sets so that it fills up all voids in cracks and holes. Two popular brands of this material are: "Polycel One", Coplanar Corp., Oakland, CA, and "Insta-Foam", Insta-Foam Products, Inc., Joliet, Illinois. The material is very effective, does not deteriorate with time and acts as an insulator as well as a sealant. It is packaged in cans of various sizes under pressure and is somewhat difficult of installation. For buildings under construction, the building contractor will subcontract out the weatherization made with "Polycel One" or "Insta-Foam", thus ensuring an excellent installation.

Where the urethane foam sealant is not used, caulking material of top quality must be used. A caulking material guaranteed for at least 10 years (and preferably with a 20-year guarantee) should be used since a draft spot, once covered with sheet rock, exterior sheathing, paneling, etc. is most difficult to eliminate. Inexpensive caulking material will do a good job on a short range basis, but will deteriorate to dust in just a few years leaving a virtually inaccessible draft source. Caulking around window glass or where the caulking will be highly visible should be done with clear silicone caulking (which has a very long guaranteed life).

The infiltration points previously detailed and illustrated by Figure 14-2 can be weatherized during the construction phase as follows

Soleplate. If the soleplate is to be laid on a concrete floor (slab construction), if the concrete is rough and not very flat, the soleplate could be laid down on the concrete floor in a bed of fresh mortar. This will seal the uneven spots. The foundation bolts should have washers and nuts installed and securely tightened to help draw the soleplate down into the fresh mortar. Also, a bead of caulking material should be spread along the inside of the soleplate against the cement floor itself (after any excess mortar is removed if the soleplate is set in fresh mortar).

If the soleplate is laid on a wood floor, foundation bolts should be provided and pulled down tight with washers and nuts. A bead of caulking material should be spread along the inside of the soleplate where it touches the wood floor.

Any holes in the soleplate (related to cable or piping penetration or a wood knot) should be sealed to prevent air flow up between the stud pairs.

Wall Outlets & Switches. To prevent air flow down between the stud pairs (wall cavity), any holes in the topplate or soleplate should be sealed. Similarly, any open seam, crack, break or hole in the outer sheathing should be sealed to prevent air from entering the wall cavities. The opening in the related electric box should also be sealed with a caulking agent (Polycel One or Insta-Foam are recommended). Precut foam rubber gaskets are now available to be placed under the plastic cover plates related to wall outlets or switches. These can be installed only after the sheet rock has been installed, acting to reduce air infiltration between the box and the wall covering by up to 97%. An air flow, most surprisingly, can also occur out of the convenience outlet openings into which the electric plug is inserted. Plastic plugs, the same as those used by parents to seal off the outlets when small children are present, are also provided to shut off this draft source. The use of the gaskets and plastic plugs is highly recommended even if all holes in the plates and outer sheathing have been repaired.

The gaskets and plastic inserts are sold at retail in prepackaged amounts, such as 8 wall switches, 8 wall outlets or such as 7 outlets, 3 switches and 10 plastic inserts in a single package. However, the gaskets and plastic inserts are sold by Energy-Saver Homes Company on an individual basis thus only the exact number needed for a home can be ordered. For free information and details, write to Energy-Saver Homes Co., P.O. Box 10083, Austin Texas 78766.

Duct System. The air-conditioning vents, mounted in the ceiling, walls or floors, can be a very serious source of drafts. If the hole cut for the vent in the sheet rock, paneling, etc., is not cut for a perfect fit with the duct-end sheet metal a gap can exist between this sheet metal and sheet rock, paneling, etc. This gap can be closed with caulking material (Polycel One or Insta-Foam is recommended). Alternately, foam rubber material, covered with adhesive material, can be fitted into the duct cover which can then be rescrewed to the duct-end sheet metal.

Another very serious gap can exist if the duct material is not firmly seated in the duct-end sheet metal. This will not only allow an air flow into or out of the room but will wastefully allow the conditioned air to escape into the attic.

Air conditioning vents, when not used for a long period, should be closed to prevent air flow up into the ducts. This would be important only if the ducts are run in the attic where, unless they are heavily insulated, they can heat or cool the air held in the ducts even with the air conditioner turned off.

Exterior Windows. Two drafts points and thus two energy wastes can relate to exterior windows. The first relates to the need for sealing the window frame itself to the window box. The second relates to the window box itself. Made from framing lumber, it usually consists of pieces of wood formed into a box just slightly larger than the window it is to hold. If the window needs to be shimmed for a tight fit (which almost always happens), the shim area (item 2, Figure 14-3) should be caulked to fill this gap. Note from Table 14-3 that filling this gap with Fiberglas (or equivalent) is not as efficient as if the gap is sealed with an expandable caulking material.

Fireplace. To reduce exfiltration of air out the fireplace chimney, all fireplaces should be equipped as follows:

(1) A positive-closure, tight-fitting damper which should be **kept closed any time the fireplace is not in use.**

(2) Ducting to provide outside air for combustion air. See "Outside Combustion Air", Section 17, Fireplaces.

(3) Glass firescreen, tight fitting, to permit outside air to be used for combustion and to shut off the fire when desired. For details, see "Glass Screens", Section 17, Fireplaces.

Vent-a-hood. Forced-draft kitchen ventilation should be used only to the minimum degree possible. A positive-closure damper should be provided to reduce air flow in and out past the damper to a minimum. For details, refer to "Controlled Ventilation", Section 18, Appliances and Lighting.

Recessed Spot Lights. These lights generate a great deal of heat which must be dissipated. The light housing is thus built to provide a vent area around the lamp, with air flowing from the house into the attic through this vent. Spotlights **must not** be covered with a box to shut off the air flow nor should they **be covered** with insulation since to do so would cause a heat buildup sufficient to start a fire.

Thus, the only remedy is to not install recessed lights. If spotlights are desired, they should not be recessed.

Exterior Doors. The two draft sources related to exterior doors can be corrected as follows:

(1) Draft between door frame and stud material (item 1, Figure 14-3) can be sealed with caulking material (Polycel One or Insta-Foam is recommended).

(2) Draft entering between door and door jamb. This can be prevented by installation of metal-clad doors using magnetic weatherstripping. For details, see "Energy-Efficient Outer Doors", Section 12, Outer doors.

If metal-clad doors are not desired, the use of a compressable neoprene gasket weatherstripping is recommended. For details, "Wood Doors — Weatherstripping", Section 12, Outer Doors.

Sliding Glass Door. A sliding-glass door, like a sliding glass window, should exhibit a high infiltration rating. For details, see "Air Infiltration Standards," Section 13, Windows and Glass Patio Doors. The facts given also hold for sliding-glass windows.

The second draft source related to sliding glass doors can be eliminated by caulking between the studs and window frame (item 2, Figure 14-3), using Polycel One or Insta-Foam.

Dryer and Bath Vents. The clothes dryer should be located outside the air conditioned portion of the house if at all possible. If this is not possible, the dryer (and washer) could be installed in an air-tight closet, with the air intake and air exhaust ports of the dryer being connected by ducts to the outside. This will provide outside air for the dryer and will exhaust the hot humid output air to the outdoors. Bath vents should be used to the minimum degree possible. They should be equipped with a close-fitting, automatic-closing damper to shut off the exhaust duct when the blower is not in use. For further details, refer to "Bathroom Vents", Section 18, Appliances and Lighting.

OTHER DRAFT POINTS

The box (fur down) made to lower the kitchen cabinets must be entirely covered with sheet rock (gypsum board) on the front and bottom and against the wall it is nailed to. The sheet rock, in other words, must extend up the full wall to the ceiling over the area related to the fur down. The joints where the sheet rock meet should be caulked if any gaps are noted. Also, attic insulation should be installed inside the furred down box to complete the thermal protection around the house enclosure.

Any wall openings in the kitchen cabinets, sink cabinet, or bathroom storage cabinets should be sealed These will normally relate to penetrations made for electric wiring and pipe runs. The opening around the wire or pipe should be sealed tight, generally by using an expandable urethane foam (Polycel One or Insta-Foam).

Electric boxes may be mounted in the ceiling or high up on walls, with electric lights being mounted on or suspended from the box. Ceiling boxes penetrate through the ceiling covering (usually sheet rock) and, unless tightly fitted to the sheet rock, can act as an air leakage point into the attic. The remedy here is to caulk up the gap between the box sidewalls and the sheet rock or to use foam rubber strips.

The outer sheathing (usually some form of rigid-foam insualtion panels) must be installed without open seams, cracks or holes. In brief, the outer sheathing should form a completely tight covering about the house exterior. If open seams, gaps, breaks or cracks are noted, they should be repaired. Large holes can be patched by fitting a patch into the opening and sealing it with caulking material plus wide contact tape. Cracks, open seams, small breaks etc. can be sealed with caulking material, preferably of the expandable urethane foam type.

Sometimes a heavy plastic film is stapled to the inside studs, top plate and sole plate and the door and window framing material to act as a vapor barrier. See "Vapor Barriers", Section 5, Insulation and Vapor Barriers. This plastic film, if tightly installed, will also act as a very fine barrier against air infiltration. However, use of such a vapor barrier-infiltration barrier should not be considered to make unnecessary the weatherization steps detailed in this section.

COST AND PAYBACK TIME

A study by Coplanar Corp. (manufacturers of Polycel One) indicates an average cost of 12¢ per square foot of living area to completely weatherize a new house in line with the new standards of air infiltration control. A recent study published by a Southwestern utility company reported an estimated savings for sealing alone for a 2,370 sq. ft. house was 3,932 KWH per year. The study also showed the estimated annual savings related to sealing against air infiltration was 225% more effective than increasing the ceiling insulation from R11 to R38 and 320% more effective than increasing the wall insulation from R11 to R19.

For a 2,000 sq. ft. house the energy savings is estimated to be 3318 KWH per year. The payback times for a 2,000 sq. ft. all-electric house would be:

Initial cost = 2,000 x 12¢ = $240.00

Energy saved	x	Energy Cost	=	Savings Per Year	=	Payback Period
3318 KWH	x	2¢	=	$66.36	=	3.62 years
3318 KWH	x	3¢	=	$99.54	=	2.41 years
3318 KWH	x	4¢	=	$132.72	=	1.81 years
3318 KWH	x	5¢	=	$165.90	=	1.45 years

In summation — the initial cost is very low, the returns are very high, the extra comfort is a bonus more than worth the initial cost — thus, not to build a tight house would be a great mistake.

Section 15

Ventilation

GENERAL

The ventilation needs of a house must be satisfied fully and in a proper manner if true energy efficiency is to be achieved. The major ventilation needs of a house are as follows:

- Selected Ventilation
- Attic Ventilation
- Whole-House Ventilation
- Under-House Ventilation
- Furnace and Fireplace Ventilation

SELECTED VENTILATION

Selected ventilation is primarily concerned with removal of household cooking odors and smoke from the kitchen and humidity from the bathrooms. The removal method is usually under control of a fan, with the exhausted air being vented out of the house through chimney-type pipes (ducts). Each duct *must* be equipped with a damper (valve) that *completely* shuts off the duct when the fan is not in use. It is of utmost importance that each damper opens only when the fan is on and closes completely (tightly) when the fan is off. Otherwise, the ducts can act as vents to draw out warm air from the air-conditioned portion of the house or allow cold air to enter. Most dampers are made of light metal and hinged such that just the air being pumped up the duct through the fan action is enough to open the damper. When the air flow stops, the damper automatically closes.

An excellent fan-damper unit is one that mounts directly on the roof and is controlled from the using place (stove, bathroom, etc.). The damper is usually electrically controlled and operates most positively, opening when the fan is turned on and closing tightly under power-control when the fan is turned off. Also, with the fan up on the roof, noise level at the using place is low.

Care should be taken to use fan-powered ventilation only to the degree required to clear the air since even a moderate-size fan can exhaust a large volume of the conditioned air each time it is used.

Ductless venting systems are sometimes used for the kitchen range, with the air over the range being pulled through a charcoal filter to be purified. This system has two drawbacks: (1) it cannot handle a heavy load of smoke or odor and (2) it does not remove heat and humidity from the kitchen. This can act as a cooling load in the summer but as a heat and humidity gain in the winter.

Ideally, the clothes dryer should be located outside the air-conditioned portion of the house but, even so, the hot-air exhaust should be vented to the outside through a damper-equipped duct. Some experimental houses feature a dual ducting system for the clothes dryer, acting to duct the hot humid air outside in the summer but being capable of switchover to deliver the hot air into the living area as a meaningful heat gain in the winter.

Note that ducting the hot-air exhaust from a dryer into the living area can be dangerous if a gas-fired model is used since the fumes from the gas fire can leak into the dryer basket.

Regretfully, controlled-ventilation systems can contribute to the air-leakage rate of a house. This is illustrated by the piegraph, figure 15-1, developed by the Texas Power and Light Company and giving average values as based upon a 50-home test in the Dallas-Fort Worth area. Note the air leakage related to a bath vent (1.5%), a dryer vent (3%) and the hood over the kitchen range (6%). This leakage related partly to the air gap existing around the duct as it passes through a wall or the ceiling and, to a greater degree, to a poorly operating damper. For details on how to reduce or eliminate this air leakage, refer to "Draft Elimination", page 23-2, Section 23.

ATTIC VENTILATION

Summer-time heat passing through the roof covering (especially if dark-colored materials are used) can build up in an unventilated attic, raising the attic temperature to a very high level. Manufacturer literature suggest attic temperatures can build up to as high as 150°F when the outdoor temperature is about 95°F. Tests by government

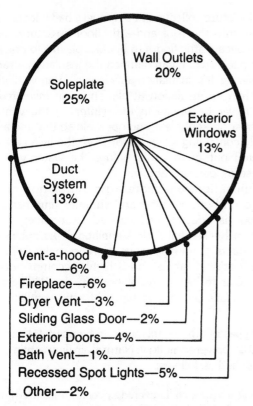

Source: Texas Power and Light Co.

Figure 15-1. Air-Leakage Test Results

Wall Outlets 20%
Soleplate 25%
Exterior Windows 13%
Duct System 13%
Vent-a-hood —6%
Fireplace—6%
Dryer Vent—3%
Sliding Glass Door—2%
Exterior Doors—4%
Bath Vent—1%
Recessed Spot Lights—5%
Other—2%

and public agencies have seldom found such extreme temperatures, most unventilated attic measuring around 130°F with an outdoor temperature of about 95°F. This extreme temperature can pass through the ceiling to raise the temperature of the air-conditioned portion of the house, with the temperature increase being somewhat proportional to the amount of insulation used. The temperature buildup in an unventilated attic can also appear as a severe load on the cooling system if the air-conditioning ducts are run in the attic. Unless heavily insulated, the attic heat can pass through the duct walls to lower the cooling efficiency of the air-conditioning system. The amount of heat passed through the duct walls is somewhat proportional to the amount of duct insulation used. Also, high attic temperatures can cause deterioration of the roof covering (shingles, tar papers, etc.), the electrical wiring run through the attic, and whatever household objects may be stored in the attic.

The solution is to provide adequate attic ventilation, ensuring an air flow sufficient to keep the summer-time attic temperature from rising much above the outdoor temperature. Winter-time need for attic ventilation will differ dependent upon whether the ceiling (attic floor) is adequately insulated or has little or no insulation.

Attic ventilation (it's need and purpose) is all too often being based upon experience gained with the houses of old — that is, houses with little or no attic-floor insulation. With such houses, the summer-time attic heat build up would pass through into the living area to a most distressing degree. Therefore, maximum attic ventilation was provided to bring in large volumes of outside air to prevent or reduce the heat build up. During the winter, since the attic floor was provided with little or no insulation, a rather large amount of heat would flow up into the attic from the rooms below. Saving this heat became important thus it was customary to cover all attic venting areas for the entire winter season so that the heat could be trapped in the attic, raising the attic temperature. When the attic temperature rose to near the room temperature, a slowdown of heat transfer occurred. This concept is entirely correct but *only* as related to houses with little or no attic-floor insulation.

Let us now consider a more modern home, one insulated to provide adequate insulation (R19 or higher) for the attic floor. Recent tests conducted by the National Bureau of Standards (NBS) found that an attic floor insulated to R19 rather completely isolated the living area from the attic temperatures. The tests indicated that adding "extra" attic ventilation "was not an effective energy conservation procedure for those houses which had moderately insulated attics." "Standard" attic ventilation is that related to FHA Minimum Property Standards (FHA MPS). That is, gable-end vents or ridge-top venting operating in conjunction with eave (soffit) vents as illustrated by figure 15-2.

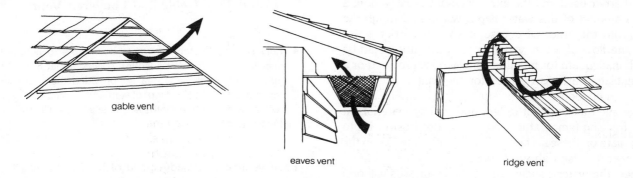

gable vent

eaves vent

ridge vent

Figure 15-2. Standard Attic Ventilation Systems

The NBS tests indicated that providing "extra" attic ventilation was found to produce less than a three percent reduction in the daily cooling load for the test houses. Over the course of a day, the energy consumed by electric-powered fans or turbines was found to exceed the amount of energy they saved by lowering the air-conditioning requirements.

The NBS stresses that "these findings should not be viewed as the last word on the energy effectiveness of (extra) attic ventilation." However, the author's house, which certainly qualifies as an energy saver, substantuates the NBS findings. The author's house is equipped with two gable-end vents and has eave vents on eight-foot centers. A large gable-end fan was used but was disconnected after one summer season with no noticeable effect upon the cooling efficiency of the house. The point to be made here is that "standard" attic ventilation is completely adequate for summer-time reduction of attic temperatures if the attic floor is insulated to R19 or higher. In general, electric-powered fans or turbines are considered to use more energy than they save.

The winter-time concept of attic ventilation is completely different for a house having a well insulated attic floor (R19 or higher) as against a house whose attic floor is provided with little or no insulation. With a well insulated attic floor, very little heat from the air-conditioned portion of the house will pass through the insulation into the attic area. So little, in fact, that the attic temperature will not be measureably raised if the venting areas are covered for the winter season. In fact, it is very important that the attic venting system is not covered or obstructed during the winter time — this to ensure that a sufficient volume of outdoor air moves through the attic space to prevent condensation of the water vapor in the attic air. That is, to keep the air moving out of the attic at a rate sufficient to carry off any water vapor rising up from the living area below before it condenses.

For maximum energy-use efficiency a house must be build "tight", this to reduce air flow into and out of the house to an absolute minimum. This means that the water-vapor level of the house air can be high since the air is not moving out of the house at the rates associated with "loose" houses of the past. Dependent upon the type of vapor barrier used and the excellence of its installation, a certain amount of this water vapor will pass through the ceiling into the attic. Of course, if a vapor barrier is not used, the flow of water vapor up into the attic could be high. If inadequate (or no) attic ventilation is provided or if the ventilation area is covered for the winter, the water vapor can condense into moisture when it strikes a cold surface such as the roof rafters and roofing material. At below freezing temperatures this can cause frost or ice to accumulate on these surfaces, thawing into water when the temperature rises above freezing. In above freezing weather, the water condensed on these surfaces will drip down upon the floor insulation as will the water developed when the ice or frost thaws.

This moisture collection has two very bad effects. One: it can soak into the roof and attic floor structure, causing wood to decay, attic floors to buckle, plaster to crack, and paint to peel. Two: it can dampen the insulation, dramatically lowering it's insulation efficiency. Wet insulation is worse than no insulation at all. Thus, an *insulated attic should never* be sealed in the winter — the ventilating areas must be kept clear and operable so that the attic air (possibly containing water vapor from the living area) can be vented out of the attic before the water vapor can condense as detailed above.

In summation, adequate attic ventilation must be provided on both a winter and summer time basis if the attic floor is adequately insulated. A booklet, "Fundamentals of Residential Attic Ventilation", as published by HC Products Company gives more complete details on attic ventilation systems and is highly recommended. For details, refer to "Attic Ventilation" in the Bibliography.

Basic details on various types of attic ventilation now follows:

Two types of attic ventilation can be used: (1) natural air flow and (2) powered air flow. Natural air-flow venting can be accomplished as follows:

- *Gable-end venting*. Louvered air vents are installed in at least two ends of the attic, each having an area of one square foot for each 150 square feet of attic surface. Ideally, the vents should be installed in opposite sides of the attic and, if possible, one should face the prevailing winds. A gable-end vent is illustrated by Figure 15-3.

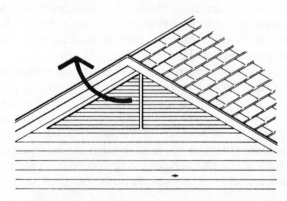

Figure 15-3. Gable-End Louvered Vent

- *Eave venting*. Rectangular vents, usually 8 x 16 inch, can be installed under the eaves (soffit), spaced about 8 to 10 feet apart. The total vent area so provided must provide a minimum of one square foot of vent area for each 150 square feet of attic surface. Installation details are illustrated by Figure 15-4.

Eave venting takes advantage of the "chimney effect". That is, hot air rises and is replaced by colder air. It is this action that causes an open fireplace or vent-fan duct to act as a passage way for transfer of air out of the house (unless closed off with a damper). For the eave vents to operate properly, roof venting must be installed to a minimum ratio of one square foot of roof vent area to each 150 square feet of attic space. This roof venting can be of two types: turbine ventilators or top-ridge venting.

- Turbine ventilators, usually wind driven, can be located on the roof per Figure 15-5. A venting ratio of one turbine per 800 square feet of attic surface is specified as a minimum with a minimum of three 8x16 inch vents being provided in the eaves for each turbine.

- Top-ridge ventilation is achieved by installing a venting cap that extends across the entire roof at the roof top (ridge). Installation details are illustrated by Figure 15-6.

Powered air-flow venting can be accomplished as follows:

- Motor-driven turbine ventilators, controlled by a thermostat, can be used instead of the wind-driven unit to increase the air flow up through the eave vents and out the turbines.

- Roof-top ventilators of low-profile and featuring a thermostat-controlled fan can be installed instead of the power-driven turbine units. Again, sufficient eave vents must be provided.

- A thermostat-controlled fan can be installed directly in back of a gable vent, ideally the down-wind vent to ensure the fan does not try to exhaust air into the prevailing wind. Two

gable vents (or more) must be provided to ensure proper air flow.

The fan must be sized in proportion to the cubic-foot area of the attic (width x length x average height). This total figure, divided by 10, will give the cubic-foot-per-minute (CFM) required to be moved by the fan.

$$\frac{\text{Cubic Ft. of Attic Area}}{10} = \text{CFM Fan Rating}$$

It should be noted that if eave-ridge venting is used, gable vents must not be installed since their effect can be to upset the natural chimney-type air flow. Another point, if eave vents are installed, care must be taken to ensure that the attic insulation (in batt or blown-in form) does not block air flow from the eave vents into the attic. Ideally, a baffle should be installed between the ceiling joists related to each of the eave vents as illustrated by Figure 15-4. Also note that if "whole-house" ventilation is used, gable-end or ridge vents are usually specified since a larger venting area is needed for efficient operation of this ventilation system. Ridge venting can provide as high as 18" of ventilating area per linear foot of ridge vent. If ridge venting is installed on top of all the roof ridges to provide a total of 20 square feet minimum of venting area, ridge vents can be installed instead of gable-end vents for the whole-house ventilation system.

The "chimney effect" system is very efficient of energy use (if a power-driven turbine or fan is not used). The system

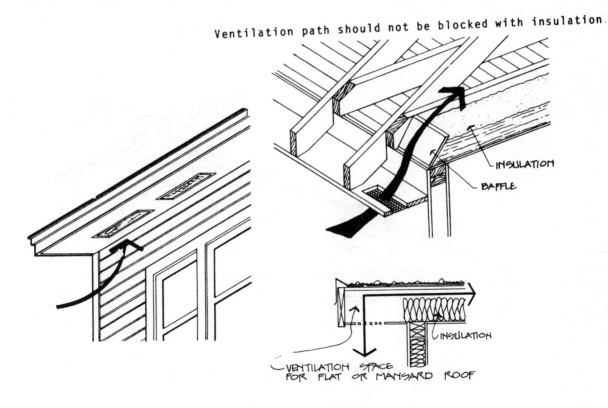

Figure 15.4. Eave (Soffit) Vents

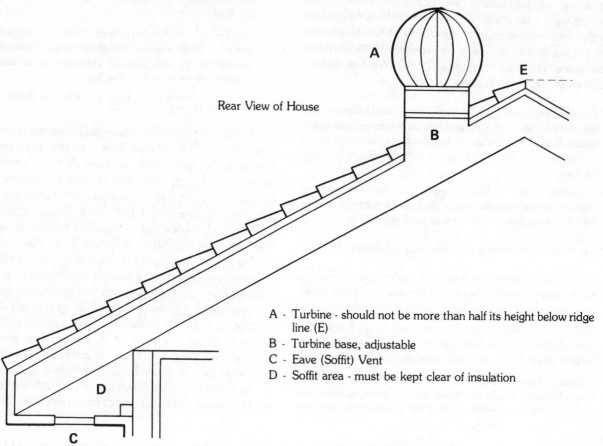

Rear View of House

A - Turbine - should not be more than half its height below ridge line (E)
B - Turbine base, adjustable
C - Eave (Soffit) Vent
D - Soffit area - must be kept clear of insulation

Figure 15-5. Turbine-Eave Venting

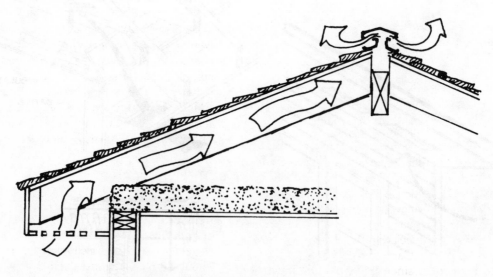

Figure 15-6. Top Ridge-Eave Venting

15-5

will drop the attic temperature to a safe value and is recommended if maximum insulation (for the climatic locale) is provided over the ceiling. In addition, if the air conditioning ducting is located in the attic, the ducting should be insulated to an R8 value. With a well-insulated attic, the living space and ducting is somewhat "isolated" from the attic heat. Thus, if the attic heat in the summer is held to 100°F by the chimney effect, air-conditioning efficiency is assured. The ridge vent system operates very well and is most inconspicuous since the ridge vent material is almost unnoticeable unlike turbine vents, roof ventilators and gable-end vents.

In any case where an attic demonstrates high humidity problems in the winter, the venting system should not be sealed off since ventilation will still be needed to keep the humidity level down. If power-drive turbines or fans are used, these could be equipped with humidity-operated switches that act to turn on the motor when the attic humidity reaches a predetermined level.

The square-foot venting area needed to provide adequate attic ventilation is somewhat difficult to establish and must be considered on a house-by-house basis and in relation to the summer-heat and winter-humidity problems of the house area. One method is to determine what the manufacturers recommend. Attic venting sizing details are somewhat outside the scope of this book thus reference to manufacturer's literature is recommended. For details, see "Attic Ventilation" in the Bibliography. In general, the house itself, by its design, will largely determine how much venting area can be provided on a practical basis. If top-ridge venting is used in conjunction with 8 x 16 inch eave vents set on 8-foot centers, adequate attic ventilation is assured. Gable-end vents are usually limited in size by the actual size of the gable end itself, with the requirement for one square foot of vent area for each 150 square feet of attic floor area being easily satisfied.

Gable-end fans are somewhat standardized as to air-flow power. Turbine vents should not be used if more than two are required to provide adequate venting. More than two makes for a most unsightly roof. Motor-driven turbines are not really much more efficient as to moving air than the wind-driven models and, generally, cannot justify the electricity they use. One last point about attic ventilation — in areas experiencing very high winds, care must be taken that blown-in insulation is not blown around in the attic by high winds entering through gable-end or eave vents. If necessary, wide-guage chicken wire (or similar) may be used, nailed to the ceiling joists in the vent area to keep insulation in place. Care should be taken not to compress the insulation since to do so will lower it's insulation efficiency.

WHOLE-HOUSE VENTILATION

Before the perfection and widespread use of refrigerant-type air-conditioning to cool a house, maximum use was made of air movement into and out of the house by opening windows and doors to catch every breeze. In some instances, a large fan (or fans) was used when there was no natural air movement due to breezes. In brief, a different lifestyle as far as house cooling was necessary before our present air-conditioning systems allowed our extremely comfortable home environment.

One return-to-the-past being brought about by the energy shortage is the whole-house fan. This fan, a large one of up to 42" in size, is centrally mounted in the ceiling where it can pull air from the "whole house." The volume of air pulled into the house through opened windows and screened doors by the fan is considerable (up to 10,000 cubic feet per minute). The fan opening can be equipped with shutters that automatically open when the fan is turned on and close when it is shut off. When a whole-house fan is used, large louvered vents should be fitted into the gable ends of the house. Alternately, ridge venting can be used. Eave vents (and turbines) need not be installed as the whole-house action will force air out of the attic and replace it with cooler air.

Whole-house ventilation—cooling the entire house by air movement alone—is based upon having a large drop in outdoor temperature during the night and a slow buildup of the outdoor temperature from sun up to a peak in the afternoon. (The system is recommended only for areas that experience night-time temperatures markedly cooler than the day-time values.) Let us consider the old-time house-cooling cycle, starting at midnight. At that time, the outdoor temperature is dropping and the house, with all doors and windows open (but screened), would be cooling off rapidly. By morning, the house would have cooled off to be near the outdoor temperature. Upon arising, the occupants would close all windows and doors to keep the outside air (now warming up) from entering the house. At the same time, shades, drapes, awnings, etc. were positioned to keep the sun off the windows.

Later in the day (somewhere between 10 AM and 2 PM dependent upon the heat of the day), the indoor temperature would rise until the effective temperature is uncomfortable. At that time, all outer doors and all unsunlit windows would be opened to allow any breeze to enter. Moving air through the house then did not lower the house temperature and could actually raise it. The occupants, however, felt cooler because the moving air lowered the humidity indoors and had a sort of reverse "chill effect." If the house was equipped with a large fan (or fans), it would generally be turned on at about the peak temperature of the day. The cycle then continued in this manner through midnight and was repeated. If a home was equipped with a fan, it would always be run during the cooler evening hours to bring cooler air into the house to gradually drop the house temperature to the outdoor level.

The system was remarkably efficient as to energy use but—agreed—was not as comfortable as a house cooled by an air conditioner. The occupants thus had to "live with the weather" by dressing lightly and accepting an indoor temperature in excess of the considered ideal of 72°F. Since the occupants really didn't have another choice, they accepted and adjusted to the hot days of the summer.

The air-conditioned house is a closed-up house since it would be most wasteful to have open windows or doors when the air conditioner is running. Yet, a partial return to the "old days" is now being practiced, adjusted to and liked. The main difference being—when the indoor temperature rises to an uncomfortable level (78°F at least), the windows and doors are closed and the air conditioner is turned on. The air conditioner remains on until the outdoor temperature drops to a comfortable level. At that point, the unit is turned off and the doors and windows are opened to permit natural ventilation. However, this requires that the home be equipped with screened windows and doors and has some chance to enjoy breezes.

Whole-house ventilation requires the movement (pulling) of air from all parts of the living area up into and out of the attic. A rather large fan (up to 42" square) may be required. Indeed, for larger homes in warmer climatic areas, two fans may be needed. Fan size required will be in relation to the cubic feet of air needed to be moved out of the house and the general climatic conditions of the house area. The cubic-foot-per-minute (CFM) rating of the fan can be calculated as follows:

- Measure width and length of area to be cooled by fan action. This gives a square-foot value.

- Multiply the square-foot value by the height of the rooms. For rooms with vaulted or cathedral ceilings, average the height and calculate these rooms separately. The net total of the square-foot figure times the height figure gives the cooling area in cubic feet.

- This figure, divided by 10, will give the cubic-feet-per-minute (CFM) figure for the fan.

$$\frac{\text{Cubic Ft. of Cooling Area}}{10} = \text{CFM rating}$$

- This figure should hold for all except very warm climatic areas. Local experience as obtained from the neighbors or the fan salesperson should also be used as a guide.

The whole-house fan may be positioned in either of three ways as illustrated by Figure 15-7.

Maximum air-flow efficiency is gained when the fan is located directly over the ceiling opening. Unfortunately, this position introduces maximum fan noise into the house. Alternately, the fan can be located directly in back of a gable-end louvered vent. If so located, choose the gable end opposite to the prevailing wind so the fan will not be operating into the wind. Or, the fan can be mounted horizontally near to the ceiling opening if it is fitted into a suction box (a plenum).

Two-speed fans are available, having a HIGH speed for rapid air movement during warm daylight hours and a LOW speed for gentle air circulation during the cooler hours of the night. A timer to turn the fan on and off at any desired time is also available.

House zoning may be used to improve the efficiency of the whole-house fan system or to make it possible to ventilate a house of larger cubic-foot volume than can be serviced by the selected fan. That is, during the day time, since the bedrooms will be seldom visited, all bedroom doors and windows can be closed and thus air will be moved only from the living area. In the evenings, the reverse would be desired, with the bedroom doors and windows open and the windows (and doors, if possible) of the living area closed. For privacy reasons, vents can be placed over the bedroom doors to permit air flow out from the room with the door closed. These vents can also be the closable type for sound privacy as well. Alternately, the bedroom door can be shortened (cut off) at the bottom to ensure about a half-inch gap between door bottom and the carpeting.

The whole-house fan system has two drawbacks—noise and fire danger. The noise problem can be reduced to an acceptable level by mounting the fan either just in back of a gable vent or in a plenum constructed to permit mounting of the fan some distance from the ceiling opening. The fire danger relates to the ceiling opening. If the fan is running when a fire starts in the house (or even in the attic), the fan would (unless shut off) supply forced air to the fire. This can be avoided by use of available devices which act to turn off the fan and close the shutters if a fire is detected.

Proper operation of a whole-house fan requires that the exhaust area be sized to permit the full air flow developed by the fan to easily pass out of the attic (if the fan is ceiling mounted). Manufacturers recommendations should be followed and be considered minimum. One manufacturer, for example, suggests a minimum of eight square feet of attic exhaust area for a 24 inch fan and a minimum of 20 square feet for a 48 inch fan. The needed exhaust area can be made up of a combination of eave (soffit) vents and gable-end vents. Top-ridge venting will usually, by itself, provide the needed exhaust area and is very effective being the highest point in the attic.

Cooling a house with a whole-house fan is remarkably efficient as to energy use but — agreed — it is not always as comfortable as related to when the house is cooled with the air conditioner. The house occupants thus must "live with the weather" somewhat and accept an indoor temperature in excess of what has long been considered ideal (72-75°F). However, experience has shown that one can accept and adjust to a higher indoor summer temperature (78°F as requested by the President) in just a few days.

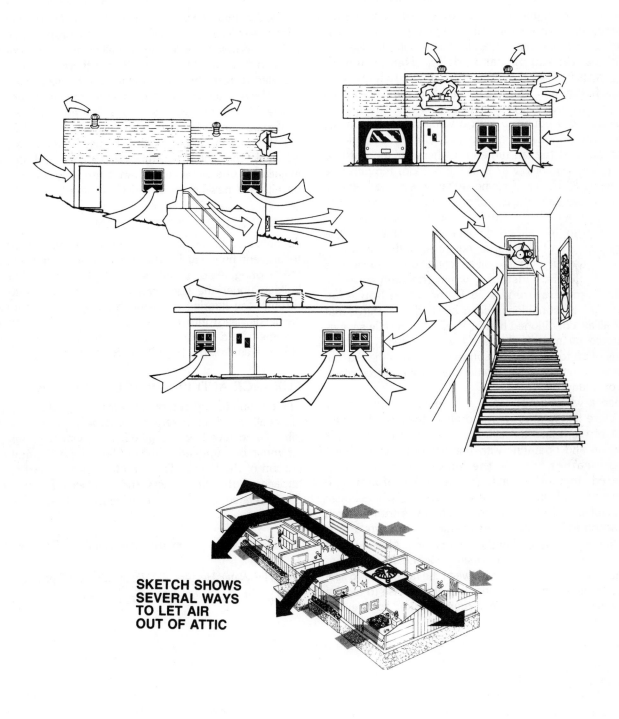

SKETCH SHOWS
SEVERAL WAYS
TO LET AIR
OUT OF ATTIC

Figure 15-7. Whole-House Fan Locations and Exhaust Areas

Very meaningful savings of electric energy have been reported by satisfied users throughout the country. The fan is rather easily installed, even in an existing house, and the capital outlay is not high. A fairly reasonable payback period of five years (or less) is indicated. Of course, if electricity is ever rationed (and it may be) or it continues to rise at the same frightening rate now prevalent across the country, whole-house ventilation will would be most attractive in those climatic areas that justify its use.

National Bureau of Standards and Department of Energy tests indicate that ventilating (cooling) a house with a whole-house fan instead of using the air conditioner can be a very effective way of saving energy. During the tests, a test house was equipped with a whole-house fan in the ceiling. The windows were opened, the air conditioner turned off, and the fan turned on whenever the outdoor temperature was below 82°F. If the outdoor temperature rose above 82°F, the whole-house fan was turned off, the windows closed and the air conditioner was turned on. For comparison, an exact-sized house in the same area was operated with the air conditioner on at all times. The energy savings of the house equipped with the whole-house ventilation over the all-air conditioned house was considerable. For instance, when the daily-average outdoor temperature was 76°F, the whole-house fan reduced the air-conditioning costs by nearly two-thirds that of the all-air conditioned house. Really worthwhile savings are stated by manufacturers. One firm listed a possible savings of up to $146.00 per summer season in the Austin, Texas area (where peak summertime temperatures reach 95°F on many days).

When a whole-house fan is not operating, the shutter *must* close tightly to prevent a draft — the flow of air into or out of the house through the attic when the house is closed up and operating with the air conditioner. When cooler weather arrives, the fan opening should be insulated. Insulation seals (made of Styrofoam-type material with a high R value) are provided by whole-house fan manufacturers that fit into the shutter from the room side, acting to both seal off the opening as to drafts and to raise the insulation level of the fan opening. Alternately, if the fan can be somewhat easily reached in the attic, insulation batts can be fitted between the fan blades to seal off and insulate the fan opening. It might be wise to tag the fan switch or to open the circuit breaker to prevent

accidental turn on of the fan during the period the fan opening is sealed and insulated.

Some fans are equipped with a two-speed motor, permitting HIGH speed operation for a rapid air flow and a LOW speed for gentle air circulation during the night or when a rapid air flow is not needed. Generally, the whole-house fan must be turned on and off manually since the windows have to be opened or closed for proper operation. If the windows can be left open at all times, a timer could be used to turn the unit on or off or a thermostat could be installed to turn the unit on when the house temperature rises above a certain point and to turn the fan off when the house temperature dropped to a desired level.

Manufacturer's literature on whole-house fans is listed in the Bibliography under "Whole-House Fans." It would be advisable that such literature be obtained and studied if installation of a whole-house fan is seriously contemplated on either a new-house or existing-home basis.

UNDER-HOUSE VENTILATION

An unheated basement or crawl space must be ventilated to prevent humidity buildup with subsequent damage to the flooring. Also, if not ventilated, the heavy humidity buildup under the floor can cause water vapor to pass through the flooring (to a much lesser degree if a vapor barrier is used) into the house. For complete details on basement and under-house ventilation, refer to "Under-House Ventilation", page 10-7, Section 10.

FURNACE AND FIREPLACE AIR INTAKE

The burning of any combustible material (natural gas, fuel oil, coal, wood, etc.) requires a large volume of oxygen (air). To achieve true energy efficiency within a home, this air *must* be supplied from outside the air-conditioned portion of the house. This air-intake need is particular to furnaces, hot-water heaters and fireplaces. For particular details related to supplying outside air to these items, refer to:

- Furnaces — "Combustion Air Input to Furnaces," page 19-4.

- Hot-Water Heaters — "Ventilation Loss," page 16-3.

- Fireplaces — "Outside Air for Combustion," page 19-3.

Section 16

Hot Water Systems

GENERAL

The heating of water for personal and household use consumes a very large amount of energy, much more than most people realize. In fact, except for heating and cooling a home, more energy is consumed in heating water and holding it to the desired temperature level than for any other purpose. Natural gas is the most efficient fuel to use for water heating, at least as related to the unit cost now in effect. Electrical heating of water is the most expensive as of now but its extra cost against gas heating may be reduced if gas prices rise as has been predicted. However, gas heating of water is still the least expensive and should be used if gas is available at the building site.

Energy efficiency as related to water heating is achieved by reducing heat losses to a minimum as associated with:

- Piping loss
- Ventilation loss (gas only)
- Air-conditioning loading
- Excessive-temperature loss
- Tank loss

TANK SIZE SELECTION

Selecting the proper tank size (in gallons) is very important. Too large a tank means an excess of water to heat and to hold to the desired temperature while too small a tank can mean a shortage of hot water at times. Proper tank size is somewhat difficult to establish since the personal habit of the house occupants plus their numbers must be taken into account along with the efficiency of the hot-water system itself. Water-saving devices can be installed on shower heads and in faucets to reduce the demand flow of hot water on a per-minute basis. The use of these devices plus some attention by the home owners as to reducing hot-water consumption can make it possible to have ample hot water with a smaller tank than would normally be selected. In general terms, a 30-gallon tank is considered adequate for a family of four with one bathroom plus a clotheswasher and dishwasher. Usually, a 40-gallon tank will suffice for a family of four or five with two bathrooms plus a clotheswasher and a dishwaster if moderate care is taken to use hot water sparingly.

The following savings have been calculated to be reasonable.

Electric heating. Initial Cost = (IC)   Operating Cost = (OC)   Lifetime Cost = (LC)

Standard unit: IC = \$200.00   OC = \$4,078.00 @ 4¢ per KWH for a 10-year life

LC = \$200.00 + \$4,078.00 = \$4,278.00

Deluxe unit: IC = \$224.00   OC = \$3,737.33 @ 4¢ per KWH for a 10-year life

LC = \$224.00 + \$3,737.33 = \$3,961.33

Standard Unit = \$4,720.00
Deluxe Unit = - \$3,961.33
Savings = \$ 316.67 for a 10-year life

With electric rates expected to increase at an average rate of 10% per year, the above values must be factored by 1.6 to correct for the actual cost of electricity over the 10-year lifespan of the hot-water tanks.

A more accurate 10-year savings would then be $521.07.

Gas heating — @ 20¢ per therm

Savings — Deluxe over standard = $253.00 for a 10-year life

Factored by 1.6 = $416.00

LP heating — @ 40¢ per gallon

Savings — Deluxe over standard = $424.00 for a 10-year life

Factored by 1.6 = $690.00

The above clearly shows that heating water electrically is the most costly, with natural gas and LP heating being considerably less over a 10-year period. The above also indicates that it is best to purchase a deluxe (higher quality) unit rather than the unit customarily installed by the building contractor.

PIPING LOSS

Heat loss from the hot-water piping can be considerable if the pipes are not insulated. A ½" diameter copper pipe, for example, can lose up to 40 BTU's of heat per foot of pipe per hour at a water temperature of 150°F. At 130°F, the BTU loss per foot is considerably less but it is still a great waster of energy. A second dollar loss associated with hot water piping is the cost of the water wasted to draw hot water from a tank through long lines (runs) of pipe.

The energy dollars and water dollars lost as related to long runs of pipe make it well worthwhile to design a hot-water system that features very short runs of hot-water piping. That is, the house design should be studied to determine the hot-water using areas within the house. In many cases, the study will show there are three rather distinct hot-water using areas: (1) the bathrooms, (2) the kitchen, and (3) the clothes washer area.

If at all possible, two hot-water tanks should be installed (if the using areas are suitably grouped). One unit could be installed as near to the bathrooms as possible and the second located near to the kitchen sink and dishwasher and to the clothes washer. Since the kitchen uses hot water many times a day, try to locate the tank as near to the kitchen as possible rather than dividing the distance between it and the clothes washer. The second unit would then service only the bathrooms, with its short runs giving almost instant hot water at a real savings in energy and water. Even with short runs, pipe insulation is still highly recommended.

If a two-tank system is possible, the kitchen tank could be a 30-gallon unit for a small to moderate family (4 people maximum) or a 40-gallon unit for a larger family. The thermostat on this unit should be set to about 125°F to 130°F to ensure good dishwashing operation. The second tank for the bathrooms may have to be either a 20-gallon or 30-gallon unit depending upon the number of people in the house and the hot-water used in the bathroom during any maximum-use period. The thermostat on the bathroom unit can be set for a maximum of 110°F, this representing an additional energy-saving benefit.

The tank size required for a given family on either a one-tank or two-tank basis is related both to the number of occupants in the house, their hot-water using habits and— the recovery rate of the tank. Since a smaller size tank initially costs less and requires less energy to keep the stored water hot, the smaller the tank the greater the energy (and dollar) savings. A smaller kitchen-clothes washer unit can be used if the unit is a quick-recovery type and the hot-water use is spaced out. For example, if the dishwasher is not run when the clothes washer is on, etc. The largest water drain at a given time will be for the clothes washer thus a smaller tank could be used if the washer loads are spaced out during a given day or several days rather than to run all washing loads in a fast series. For the bathroom unit, use of a shower instead of tub baths will result in less hot water being used—especially if a low-volume shower head is used. Again, if the showers for a large family could be spaced out rather than being taken in a fast series, a smaller tank could be used.

For a slab foundation, if the hot water pipes (tubing, actually) are to run through the concrete floor, pipe insulation should be of a high level. Alternately, the hot-water pipes could be run through the attic, slipping through holes drilled in the ceiling joists very near the side to which the ceiling sheet rock will be nailed. The piping would then be insulated by the batt insulation. Or, the pipe could be insulated, run on top of the joists, and covered by the ceiling insulation (if an R30-R40 ceiling is used).

The comfort benefts of almost instant hot water due to the short runs possible with a two-tank system are considerable. A hot-water circulating system is available that gives instant hot water upon demand. The system consists of a double run of piping to the hot-water users (bathrooms and kitchen sink) and features a thermostat-controlled water pump. The thermostat acts to close when the pipe (and thus the water) temperature drops to a certain level. The pump then circulates the water in the double-pipe loops until the water temperature is returned to the desired level. This is a most inefficient system as far as energy use since the pipes are always full of hot water and thus there is high heat loss even through well insulated piping. This system is thus not recommended and, in fact, is pointed out as most wasteful of energy.

VENTILATION LOSS

A gas-fired water heater requires a large volume of air. For this reason, the gas water heater should never be installed where it will draw upon the air-conditioned air within the house for combustion purposes. This action would draw large amounts of house air into the combustion chamber and would thus reflect a large load on the heating and cooling system.

Recent tests have shown that the heating efficiency of a gas heater is little effected if the combustion air is drawn from other than the heated portion of the house. In the case of a vented crawl-space or basement foundation, the needed combustion air can be drawn in directly through a vent in the floor. Otherwise, a light-weight ducting can be used to pull in the required air from outside the house, usually above the roof.

AIR-CONDITIONING LOADING

Hot-water tanks, even if well insulated, will give off heat as will the copper piping. While this is a benefit to the heating system in the winter, it is a loss to the cooling system in the summer (particularly in areas requiring high-volume cooling during hot days). If the subject house is in an area where summer-time cooling is a problem, it is suggested the hot water tank(s) be located outside of the air-conditioned area. If they must be located in this area, it is recommended that they be installed in well-insulated air-tight closets.

EXCESSIVE TEMPERATURE LOSS

The thermostats of hot-water tanks are generally set to 145°F or higher at the factory. This temperature level is actually very dangerous as it can cause severe skin scalding if hot water, undiluted by cold water, strikes one while showering. For hand washing, shaving and showering,

105°F to 110°F would be ideal and safe. For dishwashers without a heater element, a maximum of 130°F would suffice for proper operation. If the dishwasher uses a heater element to raise the water temperature, the hot-water thermostat could be set for a maximum of 125°F. Further, the dishwasher really needs very hot water only to free baked-on or thick materials from pots and pans and (sometimes) dishes on which particularly sticky material has dried. A little presoaking and hand scouring of the problem items will reduce the work load of the dishwasher, making operation at a water temperature of 125°F most practical.

Reducing the tank temperature permits the following energy savings to be realized:

- Reduced heat loss from tank
- Extended life of tank and heating element
- Reduced heat loss from pipes

TANK LOSS

Generally speaking, an inexpensive hot-water heater tank is a poor bargain since such a tank is usually poorly insulated and the heater portion may have a less-than-normal life. Regardless of the unit purchased, direct heat loss from the tank can raise the energy bill for water heating by a considerable amount. This loss can be dramatically reduced by adding extra insulation to the outside of the tank.

If the tank is in a closet, the walls of the closet should be insulated if an electric model is used. Note that the closet should be relatively air tight. A gas-fired model in a closet should be wrapped in a special insulation blanket now manufactured for water tanks. This method is required for a gas-fired unit since it must draw in air and thus the closet area cannot really be insulated to save tank loss. Wall insulation towards the air-conditioned area of the house is recommended however to prevent loading of the air-conditioning system during the cooling season. Also, a solid wood door should be used on the closet, particularly if it contains a gas-fired unit. The heater should be shut off when going on vacation, etc.

If the tank is not in a closet, it should be wrapped in the insulation blanket just mentioned. For a gas-fired model, be certain the blanket does not shut off the air entrance to the heater section.

TIMED USE

The tank thermostat will cycle on and off during long periods of non-use just to keep the water up to the desired temperature since there will be some heat loss even through a well-insulated tank and hot-water line system. There are two possible periods each day during which little or no hot water is used. These are: (1) the sleeping hours from about 10PM to 6AM and (2) work or school time from 9AM to 4PM approximately.

In those areas where hot water must be electrically heated, some households are practicing a new energy-saver measure. They are installing a timer in the power-supply line to the hot-water heater. The timer acts to interrupt the line at the start of any long non-use period and to close the line just before hot-water use in volume is expected. The energy normally used during non-use periods to maintain the tank temperature at thermostat setting is thus saved.

The timer system is based upon two facts: (1) that the tank will not drop much in temperature during the power-off period because of good insulation, and (2) the slight water-temperature drop can be raised in a very short time by the modern fast-recovery units. It is more energy efficient to raise the water temperature once at the end of the timed non-use period than to do so over and over during the non-use period. Of course, hot water can still be drawn but in small quantities such as used for a quick washup, a short shower, a panful of dishes, etc. The timer may be shut off at any time desired, restoring full-time operation.

This system may be used only with an electric water heater since its use with a gas or oil-fired unit requires opening of the thermostat circuitry of these units and is thus not recommended.

The timers are not overly expensive, costing between $20.00 and $30.00 plus installation. Units can be obtained that can control only one cycle (10PM to 6AM, for example) or two cycles (night-time and day-time).

The author does not have personal experience in relation to this timed-use method and thus cannot "speak from experience." The author does advise that a recent newspaper article detailed a test run by a university to determine the approximate energy savings possible with the timed-use method. While the article gave only bare details as to the size of the storage tank, the length of the no-use periods, etc., the test concluded that the possible savings were very minor, approximately 15 cents per month.

TEMPERING TANK

The water supply line to a house is run underground from the water source (which may be miles away) to the house. The incoming water is thus generally at ground temperature, usually around 50-55°F. This means that water of this temperature will flow from the supply line into the tank whenever hot water is drawn. The heater must then bring the water up from 50-55°F to the selected temperature (125°F, say), a fair temperature spread. In the summer, it would be advantageous to store the water above ground in a large-capacity tank so that it can rise to the above-ground temperature. The water temperature in the tempering tank will be dependent upon the average temperature of the tank location, being highest if the tank is located in direct sunlight. The temperature spread between the water drawn from the tempering tank and the desired water temperature within the hot-water tank can

be reduced and thus less energy will be used for hot-water heating.

Three points should be considered in relation to tempering tanks. One, if the tank is located where water in it could, during the winter, drop in temperature below the underground temperature or even freeze, the tank should be bypassed in the winter. That is, the water supply line should be reconnected direct to the hot-water tank and the tempering tank should be drained. Two, the tank should not be insulated since to do so would prevent the heat from passing through the tank walls to heat the stored water. Three, the tank should have at least twice the capacity of the hot-water tank(s), this to ensure the tempering tank can deliver pre-heated water equal to two full tanks of hot water drawn in a short period. This capacity requirement (with its attendant water weight) strongly suggests the tempering tank should not be located on the roof. If roof mounting is desired, the tank size must not exceed the capacity of the roof to support the water-weight load.

HEATING WATER WITH A HEAT EXCHANGER

Two new innovations in hot-water heating relate to use of a heat exchanger that captures waste heat from the air conditioner to heat or preheat hot water. Both methods take advantage of the very high level of heat stored in the Freon fluid-gas when an air conditioner, either a conventional model or a heat pump, is operating in the cooling cycle. That is, when in the cooling cycle, the air conditioner acts to remove heat from the house air and to dissipate this heat outdoors by means of the compressor action. A heat exchanger operates to pass some of this heat into the hot-water line or hot-water tank to heat or preheat some the water. A second benefit is realized in that some of the heat is removed from the Freon before it reaches the compressor, head pressure is reduced and the compressor operates somewhat more efficiently as a result.

One heat exchanger, figure 16-1, consists of a small box that is mounted between the compressor and the outdoor condensor coil. The Freon line is brought into the box, connecting to a pipe that is looped back and forth within the box. The Freon then flows from the box to the outdoor condensor coil. A water pipe from the bottom of the hot-water tank is brought to the box and connected to a copper pipe that lies directly above the looped Freon line. This pipe, also looped, then connects back to the top of the water tank. A circulating pump, turned on when the air conditioner operates, pumps water from the hot-water tank through the heat exchanger box and back to the tank. Thus, the hot water is either preheated or even brought up to desired temperature by capturing the waste heat. In many cases, experience has shown that the supply

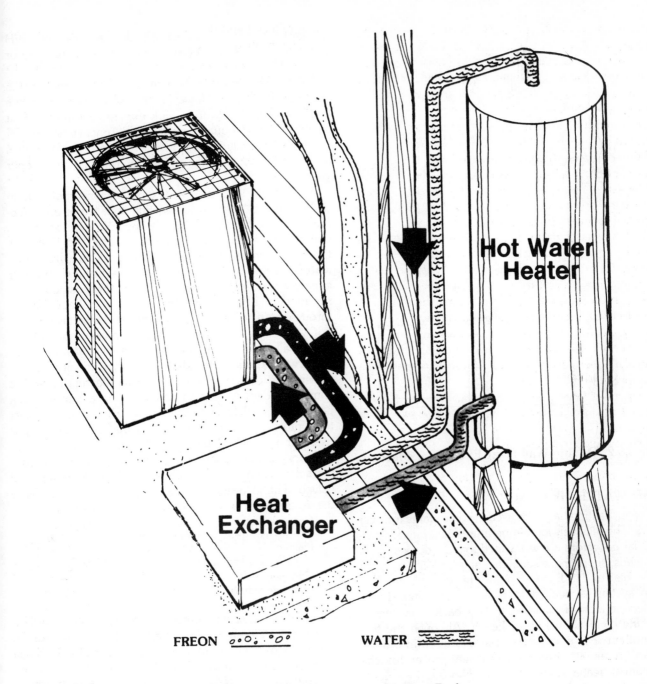

FREON °∘°∘° °∘°   WATER ≈≈≈

Figure 16-1. Preheating Water with Heat Exchanger

line to the electric heater in electric models can be opened, with the water temperature being maintained solely by action of the heat exchanger.

Another method, figure 16-2, transfers heat from the freon line directly at the water tank. A double-walled "tube-within-a-tube" heat exchanger is installed into the hot-water tank. The hot-gas (Freon) line from the compressor is connected to the input side of the heat exchanger and flows through a solenoid valve to pass down through the double-walled tube, giving up heat directly to the water. The hot-gas line then exits to be delivered to the outdoor condensor coil. A thermostat monitors the tank temperature at the hot-water output and acts to close the solenoid valve when a preset water temperature is reached. The Freon is then delivered directly to the condensor coil, bypassing the double-walled tube. The system has been ARL approved and, according to manufacturer's data, can develop up to 5 gallons of hot water per hour per ton of capacity when the air conditioner is running. A 3-ton unit would thus develop water at the rate of 15 gallons per hour running time or about 5 gallons per hour if the air conditioner was on for 20 minutes per hour.

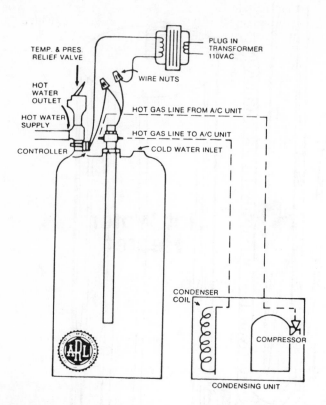

Figure 16-2. Double-Wall Heat Exchanger Method

SOLAR WATER HEATING

Solar water heating has been used in some states for over 30 years. The relatively low temperatures generated by flat-plate solar collectors are well suited to most domestic hot water needs, supplying water in the range of 165°F on a hot summer day to 115°F on a cold winter day. However, a backup system is needed to provide hot water during extended periods of cloudiness. This backup system is simply the conventional water heater. Although the flat-plate collector is somewhat effective even in cloudy weather, it usually can only pre-heat water for the conventional heater under clear conditions.

Cost Data. The feasibility of solar water heating systems hinges on several factors, wtih the primary one being cost. That is, the cost of solar system on a life-time basis (10 years at least) versus the same cost for heating water with the available energy (gas, LP or electricity). Up to 17 percent of a family's energy consumption is for hot water (based upon an average monthly demand of 100 gallons per day for a family of four). Heating with natural gas at a price of 17¢ per day (an average cost for 100 cubic feet of gas which typically heats 100 gallons of water per day) results in a monthly cost of 30 x 17¢ = $5.10. Heating

100 gallons a day in an electric tank uses about 17 KWH per day which, at a 4¢ KWH rate, totals 68¢ per day or $20.40 (30 x .68) per month.

Solar energy is often thought of as "free" which it is in the sunshine sense. However, the solar collector system and associated hardware is fairly expensive, running about $1200-$2000 for a quality installation. Annual maintenance costs will generally average from 2 to 5 percent of the initial system cost, adjusted for an inflation rate of 6 percent per year.

A study in 1976 by the U.S. Department of Energy (DOE) stated "solar water heating installed at an equipment cost of $20.00 per square foot of collector area is competitive today against electric resistance systems throughout most of the U.S." The study analyzed solar water heating in comparison with heating with other energy types and concluded that if the cost could be reduced to $10.00 per square foot of collector area, through both technical innovations and incentives, solar hot water heating would be economically competitive against all residential fuel types (electricity, gas, LP) in all but areas experiencing adverse weather conditions.

The true cost of a solar hot-water heating system is somewhat difficult to establish thus the actual payback period is also difficult to determine. Then too, one must take into account the positive fact that energy costs will rise year after year. If energy costs double during the next 10 years (as they easily could), the effective dollars savings of a solar system would be doubled and the payback period halved. The following is a somewhat practical analysis of the *true* cost of a solar hot-water heating system.

Cost installed	$1,600.00
20-year mortgage — interest at 9%	2,880.00
Maintenance — 2% of $1,600 per year	640.00
Total cost — 20-year span	$5,120.00
Cost per year	$256.00
Cost per month	$21.33

The above indicates a monthly savings of $21.33 will be required if a 20-year payback period is to be achieved. On the average, heating hot water electrically at a 5¢ KWH rate would cost about $30.00 per month. Taking an average savings of 80% of the heating cost if solar heating is used, the monthly savings would be $24.00. However, many areas now have KWH rates in excess of 5¢ and the rate will increase for all areas on an almost endless basis. Thus, a payback time of perhaps as low as 10 years can be realized on a solar hot-water heating system installed today. One thing — it will never cost less than it does now.

Collector Assembly. Most solar collecting systems use the flat-plate collector (Figure 16-3). Most collectors use water or some other liquid as the heat-transfer medium while a few systems may use air. The collector consists of:

(A) glazing, usually double-strength glass installed with gaskets or caulking, to allow for expansion and contraction due to temperature changes.

(B) water tubes, that are attached above, below or integral to the absorber plate for heat transfer.

(C) absorber plate, usually metal and treated with a black paint or dark "selective" coating to improve the plate's ability to absorb heat.

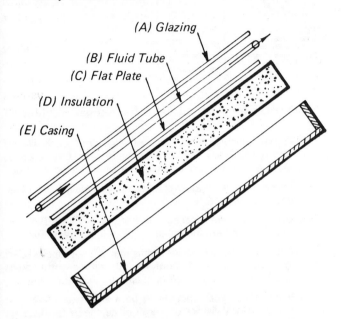

Figure 16-3. Flat-Plate Solar Collector Assembly

(D) insulation, used to reduce heat loss through the back of the collector.

(E) enclosure, acts as a container for the components listed above. The glazing (A) is fitted into the enclosure to form a weather-tight seal.

System Types. Two basic types of solar water heating systems are in common use today: (1) the open system and (2) the closed system.

The open system circulates the actual water used in the home. It is thus called an "open" system since the water is directly heated. An open system can circulate water through the collectors either on a thermosyphon or pumped basis. The thermosyphon system is the simplest and (usually) the least expensive. The thermosyphon system, Figure 16-4, features a large storage tank that is located high enough in relation to the collectors to cause cold water flowing into the storage tank and down the downcomer pipe to enter the bottom of the collectors. As the water heats, it flows up the water riser to flow into the top of the storage tank and from there down to the regular (backup) tank of the hot-water heater. A report by John Yellot, a mechanical engineer and professor of architecture at Arizona State University, stated a thermosyphon type solar heater can heat 40-50 gallons of water a day with a 4 x 8-foot collector located in an area free from shade.

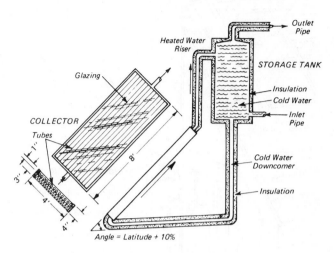

Figure 16-4. Typical Thermosyphon System

The pumped system, Figure 16-5, contains the same components as the thermosyphon system except that a pump is used to force the water up to the collectors and around (heated) back into the storage tank. The storage tank can thus be located at any desired level. However, with a pumped system, temperature-sensitive controls must be provided that will permit the water pump to turn on only when the water in the collectors is at a predetermined temperature. Otherwise, the water pump would simply pump on an endless basis with a consequent loss of energy. The open system contains water in the pipes to the collector and, since this water could freeze when the water temperature drops below 32°F, a drain-down feature must be provided to prevent the pipes from freezing and thus bursting.

A closed system, Figure 16-6, features a heat exchanger wrapped around the bottom of the hot water tank. This heat exchanger connects to the piping running up to the solar collectors. A treated water solution (water and antifreeze, usually) is circulated under pump pressure through this "closed" system. The heat developed by the collectors is transmitted to the water in the tank by means of the heat exchanger. The heat exchanger is generally external to the water tank since the piping contains antifreeze, a potentially toxic material. A closed system can also circulate the water-antifreeze mix under thermosyphon control. The closed system generally is more expensive than the open system but it has proven to have a longer operating life and lower maintenance costs.

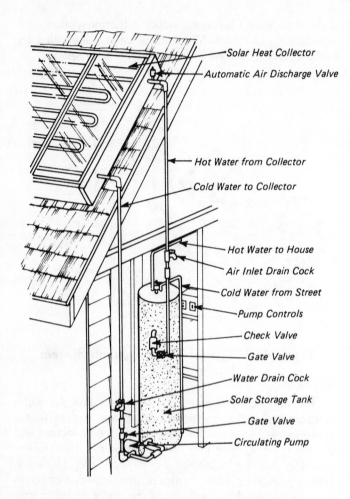

Figure 16-5. Typical Pumped System

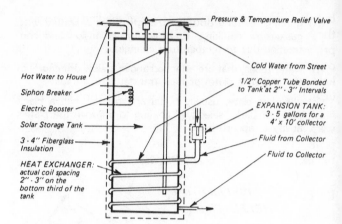

Figure 16-6. Typical Heat Exchanger System

The Final Decision. Solar water heaters are a field in themselves and one in which much expertise has recently been developed. However, most building contractors are uninformed as to solar hot water heating systems; thus it would be best to deal directly with a local firm specializing in solar systems. The National Solar Heating and Cooling Center Information Center suggests the following be considered when buying a solar hot-water heating system:

(1) Ask for proof that the product will perform as advertised. An independent laboratory or university report should be consulted.

(2) Examine the warranty carefully. According to law, the manufacturer must state whether the warranty is full or limited. Ask the seller what financial arrangements, such as an escrow account, have been made to honor the warranty.

(3) Solar components must work well together if efficiency and long life is to be realized. It is best to buy the system as a whole package as developed by one manufacturer. If the seller assembles the solar system from items developed by more than one manufacturer, determine the seller has a broad experience in choosing compatible components.

(4) Get in writing who will service the system if anything goes wrong since service on solar water systems requires experience. Not just any plumber or handyman will do.

(5) Do not try a do-it-yourself kit unless you really have a solid background as a handyman.

(6) Check with your local consumer office or Better Business Bureau to determine whether the seller is reputable.

(7) If the seller makes verbal claims that are not "spelled out" in the literature handed out, have the claims written down and have the seller sign his name to the statement.

(8) If you have what appears to be a legitimate complaint, notify the local district attorney's office, the Better Business Bureau, and the local consumer protection agency. Be specific in your complaint and give as much documentation as possible.

Roof Pitch and Orientation. The roof pitch (steepness) and the house's orientation to the sun are of extreme importance if solar water heating is desired. Ideally, the roof to mount the solar collector array should face true south for maximum sun exposure. However, collector orientation 20 degrees either side of true south is considered acceptable. A greater deviation than that will result in a low-performance system. Best collector tilt is equal to the site latitude but a variation of 10 degrees from this angle is considered acceptable.

Collector tilt (slant to the average sun-ray angle) can be adjusted to the desire degree by propping up the collector at top or bottom. A flat roof generally permits the collector to be positioned to due South. If positioned near the center of the roof, the collector may be all but invisible from the ground. The collector, of course, will have to be propped up (tilted) to the required tilt angle.

Solar Shading. Before a solar hot-water heating system is decided upon, a very careful study should be made to determine if the solar collector will be shaded at any time by trees, chimneys, the house next door, etc. One should consider not only actual shading problems apparent today but should take into account potential shading problems of the future. Such as: will a tree, now too small to be a shade problem, become a problem when fully grown? — if a lot on either side of your house is now not built upon, what kind of house may be built on it in the future; if a two-story, would it block the sun from the solar collector? Solar rights are not yet established in the legal sense so one probably will not be able to stop others from building a house, planting a tree, etc. that could interfere with one's solar rights.

INITIAL COST PAYBACK PERIODS

Estimates related to energy and dollars saved and the payback periods for the energy-saving features detailed in this section are:

- Deluxe hot-water tank versus standard unit.

  Initial cost difference is between $25.00 and $50.00. For an electric unit, payback period is two years or less. For a gas unit, payback period will be less than three years and for an LP unit, less than two years.

- Piping Insulation.

  An initial cost of $50.00 to $75.00 is indicated. An annual savings of five percent of the total water-heating bill is reasonable to expect. Payback time is three years or less for gas or LP unit and two years for an electric unit.

- Two-tank system.

  Two savings are made here: less water, hot and cold, is wasted to get hot water to the using point. Less copper pipe and pipe insulation is needed.

  A minimum savings of 5% to 7.5% on the total water-heating bill is indicated dependent upon the amount of water drawn each day. The cost of the extra tank is somewhat compensated by the fact that both tanks will be smaller and thus less expensive per each.

  It is considered that the extra cost will be repaid in five years. The comfort factor alone would make the extra cost worthwhile.

- Excessive temperature reduction.

  No initial cost since thermostat(s) need merely be turned back. Savings are estimated to be between $10.00 and $50.00 per year, dependent upon the amount of water used.

- Tank insulation.

  Insulating the tank itself usually costs about $25.00 or less. A savings of 5 to 8% on the hot-water heating bills are listed in manufacturer's literature. Payback time is one year or less.

  Insulating a closet will be more expensive, perhaps $100.00 or less. Payback time may be as long as five years.

- Timed use.

  An initial cost of $30.00 to $50.00 installed per timer and a questionable dollar and energy savings makes timed-use a debatable energy-saving feature. Tests by the University of Texas indicate "a possible savings of 15¢ per month."

- Tempering tank method.

  Initial cost and payback data is not currently available. Initial cost will be determined by the type and size of tempering tank used, the extra piping and drain valve required, etc. Total cost will be less if self installed.

  The payback should be relatively good (between $50.00 and $100.00 per year as an estimate.)

- Heating water with a heat exchanger.

  Cost of the heat-exchange box is between $300.00 and $450.00 installed. Cost of the double-wall heat exchanger, installed, is about $400.00 — and appears to be more efficient than the heat-exchange box.

  A payback time of two years or less is indicated for both systems.

- Solar water heating.

  The high initial cost installed would require a very high yearly dollars savings to result in a reasonable payback period. Hot-water heating averages about:

Electric Heating	— $360.00 a year (at a 5¢ KWH rate)
Gas heating	— $200.00 (or less)
LP heating	— $250.00 (or less)

  With an installed cost of between $1,000.00 and $2,000.00 and an estimated maintenance factor of 2% per year, a payback time of 10 years is generally considered to make the installation worthwhile. As energy costs increase, this 10-year payback period may be shortened considerably. For a quality installation, a unit life of 20 years is considered possible.

  If the conditions of a given area are somewhat ideal (many hours of sunshine, winter and summer — ideal or near ideal orientation of collector — no solar shading problems now or in the future), installation of a unit is recommended by both the Government and by gas and electric companies. The uncertain future of energy prices also makes an installation more attractive.

Section 17

FIREPLACES

GENERAL

Many home owners desire a fireplace in the living room and even a second unit in the family room. Indeed, in many areas a house without a fireplace is somewhat difficult to sell. Yet, as will be detailed, a fireplace can actually be a serious energy waster unless designed for heat-producing efficiency.

Two types of fireplaces are in common use today: (1) in-wall units and (2) free-standing units. The in-wall unit may be built into either an inner or outer wall and consist of two basic types: (1) all-masonry and (2) prefabricated (of metal, whole or in part). Unless specially designed for heat-producing efficiency, an in-wall open-front fireplace is a heat waster. A free-standing fireplace is made of metal and may be placed anywhere in a room as a "free-standing" unit. A minimum distance from combustible material, however, must be maintained. The heat-producing efficiency of a free-standing unit is always better than that of a "standard" in-wall unit, with the amount of heat developed by a given unit being largely determined by its design.

FIREPLACE FACTS

The energy shortage and the ever-increasing cost of fuel (natural gas, oil) and electricity as used for heating has caused a wide-spread return to using a fireplace as a heat source. Many people have "dusted off" their old fireplace and are now using it through the worst part of the winter, not being aware that they are actually losing more heat than the fire is developing. Homes are still being built with in-wall fireplaces of "standard" design, with leaky (or missing) dampers, to be used as heat producers mistakenly. Thus if a fireplace is to be used as a true heat source in a new home, a true-heat producing fireplace of worthwhile efficiency should be built into the home. For an existing home, the fireplace (almost always an in-wall unit) should be equipped with the accessories now available to turn it into a true heat producer.

If a fireplace is to be used as a heat producer, a serious study should be made of the heat-producing efficiency of the many fireplaces now on the market. This book canno[t] cover them in any detail — there are so many types, s[o] many designs. This section will give informative details o[f] the two major types of fireplaces — in-wall and fre[e] standing. Stoves and furnaces of a bewildering variety ar[e] now on the market but will not be covered in this book. T[o] do so would enlarge it by many pages.

Two other aspects of the use of a fireplace as a hea[t] producer should be considered. One: how available [is] fireplace wood and what does it cost? Here in Austi[n,] Texas (a heavily wooded area) the price of firewood ha[s] zoomed from $35.00 per cord in 1976 to $80.00 plus i[n] 1978. This specifies that unless a fireplace has a rather hig[h] heat-producing efficiency, the cost of wood will more tha[n] erase any energy-cost savings. Secondly: certain area[s] within a town or city can, under certain wind condition[s,] hold the smoke pouring from a multitude of fires. Thi[s] thought should be considered based upon local observa[-] tions now and as related to the projected use of fireplace[s] in the future.

IN-WALL FIREPLACES

An in-wall fireplace is a wonderfully heartening sight on [a] cold day but it must be understood that, unless speciall[y] designed and equipped, it is not a true heat produce[r.] Facts on a "standard" in-wall, open-front fireplace are a[s] follows:

- Develops heat mainly by radiation, with a minor amount bein[g] developed by conduction (heating of the fireplace stone o[r] brick).

- While burning, the fire can draw from 12,000 to 15,000 cubi[c] feet of house air per hour to be used as combustion air or t[o] wastefully flow up the chimney.

- This lost house air is then replaced by cold air drawn into th[e] house from all possible draft points. This cold air flow is suc[h] that while the fireplace room may be warm, the remainder o[f] the house will lose heat.

- When it is desired to let the fire burn down, the damper mus[t] be left open until the fire is completely out. Thus, for literall[y] hours house air will flow up the chimney until the fire has die[d] down to the point the damper can be closed.

- Many existing in-wall fireplaces were built without a damper while others have poor-fitting dampers. This results in a constant air flow into or out of the house on a year-round basis. A 50-house test revealed that, on the average, a "good" damper leaked enough to account for 5.5% of the drafts into or out of the house. (For details, refer to Figure 14-2, page 14-3.)

The above specifies that a "standard" in-wall open-front fireplace can lose more heat than it develops. Fortunately, many things can be done to improve the heat-producing efficiency of an in-wall fireplace. And, excellent heat producers can be installed when a home is being built. These will now be discussed.

EXISTING IN-WALL FIREPLACE—ACCESSORIES

Dampers. To be draft proof, a damper must close tightly. The best built-in damper is one mounted in a cast-iron frame to which the damper can be tightly closed to make a very good seal. A damper should be inspected yearly and repaired if defective. Replacement is sometimes most difficult. For a damper that cannot be repaired or if a damper is missing, a special damper that mounts on top the chimney is available. This damper can be opened and closed by a lever mounted in the fireplace opening. The damper makes a positive seal and also acts to keep birds from nesting in the chimney.

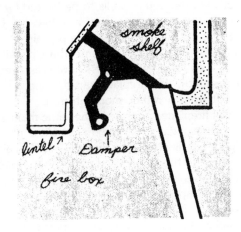

Figure 17-1. Standard Fireplace Damper

Heat Reflectors. Heat reflectors — in the form of a large metal plate — can be fitted against the back of the fireplace. The plate acts to reflect more of the radiant heat out into the room than would the soot-blackened masonary wall. Cost is about $30.00, installation is easy and they are somewhat effective. Note they should be cleaned with a wirebrush when they become soot laden — this to prevent the soot from absorbing the radiant heat.

Convection Heat Tubes. A special grate — constructed of large-size pipe — can be used instead of the conven-

tional iron-bar grate. The special grate is formed of six pipes (normally) as illustrated by Figure 17-2. The fire heats the air in the pipes which then flows out the top of the pipes into the room and is replaced by colder room air. This convection heat flow can improve the heat-producing efficiency of a fireplace to a meaningful degree. Some of these grates are built with the pipes all being connected at the bottom into a long rectangular box (a plenum) (Figure 17-3) through which room air is pumped into all pipes under motor control. This type is, of course, more efficient as a heat producer since the hot air in the pipes is replaced with room air on a more rapid basis.

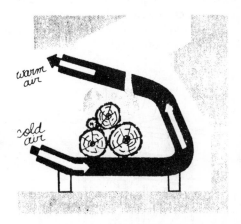

Figure 17-2. Hollow-Pipe Grate

Glass-Screen Front. A fireplace screen, fitted with sliding glass doors, is available — designed to fit nearly airtight into the fireplace opening. The screen is provided with adjustable vents (2) at the bottom which can be opened to permit room air to be drawn in as combustion air for the fire. The vents are usually opened fully and the glass doors opened when the fire is started. Once the fire is burning well, the glass doors are closed and the vents are used to regulate the fire. The radiant heat from the fire passes through the glass doors with little loss. The air vents both allow the fire to be regulated and can shut off all combustion air to the fire when it is desired the fire should die down. This means that house air will not be flowing up the chimney during the period the fire is dying down. Also, the vents control the amount of room air used as combustion and thus can act to make a fire burn longer for a given load of wood.

The glass-door screen can be mated with the special grate just described. The mating gains the benefits of both and results in a fireplace with a vastly improved heating efficiency. If a "standard" in-wall fireplace is to develop part or all of the heat for a house, the glass-door screen/pipe grate is highly recommended. As illustrated by Figure 17-3, a blower motor can be used to force room air through the grate tubes to exit at the top heated to a much higher temperature. Note a plenum on the left-hand side permits outdoor air to be brought into the fire opening for combustion purposes. If outside air is provided, the room-air vents should be closed to prevent room air being drawn up into the chimney. The combination indicated below will produce a very high level of heated air for a given amount of wood burned and is highly recommended.

Outside Air for Combustion. The last step in improving the heat-producing efficiency of an in-all fireplace is to obtain outside air for combustion. One method is illustrated by Figure 17-3, with the air being brought to the glass-door screen through a rectangular duct. This duct can connect through the floor to a ventilated basement or crawl space or it can be run out through an outer wall. This specifies the fireplace should be built into an outer wall if outdoor air is to be obtained.

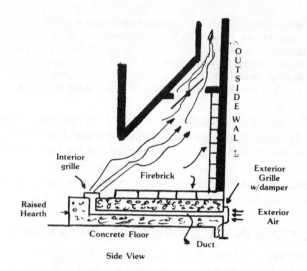

Figure 17-4. Outside Air Via Ash Pit

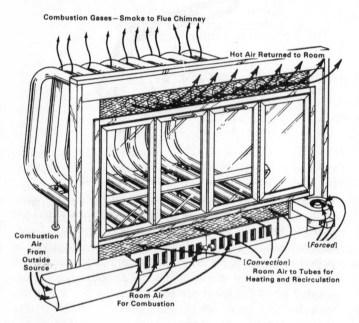

Figure 17-3. Glass-Door Screen & Heat-Pipe Grate

A second method is illustrated by Figure 17-4, with the air being drawn into the fireplace opening through the ash pit. The circulating ash dump should be built into the fireplace base as near to the front as possible. The cleanout door is vented and equipped with a screen to keep insects out. The system both supplies outdoor air to the fire and permits removal of ashes.·

PREFABRICATED IN-WALL FIREPLACES
Prefabricated fireplaces, generally made entirely or in part from steel plates, are now being installed in homes that are being built. The fireplace is somewhat cost-competitive with an all-masonry fireplace but has an inherently higher

heat-producing efficiency. The prefabricated fireplace is set into the wall, either an inner or outer wall, and closed in with stone or mortar as illustrated by Figure 17-5. The prefabricated units are built as either a double-wall or triple-wall unit as illustrated by figure 17-5.

Note the double-wall unit uses a fire-brick base. Two side vents are provided to pull in floor-level room air which passes between the double walls to be heated by the fire, exiting from two top vents in the sidewalls. In some models, a motor-driven fan is used to pull air in and push heated air out in a higher volume than possible with convection. If equipped with a glass-door firescreen and an outside-air source, this fireplace can develop a very high level of heat from a rather moderate fire.

Triple-wall fireplaces operate in the same manner as the double-wall units except that the three walls act to develop two air spaces as illustrated by Figure 17-5. One air space, the one closest to the fire, is used to pull in room air at the bottom through a vent. The air is then heated as it passes through the air space, exiting from top vents either as a hot-air flow or as driven by a fan. The second air space can also be used as a hot-air heating space or it can be used to pull air down into the firebox from the attic. In either case, the two air spaces act to drop the wall temperature to the point the fireplace may be placed against a combustible wall with "zero clearance" without concern for fire danger. These prefabricated fireplaces are thus called "zero-clearance" units. This unit, like the double-wall unit, can be equipped with a glass-door screen to increase its heat producing efficiency.

All prefabricated fireplaces feature a positive-closing damper. The units, not having a rain shelf like found in a brick-built fireplace, must use a chimney cap to keep rain from falling down the chimney directly onto the fire box.

Some prefabricated double-wall and triple-wall fireplaces are equipped with ducts that may be used to deliver air

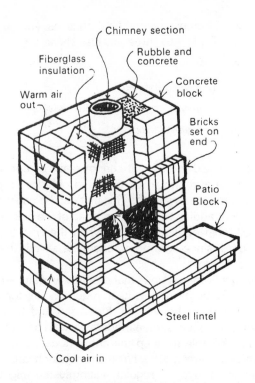

Double-Wall Unit

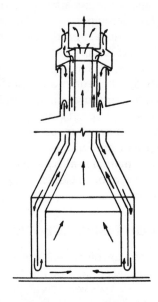

Triple-Wall Unit

Figure 17-5. Prefabricated In-Wall Fireplaces

heated in the multi-wall air space to other parts of the house. A fan of suitable size is customarily used to push the hot air though the ducts to the receiving rooms. This fireplace can, under somewhat ideal circumstances, heat an entire house with a moderate use of firewood per heating season.

Certain prefabricated units can be equipped with a special grate or a hollow-pipe grate that permits coal to be burned without damage to the fireplace base or the hollow-pipe grate. A much hotter and slower burning fire results if coal is used. Be certain to determine if your prefabricated fireplace can burn coal before actually burning coal in it.

FREE-STANDING FIREPLACES

The "free-standing" fireplaces are like the "pot-bellied" stoves of old in that they are not built into a wall but stand by themselves any place desired in the room. The units, however, must be kept a certain distance (in inches) from combustible material and have a noncombustible hearth under them. The chimney, made up of fit-together sections, runs from the stove up through the ceiling and roof by means of special fittings called firestops.

The free-standing fireplaces develop both radiant heat (out the opening) and conductive heat through the fireplace itself and the chimney run. These units are thus relatively good heat producers. In fact, in homes of about 1500 square-feet living space or less, a small free-standing unit can keep the entire house warm if the outdoor temperature is about

40°F or higher. To distribute the developed heat throughout the house, the air-conditioning fan should be set to "ON". The fan can then pull the heat back into the air handler for distribution through the air-conditioning duct system. If part of the house can be shut off so it does not need heating, a free-standing fireplace has been known to keep the remainder of the house at a liveable temperature without air-conditioner participation even when the outdoor temperature was as low as 25°F. This assumes a moderate-size well-insulated, energy-saver type home, however.

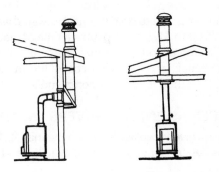

Figure 17-6. Free-Standing Fireplaces

Free-standing fireplaces have been used throughout Europe for literally centuries. These European fireplaces are slow-burning types in that the air input into the firebox can be regulated to produce a fire rate that generates moderate heat with low fuel (wood) consumption. These units are often made from porcelain and are rather attractive. In fact, there is now a fad starting for units imported from overseas.

Another slow-burning, excellent heat-producing fireplace is just coming into use in our country. This unit has a thermostatically-controlled air input that ensures constant slow burning of the fuel (wood). These units are reported to develop considerable heat with a very low air intake and with low fuel consumption. Fireplace shops in larger cities may have further information on these units as well as the porcelain units being imported from Europe.

Regretfully, no further information is at hand as of now but these units seem interesting enough to encourage local inquiries of the fireplace shops, etc.

ENERGY LOSS THROUGH FIREPLACE WALL

A masonry fireplace built into an outer wall customarily consists of two masonry walls separated by an air space. The resistance (R) value of masonry is very low as indicated under the "Wall Comparison" portion of Section 6. A discussion of the energy efficiency of a fireplace masonry wall versus a well-insulated stud wall is given under the "Solid-Masonry Outer Walls" portion of Section 11. The discussion illustrates how a masonry outer wall amounting to only 32% of the total outer wall area will have a 79.6% energy drain. The remaining 68% of the wall area (of R20 value) then accounts for the remainder of the energy drain (20.4%). This is a heat loss or gain ratio of 4 to 1.

This high energy loss through a solid-masonry wall can be greatly reduced by using a prefabricated zero-clearance unit, set inside of a fully-insulated stud wall. (Manufacturers' literature shows the method.) The masonry can then be laid up against the stud wall, resulting in a fireplace identical in appearance and operation to the "standard" all-masonry fireplace. And, a well-insulated wall results with very low energy drain.

Taking a fireplace masonry wall of 8' high by 8' wide as an average, the extra cost to build the insulated stud wall would be about $75.00 to $125.00. A payback time of more than 5 years is indicated at today's energy costs but, considering the comfort benefit and the higher cost of fuel in the future, the stud-wall method is highly recommended.

FIREPLACES AS ENERGY SAVERS - SUMMARY

The ability of a given fireplace to deliver meaningful heat into the house is dependent upon the type installed and how it is used. As heat producers (and thus as energy savers), fireplaces divide into three groups. These are:

1. In-wall, standard
2. In-wall, multi-walled, with blowers
3. Free-standing

The standard in-wall unit cannot really be considered a heat source and should be operated only for its pleasant sight and radiated warmth. This unit can be considered, at best, as not adding to the heating load of the heater system (gas, oil, coal or heat pump). When the cost of wood is considered, since little or no energy is saved, there is an actual dollar loss.

The special in-wall units that output warm air can actually supply part or all of the heat requirements for a home dependent upon home size, type used and the outdoor temperature. That is, on a moderately cold day, the special unit may be able to keep the entire house warm without need for supplemental heat from the regular heating system. On very cold days, the regular heating system might have to assist to hold the house temperature to an acceptable level. This unit is thus a heat producer and an energy saver. However, when the cost of wood is considered, an actual dollar savings might not be realized.

If part of the house is capable of being shut off (sleeping area in the day time) a special in-wall unit might be capable of supplying all required heat in the living area even for very cold days.

The free-standing units are somewhat equal in heat producing capabilities with the special in-wall units and thus can be considered energy savers. Again, when the cost of the fuel (wood) is taken into account, an actual dollar savings might not be realized.

Fireplaces, in brief, should not be considered as real energy savers while saving dollars at the same time. The initial cost of the units is fairly high (up to $500.00 or more for a special in-wall unit) and the fuel costs can be considerable. However, in areas where wood is cheap or free, the fuel cost can be disregarded.

Generally, a fireplace should be considered for its architectural beauty and because it adds a certain flair to a home—and because it is such a lovely sight when burning. Practically speaking, the dollars saved by the energy savings realized by a fireplace will not be great in relation to the total cost of the unit installed.

Table 17-1

COMPARISON OF HEATING VALUES FOR SEVERAL SPECIES OF WOOD

Species	Density of Wood @ 20% Moisture Content(1) (pounds/cu. ft.)	Average Weight of 85 cu. ft. of Wood @ 20% Moisture Content (pounds)	Possible Recoverable Heat Units Per Cord of 85 Solid Cubic feet and assuming 100% Efficiency(2) (in millions of BTUs) 20% M.C.	Available Heat Per Cord at 50% Heating Efficiency (in millions of BTUs)	Units Needed to Give 1,000,000 BTUs of Available Heat (cords)
Hickory (Avg. of Several Types)	50.9	4,327	27.7	13.8	.072
Eastern Hophornbeam	50.2	4,267	27.3	13.7	.073
Apple	48.7	4,140	26.5	13.2	.076
White Oak	47.2	4,012	25.7	12.8	.078
Sugar Maple	44.2	3,757	24.0	12.0	.083
Red Oak	44.2	3.757	24.0	12.0	.083
Beech	44.2	3,757	24.0	12.0	.083
Yellow Birch	43.4	3,689	23.6	11.8	.085
White Ash	43.4	3,689	23.6	11.8	.085
Hackberry	38.2	3,247	20.8	10.4	.096
Tamarack	38.2	3,247	20.8	10.4	.096
Paper Birch	37.4	3,179	20.3	10.2	.098
Cherry	36.7	3,120	20.0	10.0	.100
Elm (White or American)	35.9	3,052	19.5	9.8	.102
Black Ash	35.2	2,992	19.1	9.6	.104
Red Maple (Soft Maple)	34.4	2,924	18.7	9.4	.106
Boxelder	32.9	2,797	17.9	8.9	.112
Jack Pine	31.4	2,669	17.1	8.5	.118
Norway Pine	31.4	2,669	17.1	8.5	.118
Hemlock	29.2	2,482	15.9	7.9	.127
Black Spruce	29.2	2,482	15.9	7.9	.127
Aspen	27.0	2,295	14.7	7.3	.137
White Pine	26.3	2,236	14.3	7.2	.139
Balsam Fir	26.3	2,236	14.3	7.2	.139
Cottonwood	24.8	2,108	13.5	6.7	.149
Basswood	24.8	2,108	13.5	6.7	.149
N. White Cedar	22.5	1,913	12.2	6.1	.164

(1) Density = Weight and volume at 20% moisture content.
(2) Conversion Factors: at 20% moisture content, there are approximately 6400 BTUs per pound of wood.
By Lewis T. Hendricks, Extension Specialist, Forest Products, University of Minnesota.

COMPARISON OF ENERGY SOURCES FOR HEATING

Fuel	Unit	Heating Efficiency	Heating Values 1000's of BTUs Per Unit Total	Available(4)	Units Needed To Give 1,000,000 BTUs of Available Heat
Natural Gas	mcf(1)	70%	1,000	700	1.43(4)
#1 Fuel Oil (Kerosene)	gallon	65%	135	87.8	11.4
#2 Fuel Oil	gallon	65%	141	91.7	10.9
Propane	gallon	70%	91	63.7	15.7
Electricity	KWH	100%	3.413	3.413	293
Coal					
Anthracite	ton	60%	25,400	15,240	0.066
High-Volatile Bituminous C	ton	60%	22,000	13,200	0.076
Low-Volatile Bituminous	ton	60%	28,600	17,160	0.058
Lignite	ton	60%	13,800	8,280	0.12
Charcoal	pound	60%	13	7.8	128
Wood					
Aspen	cord(2)	50%	14,700(3)	7,300	0.137
Jack Pine	cord	50%	17,100	8,500	0.118
Paper Birch	cord	50%	20,300	10,200	0.098
White Oak	cord	50%	25,700	12,800	0.078

(1) Thousand Cubic Feet
(2) 128 Cubic Feet
(3) Assuming 85 Cubic Feet of Solid Wood Per Cord At 20% Moisture Content.
(4) For Other Efficiencies: AVAILABLE HEAT = TOTAL HEAT X EFFICIENCY
    UNITS NEEDED = 1,000,000 ÷ AVAILABLE HEAT.

By: Lewis T. Hendricks
    Extension Specialist, Forest Products
    University of Minnesota

Section 18

Appliances and Lighting

GENERAL

The electrical power drawn by home appliances and lighting systems account for between 35 and 45 percent of the total electrical consumption of a home. Very meaningful energy savings (and thus dollar savings) can be realized by careful purchase selection and use of appliances and lighting systems.

APPLIANCES

The major appliances, on a national average, use up to 28 percent of the electricity consumed in a home with the minor appliances accounting for an additional six percent.

Refrigerator	18%
Food Freezer	6%
Clothes Dryer	4%
Minor Appliances	6%
Total	34%

Refer to piegraph figure, page 9-7

The electrical power used by garbage disposals, mixers and blenders, can openers, trash compactors, meat slicers and other such small appliances is relatively small. Within this group, any savings in electrical use can be gained only by careful use. Careful purchase selection as to energy conservation is indicated as related to the dishwasher and clothes washer and the major appliances (refrigerator, food freezer and clothes dryer).

Dishwasher

The dishwasher consumes very little electricity during the washing and rinsing cycles, drawing heavy power only during the drying cycle. Many tests have shown that the dishes will dry quickly and properly without going into the dryer cycle if the door is opened after the last rinse cycle. Newer model dishwashers feature an "energy-saver" switch that can be set to turn off the heaters during the drying cycle, leaving the blower motor running to exhaust the moisture. With such units, the door need not be opened to exhaust the moisture-laden air. If a "powerless drying" cycle

is used, the dishwasher will consume only a low level of electricity and, since it is very efficient as to hot-water use, can actually be less expensive as to energy use than hand washing and rinsing.

The temperature of the water in the hot-water tank can be lowered to as low as 120°F for proper and safe use in the kitchen and bathrooms but should be 130°F for dishwashing. Thus, it is recommended that the dishwasher should have a heater that turns on to boost the water temperature. With such a unit, the thermostat on the hot-water tank can be set to 125°F to realize excellent energy savings while still washing and rinsing dishes at a safe water temperature.

For energy-efficient use of dishwashers, refer to "Dishwasher," page 21-3, Section 21.

Clothes Washer

The clothes washer consumes relatively little electricity during the washing and rinsing cycles. If the hot water used by the clothes washer is heated by electricity, considerable savings of electricity can be gained if the clothes washer features hot-water saving washing and rinsing cycles and permits water-level selection for light, medium and heavy loads. With the newer clothes washing soap powders, clothes may be washed and rinsed in cold water if the clothes are not excessively dirty (soiled with oil, grease, etc.). The newer models of dishwashers thus provide for cold wash-cold rinse, warm wash-cold rinse, warm wash-warm rinse, hot wash-warm rinse and hot wash-hot rinse cycles. These units also feature load selection on the basis of light, medium and high loads with corresponding savings in water used.

For energy-efficient use of clothes washers, refer to "Clothes Washer," page 21-3, Section 21.

Clothes Dryer

A gas-fired clothes dryer is about 2.5 times more efficient basically than an electrically-heated dryer. A gas dryer should thus be purchased over an electric model if gas is available at the house site. In either case (gas or electrical model), energy waste relates to overdrying. That is, the dryer is set to operate for a longer time period than actually required to dry the clothes. Newer clothes dryers feature a humidity switch that constantly checks the humidity within the dryer. As the clothes dry, the humidity level drops until it reaches the preset humidity level. At that point the dryer is turned off, the clothes are dry and are not "overly" dry and energy has been saved. A clothes dryer featuring the humidity switch is thus highly recommended.

For energy-efficient use of clothes dryers, refer to "Clothes Dryers," page 21-4, Section 21.

Food Freezer

An energy-efficient food freezer features thick insulation, magnetic weatherstripping and an efficient cooling mechanism. Generally speaking, the thicker the insulation in the walls, floor and lid (or door) of the unit, the less electrical power will be required to maintain the required internal temperature. Magnetic weatherstripping is standard on all high-quality food freezers and is very efficient.

For energy-efficient use of the food freezer, refer to "Refrigerator-Freezer," Page 21-1, Section 21.

Refrigerator

The refrigerator uses, as a national average, up to 18 percent of the electricity consumed in a home. Fortunately, refrigerator manufacturers are now actively redesigning their units for improved energy efficiency. This redesign is highlighted by a refrigerator series just now appearing on the market. Under "standard" test conditions, the manufacturer states their 16 cubic-foot model, as an example, uses only 48 killowatt-hours per month (48 KWH). This contrasts against other 16 cubic-foot models of comparable quality which use as high as 200 KWH per month. Two representative 16 cubic-foot models, tested under the same conditions, used 137 KWH and 179 KWH per month. The energy efficient model costs between $100.00 and $125.00 more than a comparable-quality model of the same size and with the same features. With the national average for electricity now 3.5 cents per KWH, the savings are:

Model	KWH Used Per Month	Monthly Cost	Yearly Cost	Yearly Savings	Payback Time
A	48	$1.68	$20.16		
B	137	$4.80	$57.60	$37.44	3.34 yrs
C	179	$6.27	$75.24	$55.08	2.26 yrs

1976 average KWH cost = 3.5 cents

Raising of the energy-efficiency level is gained by using thicker insulation in the walls and doors of the unit and by improving the cooling mechanism itself. The use of magnetic weatherstripping is now about standard. This method of keeping the cold air within the unit from leaking out through the door opening is ideal but it does have one drawback. Under certain levels of humidity the weatherstripping can actually freeze solid to the door facing. To avoid this problem heater strips have been built into the unit walls to heat the weatherstripping. This is, of course, a waste of energy. New thinking now reveals that the heaters need only be activated when the humidity level is critical. Since this will not happen if the home is air conditioned or heated (the humidity level is automatically reduced to a "safe" level), the heater strips need to be activated only when the house is not air conditioned and door sticking indicates the humidity is a problem. Thus, newer refrigerator models provide a switch to permit control of the heater strips. The energy savings has been found to be considerable.

For energy-efficient use of a refrigerator, refer to "Refrigerator-Freezer", Page 21-1, Section 21.

LIGHTING

Home lighting uses, as a national average, up to 11 percent of the electricity consumed in a home. Most experts consider that with proper design and use, a savings of 50 percent can be realized. This reduction in electricity use can be brought about as follows:

- Optimize use of natural light. Careful placement of windows and skylights can brighten a room during the daytime, thus eliminating the need for day-time lighting. However the gain in light must be balanced against the heat loss or gain associated with windows and skylights. North-facing windows and skylights admit the best light.

- Use light colors. Light-colored paint or paneling on the inside walls and under the soffit reflect more light than dark-colored items and thus reduce or even eliminate the need for daytime lighting. In addition, the light-colored walls will reflect a maximum of artificial light and thus will permit the illumination of the room to be raised to a required level with less total candle power than if dark colors were used.

- Plan lighting system for optimum energy efficiency. The light level (total candle power) required for a particular room or area is directly related to the normal activity of the room or area. For example,

machine sewing	requires 50 foot candles
formal dining	requires 15 foot candles
hand sewing, food preparation, reading, etc.	requires 150-200 foot candles

Too bright a room is tiring to the eyes and wasteful of energy while too dark a room is dangerous to the eyes and must be avoided. Most room lighting today is in the form of spot lighting. That is, where light is obtained in a small given area from a table or floor lamp or a wall lamp—each used only as needed for added illumination.

A 100-watt incandescent lamp, burning for 10 hours, uses 11,600 BTU's or the equivalent of 1 pound of coal or one-half pint of oil. A higher-wattage bulb will develop the needed light level. A single 100-watt bulb actually develops more light than two 50-watt bulbs. This specifies that a single bulb of the proper wattage is more efficient than two bulbs totalling the same wattage.

Fluorescent lighting is highly efficient, developing from three to five times the lumens (light power) developed by a same-wattage incandescent bulb. Fluorescent lighting is particularly useful in the kitchen, bathrooms, service area, basement and garage. Also, fluorescent lights (tubes) last a great deal longer than incandescent bulbs, up to five times the life period and more. Fluorescent tubes whose output closely approximates natural light should be used.

Where fluorescent tubes are used in a dropped-ceiling over a kitchen area, the box area containing the tubes should be painted with the brightest, whitest and most glossy white paint obtainable. All too often the contractor does not paint the sheet rock facing the box area. This results in a dark cast to the light while all too much is absorbed by the grey-colored sheet rock.

Section 19

Heating and Cooling Systems

GENERAL

The energy required to heat and/or cool a home can be considerable, ranging from 25 to 50 percent (or more) of the total yearly energy bill depending upon the following:

- Local climatic conditions
- Available fuel and its energy efficiency
- Energy-efficiency level of home
- Proper-sized capacity
- Ducting system used

Since heating and cooling a home is very expensive at current energy costs and will be more expensive in the future, extra thought and extreme care should be taken to ensure that the "very best" air conditioning system is installed in the home. Generally, the selection of the air conditioning system is left up to the building contractor. Yet, this is *not always wise* since you and the building contractor may see the matter from almost opposite viewpoints—he, for economy of equipment and installation and you, for long-range fuel and maintenance economy with ideal home comfort.

EQUIPMENT SELECTION

The importance of selecting just the right air conditioning system for your new home cannot be overemphasized, since the "perfect" system can mean so much as to energy efficiency and home comfort. The building contractor, because of past building experience and habits and/or a desire to reduce costs, may suggest a "less-than-desirable" air conditioner for the following reasons:

- Least expensive unit, considering cost without much consideration for energy economy and long-term trouble-free operation.
- Least expensive installation, particularly as to return-air ducting—resulting in less efficient operation and a reduction in home comfort.

- Out-of-date selection—does not keep up with new features.
- Customary oversizing of unit—based on an incorrect belief that an over-sized unit is better.

Agreed—how can you, a non-student of air conditioners, determine if your building contractor is selecting the very best heating and/or cooling system for your home? Where can you go to get non-biased, factual and up-to-date information? The answer—contact your local gas and electric companies. Most gas and electric companies have experts whose task is to assist you, a potential customer, in the selection of heating and/or cooling equipment that will operate with maximum energy efficiency. This service is free and is highly recommended. If your heating fuel is oil, perhaps your oil supplier has a similar service.

Even if expert help is available from your oil, gas or electric companies, some self-education as to heating and cooling systems would be advisable. For example, how efficient is your present system, how has it compared with that used by others in your immediate area? Further, a visit to a well-established company selling and installing heating and cooling systems could be most informative since such companies will certainly keep up to date on recent developments and advancements in their field.

You might consider, for example, having your building contractor bid the house with and without the heating and cooling system installed. This will give you the approximate amount the building had allotted for the system(s). You should then ask your builder to discuss with you, over the house plans, how he plans to install the system(s). You can then call several well-established air-conditioning firms, make an appointment for a bid session (determining first there will not be a fee), take along your house plans, and discuss the whole system. Get at least two bids and compare them against each other and that of the building contractor for energy efficiency versus total cost today against the long-time savings related to energy efficiency.

Your talks with the building contractor and the air-conditioning contractor will have more meaning to you and you will be able to ask more searching questions if you have a basic understanding of what constitutes an energy-efficient heating and cooling system. The basic facts to follow are just that—basic facts—and are given only to enlarge your knowledge of air conditioning systems to the end you may ask questions and understand the answers based on some knowledge of the air-conditioning field. It is hoped that this basic information plus your talks with the building contractor and air-conditioning contractors will guide you to the selection of a heating and/or cooling system that will operate efficiently and assure a high level of home comfort.

BASIC FACTS - HEATING SYSTEMS

Heating by natural gas is the most efficient (least expensive) means of heating at present. Yet, with the ever increasing cost for natural gas and the very real possibility of future cutbacks and extreme shortages, gas heating may be much more expensive in the near future and unreliable as to delivery. Gas-fired furnaces are considered to operate at 80-percent efficiency when operating full time or nearly full time.

Oil-fired, hot-air furnaces are considered to operate at 70% efficiency when operating full time or nearly full time. Coal-fired furnaces have an average efficiency rating of 65%, this being somewhat dependent upon the method of feeding the firebox and the quality of the coal used.

All automatically controlled gas-fired or oil-fired furnaces should be equipped with an automatic electronic ignition switch, suitably equipped with a flame-failure safety switch to prevent fuel flow if the ignition system fails. Pilot lights consume, on a yearly basis, a rather large volume of fuel most wastefully. If a pilot-light system is used, the pilot light should be turned off for the summer (non-heating) period, when going on vacation, etc.

Heat pumps are a very efficient electric-powered heat source, delivering up to 2.5 times the heat per unit of electricity (KWH) than that delivered by an electric-strip furnace. A heat pump is such an efficient heating system it is actually nearly competitive fuel-wise to a gas-fired furnace, this depending upon the severity of the winter in the house locale and the local cost of natural gas versus the KWH cost.

Table 19-1. Energy Costs vs Fuel Type

Electricity (Strip Heating)	-	$\dfrac{3,240,000 \text{ BTU's}}{3412 \text{ BTU's per KW} \times 1.0 \text{ effic.}}$	= 950 KWH
Electricity (Heat Pump)	-	$\dfrac{3,240,000 \text{ BTU's}}{3412 \text{ BTU's per KW} \times 2.25 \text{ effic.}}$	= 422 KWH
Natural Gas	-	$\dfrac{3,240,000 \text{ BTU's}}{1000 \text{ BTU's per cf} \times 0.80 \text{ effic.}}$	= 4050 cf
Coal	-	$\dfrac{3,240,000 \text{ BTU's}}{12500 \text{ BTU's per lb} \times 0.65 \text{ effic.}}$	= 399 bls
Oil	-	$\dfrac{3,240,000 \text{ BTU's}}{140000 \text{ BTU's per gal} \times .7 \text{ effic.}}$	= 33 gals

For additional details on the heating (and cooling) efficiency of a heat pump, refer to "Heat Pumps", page 19-6.

The heat loss through a 1500-square foot wall (insulated to an R20 value) of a house located in Austin, Texas calculates out to 3,240,000 BTU's per year. (See Section 6, "Measuring Heat Loss or Gain" for details). The cost to replace the lost heat using electricity, natural gas, oil or coal is given by Table 19-1.

Using the average unit price for fuels in Austin, Texas during 1978, the heating costs would be:

Electricity, Heat Strip	= 950 KWH x 4.7¢ per KWH	= $44.65
Electricity, Heat Pump	= 422 KWH + 4.7¢ per KWH	= $19.83
Natural Gas	= 4050 cu ft x 0.0308¢	= $12.47
Fuel Oil	= 33 gallons x 45¢	= $14.85

The national average per KWH during 1976 was 4.7 cents. The heat pump charge would thus be $19.83 or not much more than the gas cost. However, note the assumed efficiency (SPF) rate of 2.25 holds only for areas experiencing rather moderate winters (seldom below 25°F). For additional details, refer to "Heat Pumps", page 19-6.

Proper use of the thermostat for heating control is essential both for energy-saving and equipment-life reasons. For details, refer to "Thermostats", page 19-4.

BASIC FACTS - COOLING SYSTEMS

Almost all home-cooling systems used today are of the refrigerant type; only a very few being cooled by water-absorption or gas-absorption systems. The measure of efficiency of a refrigerant-type air conditioner is its Energy Efficiency Rating (EER). The EER is simple to calculate, being:

$$\text{EER} = \frac{\text{BTU's of heat removed from air}}{\text{Watts used to power unit}} = \frac{37,000,000 \text{ BTU's}}{4,625,000} = 8$$

Obviously, the higher the EER number, the greater the system efficiency and thus the greater the energy (and dollar) savings. Today, an EER of 7 should be considered as a minimum value for a unit to be considered as efficient. Many cities now specify an EER of 6 or 7 as a minimum.

Since an air conditioning unit has an anticipated life of at least 15 years, energy efficiency should be considered over first cost. However, cost effectiveness must be kept in mind. For example, a recent unit on the market advertises an EER of 10—most excellent but, the equipment cost is nearly double that of a comparable quality unit with an EER of 7. On the other hand, the cost difference between an EER7 and an EER8 unit may be between $100.00 to $150.00. A heat pump, operating as a cooler, generally has an EER of 8. However, its excellence as a heater more than compensates for its moderate EER value.

The decision as to what level of EER to choose will be largely dependent upon the cost difference over less efficient (lower EER) models, the number of hours the unit will operate per summer, and the present and anticipated cost of electricity in the house locale. With the future cost of electricity so uncertain and with the very real possibility that some form of rationing may be imposed on electrical use in the very near future, care in selection of a unit with an EER of at least 7 is highly recommended.

Proper use of the thermostat with an air conditioning system is essential both for energy-saving and equipment-life reasons. For details, refer to "Thermostats", page 19-4.

DUCTING AND VENTS

The purchase of an efficient heating and/or cooling system must be complimented by installation of a well-designed and well-insulated ducting and vent system if true energy efficiency as to heating and/or cooling is to be achieved.

The first consideration in duct-vent design relates to the climatic conditions in the house locale. That is, will the ducts be used for heating purposes only, for cooling only, or for both heating and cooling to a certain degree. An entirely different forced-air output to return-air system is needed if the system is to be used for heating mainly or for cooling mainly. This difference is based upon the fact that warm air (since it is expanded and light) tends to rise while cool air falls (since it is contracted and thus dense).

If heating is the main problem, the forced-air outlets must be at floor level, preferably located against the outer wall (generally in line with the windows). The warm air will thus flow up the walls and over the windows to warm the coldest part of the house—that part in direct contact with the cold outside. Forced-air vents placed high on the walls or in the ceiling would be rather inefficient since the warm air would not be forced all the way down to floor level unless a very high air-flow action is used. Such an air flow could produce very high and uncomfortable drafts. The return-air vents for a heating-mainly system should be located high in the inner walls or in the ceiling near the inner walls. Such a location captures the hot air as it rises and returns it to the furnace in maximum amount.

If cooling is the main problem, the ideal duct-vent system would be the exact opposite of the ideal system for heating. That is, the forced-air vents should be placed high on an inner wall or in the ceiling near an inner wall. The return-air vents should be placed low in the outside wall or in the floor against the outside wall. For climatic conditions where both heating and cooling is required, an acceptable compromise must be made. This compromise must favor the "greatest use," be it either heating or cooling.

For a "heating-only" system within a house built over a sealed and insulated crawl space foundation, warmer floors and increased heating efficiency can be gained by using the crawl-space itself as the forced-air duct. Users of this method state an energy saving of from 10 to 15 percent can be realized on the heating bills and that increased comfort is

gained since the floors are always kept warm. For further information, refer to "Crawl-Space Foundations," page 10-2, Section 10.

Using the crawl-space as a forced-air duct is not recommended for delivery of cold air to floor vents as detailed for heating-only above. Cold air, being heavy, would require considerably higher air pressure to be forced across the underfloor area and up the floor vents. This would impose a severe strain on the air handler (fan) and would generally result in poor distribution of cooled air within the house.

A sealed and insulated crawl space can be used as a return-air plenum for a cooling-only system. A crawl-space cannot be efficiently used as a return-air plenum for hot air since it will be most difficult to draw hot air (which tends to rise) downwards from within the rooms without using a very high fan action.

For concrete-slab foundation, special care must be taken to insulate the duct work buried in the concrete from physical collapse under the weight of poured concrete and to prevent heat loss or gain from the slab itself. Duct work run in the attic must be well insulated to isolate the duct air from the attic temperature. If possible, the forced-air duct system should be run inside the air-conditioned part of the house. If so run, the ducts need not be insulated except for sound purposes (if desired).

In the majority, houses built on slab foundation usually do not provide return-air ducts within the slab itself. Instead, the air conditioner is closet-mounted in the living area, with large filtered vents being placed in the closet walls facing the living area. The air return is then just a gentle, slow movement of air from within the entire house back to the air handler in the closet. This system is relatively efficient, especially if a vent is provided in the closet walls to each separate area of the living space. That is, the air-conditioner closet should be centrally located so that a wall vent in the closet will pull air back from the living and sleeping areas. Note that this method must not be used if a gas-fired or oil-fired furnace is used.

MULTI-LEVEL AND SPLIT-LEVEL AIR CONDITIONING

Multi-level and split-level homes present a special air-conditioning problem. That is, hot air tends to rise and cold air tends to fall. Thus, in the winter time the hot air from the downstairs portion(s) will flow up the stairway to make the upper portion(s) much warmer than the downstairs area whose temperature may drop to a below-comfort level. In the summer time, the air flow reverses with the cold air from upstairs flowing down to the lower level(s). The upstairs may then be comfortable while the lower level(s) are too cold.

A fairly acceptable temperature balance throughout a multi-level or split-level home can be achieved as follows:

1. In the winter time, shut off one or two of the forced-air vents in the upper level of the home. Warm air from the lower level(s), flowing up the stairway, will act as a replacement.

   In the summer time, shut off one or two of the forced-air vents in the lower level(s) of the house. The cold air from the upper level, flowing down the stairway, will act as a replacement.

2. If the fan on the air handler can be set for continuous operation, this should be done. The air from all levels will then be constantly recirculated and a more even temperature will be realized throughout the house.

COMBUSTION AIR INPUT TO FURNACES

At one time it was thought that the combustion air for a gas or oil fired furnace should be taken from the air-conditioned area. With the recent sharp rise in energy costs came a re-evaluation of energy efficiency of fuel-fired furnaces. Efficiency tests have shown quite clearly that the old habit of taking the combustion air directly from the air-conditioned area is completely wrong. The slight drop in heat development brought about when cooler exterior air is brought into the combustion chamber is more than compensated for by not having to use already-heated air from within the house. It is now highly recommended that a duct (pipe) or flue system be used to bring air from outside the air-conditioned space to the combustion chamber of any fuel-fired furnace.

The required use of exterior air thus dictates that the furnace should not be located in the air-conditioned area. If the furnace must be located in the air-conditioned area, the unit should be mounted in a closet with a tight fitting door to prevent drawing air from within the house into the closet. Air can then be drawn up through a floor opening (crawl space or basement foundation) or by means of ducting (slab foundation). Note that if the crawl-space area is used as a plenum, the furnace must not be allowed to use underfloor air for combustion. In this case, air must be brought in by a duct from the outside.

THERMOSTATS

The thermostat controls the air conditioning system and has, with the advent of the energy crisis, assumed a greater importance as to the operational efficiency and longevity of the system. A well designed thermostat should perform as follows:

- Control ON and OFF cycling on a wide range of temperature differences rather than over a narrow range. Most people can tolerate a temperature difference of between 3° and 5° without discomfort. That is, if the thermostat is set for 72°F, a slow drop in room temperature down to about 68°F would not be noticed. A slow rise to about 76°F would also be virtually unnoticeable.

- If a thermostat acts to turn the heater or cooler ON and OFF

over a 3° to 5° temperature change rather than a 2° change, the heater or cooler will cycle less often. This is of particular importance in relation to a heater since all fuel-fired furnaces operate at peak efficiency when used full time. Thus, it is better for the heater to turn on less often and run longer. Also, the fewer times a heater or cooler cycles on and off, the longer the trouble-free life of the equipment.

- During the summer there are times when a house can be cooled to an acceptable degree by merely moving the air throughout the house with the windows and doors opened. Also, for multi-level and split-level homes, constant air circulation between the upstairs and downstairs areas may be required to equalize air temperature throughout the house. Thus, it would be an advantage if the thermostat has a switch that permits the fan to be set to run on a continuous basis while the thermostat can still control the air conditioner as dictated by the temperature setting.

The thermostat must be carefully positioned to ensure good comfort-level operation. The unit should be located away from any heat source such as lamps, TV, radios, etc. preferably being mounted about half-way up the wall in an area generally not affected by drafts, etc.

Many studies in depth have shown that meaningful savings as to both heating and cooling costs can be realized if the thermostat is:

(1) Winter time — set back by 10°F or more during the sleeping hours.

(2) Summer time — set up by 5°F or more during the sleeping hours.

(3) Winter or summer time — set back or up by 10°F or more during any time the house is unoccupied.

The savings realized for a 10°F nighttime setback and a 5°F daytime setup for various cities is given by Table 19-2. The savings are considerably higher (up to 75% more) if the thermostat is set back or up during the time a house is unoccupied during the day (usually).

Table 19-2. Thermostat Setback/Up Savings

CITY	HEATING-Night set back 10°F	COOLING-Day set up 5°F
ATLANTA	15%	10%
CHICAGO	11%	16%
DALLAS	15%	8%
LOS ANGELES	16%	20%
MINNEAPOLIS	9%	9%
PITTSBURGH	11%	10%
ST. LOUIS	12%	10%
SEATTLE	12%	9%

The thermostat, of course, can be adjusted manually to raise or lower the point the furnace or air conditioner turns on and off. This is rather a bother and requires that someone must rise earlier to turn the thermostat up or down to the "normal" temperature. Fortunately, many automatic thermostats are on the market now and more are scheduled to appear this Fall. Units can be obtained that will, at a preset time, raise or lower the temperature point at which the furnace or cooler will cycle on and off. Then, after a preset period, the unit will return thermostat control back to the "normal" temperature point. Such a unit is called a "two-step" unit. Other units are called a "four-step" unit and can, in addition, be set to raise or lower the thermostat control point at a precise time related to the period the house will not be occupied. After a preset time period, the unit will then return thermostat control to the "normal" temperature. This period might be from 8 AM to 4 PM.

Units are available that can be set to perform the two-step or four-step function on a 5-day, 6-day or 7-day week basis as related to the "house unoccupied" steps. Other units can be set to lower or raise the thermostat control point and to return control to normal after the passage of as much as 100 days. Still others alternately display the time and house temperature on a digital display while others feature a battery operated clock to ensure clock operation during any period of power loss. Most units provide a switch to restore "normal" operation when desired.

Most units advertise "simple installation, using existing thermostat wiring". Others may require installing two or three new small-guage wires to permit full control to be gained. All control wiring is low voltage (12 to 18 volts) and is not considered dangerous though precautions against grounding oneself while making the connections should be taken. Opening the circuit breakers (two are often used) is recommended before installing a new thermostat.

Heat pumps (to be discussed) present a particular problem in that they are designed to turn on a supplemental heat source (oil, gas or electricity) if the heat pump cannot hold house temperature to the desired point. However, certain of the multi-function thermostats now available operate to inhibit the supplemental heat source during the period the heat pump is running to return room temperature from the setback point to the "normal" point. Thus, if a heat pump is used, be certain the thermostat selected is designed to operate with a heat pump on a heating-cycle basis.

Costs range from a low of about $40.00 (simple two-step model) to a high of $200.00. The savings realized will vary dependent upon the climatic conditions of the house locale, the degree of thermostat set back or set up, and the time period of the setback or setup period. Manufacturer's literature suggests energy-cost savings as high as 30% for heating and 20% for cooling. Further ad statements suggest a payback period of as little as one season (winter or summer). For the most expensive heating system (electric-strip heating), a payback time of one year is clearly possible for a unit costing not over $200.00. For gas or oil heating in conjunction with electric air conditioning, a payback time of two years or less for a $200.00 or less unit can be anticipated.

The energy-dollars saved on both a heating and cooling basis by thermostat set back or set up from 65°F (heating season) and 78°F (cooling season) can be calculated from the data illustrated by Figure 19-1.

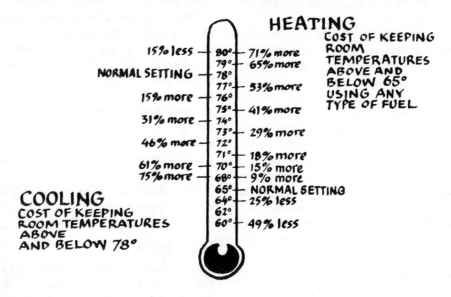

Figure 19-1. Temperature to Operate Cost Relationship

UNIT SIZING

The heater and/or cooler for a house must be most carefully sized. Basically, rather exact calculations as to heat loss (winter) or heat gain (summer) must be run up on each house as an individual unit. The results on a heat-loss basis are then used to size the heating source while the heat-gain figure is used to size the cooler. These calculations are rather complex and an explanation of the method is outside the scope of this manual. The calculations can be run up by your heating and cooling contractor or you can (in some areas) have it run up for you by your local fuel supplier (gas and electric company, mainly).

However, it should be noted here that even the "experts" cannot agree upon how to make ther actual load calculations; one group favoring a certain form and method and another group favoring a somewhat different form and method. Then too, much of the factoring material is out of date in line with the newer concept of how to build and equip an energy-saver home using the newest of materials and building methods. And further, the experts almost always tend to oversize a unit rather than to install a more practical size. In actual fact, it is more economical of energy use and first-cost to install a slightly undersized unit than to install an oversized unit.

Few air-conditioning contractors have had any real experience with a house designed and built to achieve a really high level of energy efficiency. In particular, the "experts" just won't believe the very great reduction in heat loss or gain that can be achieved by a properly designed and equipped house. The whole new concept is just coming into general knowledge and many building contractors, air-conditioning contractors, etc. will require updating of their basic understanding of house building and the related air-conditioning requirements.

It is thus felt that it will be difficult to find a building contractor and/or an air-conditioning contractor that are truly "up to date" and can accurately size the air conditioning requirements of the house. Remember, the American Institute of Architects states "a savings of up to 80 percent can be gained if a house is properly equipped and constructed." It is thus recommended that you discuss your air-conditioning requirements with several "experts"—such as air-conditioning contractors and those at your gas and electric company, and consider installing the equipment related to the "smallest-size" calculations rather than one that indicates oversizing. Knowledgeable experts have recommended installation of a 2-ton cooling unit when "old-time" experts felt a 3 or 3½ ton unit was minimum, etc.

In general, two capacity sizing are required. These are:

- *Air Handler* - sized to provide the proper air pressure through the forced-air duct system to assure all rooms receive a proper flow of conditioned air. Plus, enough fan size to pull back air through the duct system (or centrally-located intake) to ensure a good air-return movement within the house. The fan size will thus relate to the cubic feet of air required to be moved efficiently.

- *Heating Unit* - must be sized to have just sufficient capacity to replace lost heat at the rate determined by the load calculations. For an oil or gas fired furnace, maximum efficiency is gained when the unit operates for a relatively long period when turned on rather than cycling on and off quickly. An extension of the life span of the unit is also gained when the unit is operated less often. This specifies that a bit undersized is better than a bit oversized.

  For an electric-strip heater, sufficient resistive heaters must be installed to develop the maximum heat determined by the heat-load calculations. The power cabling to the resistor strips should be of sufficient capacity to allow additional resistive heaters to be installed (if found necessary under actual living conditions).

- *Heating Unit-Heat Pump* - if a heat pump is used for heating and cooling, it must be sized for the maximum use period: heating or cooling. For additional details, refer to "Heat Pumps," this section.

- *Cooling Unit* - must be sized to remove the required amount of heat (BTU's) to maintain acceptable living comfort. Oversizing of the cooling unit is all too common, the theory being "if the calculations call for a 3-ton unit, 4 tons would be better and 5 tons won't hurt." This thinking is definitely outmoded and must not be followed. If the exact tonnage compressor required by the cooling calculations (as a minimum) is not manufactured, the next lower rating should be chosen rather than the next higher-sized unit.

For information sake, 1 ton of air conditioning is needed to remove 12,000 BTU's of heat from the house air per hour.

Homes with large living space may require zoning of the heating and/or cooling equipment. That is, two units (or more) may be required if smaller units (which may be individually controlled) can be used more efficiently than one large unit. Alternately, the house may be designed to be easily "divided" into a living area and a sleeping area with an air-conditioning system provided for each area. When an area is zoned, the total capacity of the provided units may exceed the calculated whole-house capacity because air-conditioning systems are not manufactured in equal-steps as to capacity.

For additional details on air-conditioning zoning, refer to "Air-Conditioning Zoning", page 9-2, Section 9.

HEAT PUMPS

The heat pump is both a heating and a cooling system. It is called a "heat pump" because it is designed to *pump heat* into the house in the winter and to *pump heat* out of the house in the summer. Basic operation of a heat pump as a heater and as a cooler is illustrated by Figure 19-2.

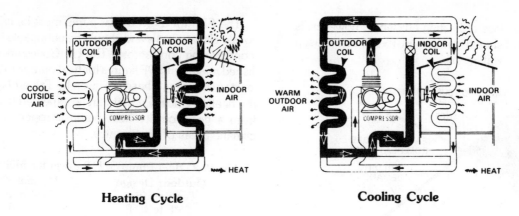

Heating Cycle   Cooling Cycle

Figure 19-2. Heat Pump — Operation Cycles

A heat pump is entered into the heating cycle when a valve reverses the flow of refrigerant between the indoor and outdoor coils. As the refrigerant is pumped through the outdoor coil, the coil is made cooler than the outdoor air by the refrigerant and thus acts to pick up heat from the air. The heat cycle is based upon the fact that heat exists in air down to –460°F. For example, 82% of the heat stored in 100°F air is still present when the air temperature has dropped to 0°F.

As the refrigerant absorbs heat through the outdoor coil, the liquid turns to gas. This gas is then pumped back through the compressor to the indoor coil being returned to a liquid in the process. The compression process in the indoor coil gives off the stored heat which is then blown by a fan through the duct system to the rooms to be heated. The cycle is then repeated.

A heat pump is changed from the heating cycle to the cooling cycle when the reversing valve is activated to reverse the flow of refrigerant between the outdoor and indoor coils. In this case, when the household air is blown past the indoor coil, the refrigerant picks up some of the heat from the air. The refrigerant turns to gas in the process. The gas is then pumped by the compressor to the outdoor coil, being compressed again into a liquid. In the process, the stored heat is released by the outdoor coil to the outside air. The liquid refrigerant is again pumped through the indoor coil and the process is repeated.

The above discussion points out that the heat pump is basically a reversible air conditioner. When heat pumps first appeared upon the market (about 1952), they were just that—basically a standard air conditioner with a reversing valve. In actual use, the early units had a very bad history of frequent failure and many troubles. Also, the early units were poorly understood by the service organizations and they were not built for really rugged service—that is, to operate in the summer as a cooler and in the winter as a heater. The heat pump operates on a double-use basis and thus the early units failed because they were not really designed for such usage.

The new units have been designed to be much more rugged and now have a life span and repair rate about equal to a comparable-quality "regular" air conditioner. In fact, most manufacturers now offer identical guarantees for their heat pumps and regular air conditioner units. Unfortunately, the past "bad" history of the heat pump is still remembered and causes some air conditioning contractors to be reluctant to handle and install heat pumps. Thus, if it is decided to use a heat pump, be certain the person who will install and maintain the unit specializes in heat pumps and is enthusiastic in relation to their use in the home.

The main benefits to heat-pump use for heating and cooling are:

- Can develop up to three units of heat for each dollar of electricity used. A test made at The University of Texas found that a home in Austin, Texas heated to 70°F by a heat pump used 1,900 KWH's per year against 4,800 KWH's required by an electric-strip heater. This resulted in an efficiency factor of 2.53 and a reported savings of $120.00 per winter.

- Provides both a heating and cooling unit in the same package, using the same duct and vent system.

Since the heat pump extracts heat from the outdoor air, as the outdoor air temperature drops, less heat is available in the air and thus the output of the heat pump will drop off in somewhat the same ratio. Dependent upon unit design and type of refrigerant used, if the outdoor temperature drops to a particular level the heat pump may not be able to develop enough heat to satisfy the thermostat setting. In brief, it will not be able to maintain the desired indoor temperature. This is known as the "balance point" and is illustrated by Figure 19-3. At this point, the heat pump acts to either turn on electric heat-strips built into the system or to turn on a gas or oil-fired furnace. When the outdoor temperature rises above the balance point, the heat pump senses this and turns off the auxiliary heat. The overall heat-producing efficiency of a heat pump is, of course, reduced in proportion to the time auxiliary heating must be used. This loss of heating efficiency, however, is generally minor and should not be considered as a reason for not installing a heat pump.

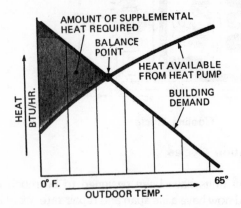

Figure 19-3. Supplemental Heat — Balance Point

The net heating-efficiency factor of a heat pump is known as SPF (Seasonal Performance Factor). The SPF is obtained from the following basic formula:

$$SPF = \frac{X}{Y + Z}$$

X = Heat developed, expressed in KWH
Y = KWH drawn by motors during winter
Z = Supplementary heat (if any) used by heat strips during winter, in KWH

If supplemental heating is never needed, the SPF figure will relate only to the electric power drawn by the heat-pump motors. This figure would be the same for any geographical area thus it is the power drawn by the supplemental heating system that will lower the SPF. This is indicated on a somewhat general basis by Figure 19-4.

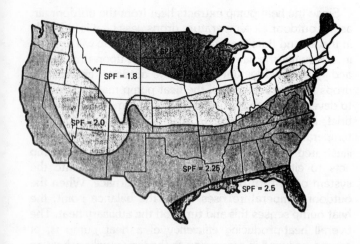

Figure 19-4. Seasonal Performance Factor Chart

The SPF for a given heat pump must be calculated on a locale-climate basis and should be obtainable from local air-conditioning contractors. The US Government has established *minimum* SPF figures for heat pumps to be installed in military housing. These are given by Table 19-3 and indicate the heating efficiency that can be expected (as a minimum) from a good quality heat pump as operating in various climatic areas of the country.

Table 19-3. Heat Pump SPF Ratings for Military Housing

Outdoor Design Temperature	Minimum SPF Permitted
35°F to 45°F	2.25
20°F to 34°F	2.00
1°F to 19°F	1.50
–20°F to 0°F	1.25

The table indicates that a home-size heat pump has an inherent heating efficiency ratio over an electric-strip heater of between 2.25 and 2.5 (in moderate winter areas) to 1.25 minimum (in areas of rather severe winters). The outdoor design temperature relates to the minimum outdoor temperature expected in the house locale. For Austin, Texas the design temperature is taken as 35°F, resulting in a minimum SPF of 2.25.

Further benefits of a heat pump:

- Heating cycle is very efficient and, in areas experiencing relatively mild winters, can be competitive to an oil-fired furnace and even a gas-fired furnace if gas cost is high and electricity costs are low.

- A safer and cleaner heating unit in that neither oil nor gas is used, also fuel storage for oil is not required and fire and carbon-monoxide fumes are not a problem.

- Changeover from heating to cooling can be completely automatic (accomplished by thermostat) or the changeover can be made manually at the thermostat by thermostat settings.

- Unit is identical in appearance and size to a "regular" air conditioning system and costs no more to install. Unit is not any noisier than a regular unit. The same duct and vent system is used for both heating and cooling.

Heat pumps do have some disadvantages. These are:

- Costs somewhat more (up to 20% more) than a *comparable-quality* "regular" all-electric heating-cooling system. When used instead of a gas or oil-fired heater, first cost can be less since fuel piping and venting is not required. Extra cost may run from $200.00 to $400.00 depending upon unit size.

- Since unit operates as both a heater and a cooler, unit is in service many more hours per year than a "regular" air conditioner. However, unit is built to higher performance (thus the extra cost) and new units have demonstrated equipment life spans about equal to "regular" units. Freedom from repairs is also about equal to "regular" units.

- As indicated by Table 19-3, the heat pump heating efficiency drops off as the outdoor temperature drops. Most heat pump units contain auxiliary heater strips which, dependent upon local climatic conditions and personal preference, can be set to come on automatically to help the heat pump maintain the desired indoor temperature. Of course, each time the auxiliary strips are turned on, the heating efficiency drops. However, auxiliary heat is generally required only enough to cause a possible maximum drop in efficiency of about 20% in areas experiencing severe winters.

- When the outdoor air temperature and humidity are at "critical" levels, the outdoor coil can freeze over. The unit senses this and goes into a reverse (cooling) cycle. The unit then extracts heat from the indoor air and exhausts it through the outdoor coil, causing the ice to melt. This cycle is usually very short, a minute or two and, on many units, automatically turns on an auxiliary heater strip to maintain indoor air temperatures.

- The refrigerant liquid used in the system is designed for maximum efficiency when used as a heating medium. This means the cooling efficiency (the EER) will be somewhat lower than that obtainable by a comparable-quality regular air conditioner. However, heat pumps with a possible SPF of 2.5 and an EER of 8+ are now on the market and are highly recommended. The efficiency difference between an EER7 heat pump and a regular unit with an EER8 figure is 12.5%. However, the winter-time savings (for an SPF of 1.5 or better climatic area) will more than compensate for the 12.5% difference in EER ratings. A discussion on this aspect follows.

All heat pumps detailed to this point operated by extracting heat from the outdoor air. Another type of heat pump is available that operates by extracting heat from water. This water can be obtained from the water mains (usually a prohibitively expensive source) or from underground or as piped up from a surface lake or stream. Underground water is the best heat source since it tends to stay at somewhat the same temperature, winter or summer. This is between 50°F and 60°F dependent upon the depth of the water source and the house area. Water from the water mains will generally be somewhat cooler dependent upon the depth of the pipes and the outdoor temperature. Water from lakes and streams will be the coldest but, if taken from a deep lake or stream, should never drop below 32°F.

A water-based heat pump is much more efficient than an air-based unit since it will never be operating with a heat source of less than 32°F. Supplemental heating should thus never be required. When operating with underground water, the constant 50-60°F water will permit the heat pump to extract a very large amount of heat at all times it is turned on. Units with an EER of 10.2 are available as a cooler and with a COP of as high as 3 (is three times as efficient as if electric-strip heating were used).

The units are generally smaller than the air-based units. When cooling is desired, the warm house air is circulated across a refrigerant coil which is maintained at 40°F by the refrigerant action. As the air passes over the coil it gives up its heat to the refrigerant. The refrigerant is then compressed (reaching a temperature of over 200°F) and then is pumped to a water-transfer coil where it gives up its heat to the water. The water then carries the heat away.

For the heating cycle, the events are reversed. Water is passed over the refrigerant coil, with the refrigerant absorbing heat from the water. The refrigerant is then compressed, developing a temperature of up to 200°F. The hot refrigerant is then pumped through the indoor coil, with the circulating air from the air handler carrying the heat through the duct system to the house area. Clearly, a most efficient system and one well worth looking into if one lives near an available water source such as a stream or lake or underground water is available at a reasonable depth.

The four-house energy-use comparison for heating and cooling given in Section 7 illustrates the heating efficiency of a heat pump. The energy (and dollar) savings enjoyed by House D (built to a much higher level of energy efficiency than FHA Min. Prop. Stds.) versus Houses A & B (upgraded somewhat from FHA Min. Prop. Stds.) are given by Table 19-4. The heating values used in the table were obtained from Table 7-1, Section 7.

Table 19-4. Heat Pump Heating Efficiency

House	Heating KWH Usage		House D KWH Usage		KWH Used Difference		House D Savings
A	*12,811	-	5,872	=	6939 @4.7¢		$326.13
B	* 9,534	-	5,872	=	3662 @4.7¢		$172.11
D	* 5,872						

*Jan, Feb, ½ Mar, ½ Oct, Nov. & Dec.
Figures from Table 7-1

House A vs House D - 12,811 vs 5,872 = House A used 2.18 times more electricity than House D. House D thus used 54% less power than House A.

House B vs House D = 9,534 vs 5,872 = House B used 1.62 times more electricity than House D. House D thus used 39% less power than House B.

The average efficiency of the heat pump (House D) versus the electric-strip heaters (Houses A & B) is 2.18 + 1.62/2 = 1.9 = 99%. The average savings is $249.12 per year.

Table 19-5. Heat Pump vs Electric-Strip Units

Assume: Heating BTU's per winter = 22,000,000
Cooling BTU's per summer = 35,000,000

$$\text{Total Heating KWH Electric-Strip} = \frac{\text{Total Heating BTU's}}{3412 \text{ BTU-s per KWH} \times 1.0 \text{ eff.}} = \frac{22,000,000}{3412} = 6448 \text{ KWH}$$

$$\text{Total Heating KWH} = \frac{\text{Total Heating BTU's}}{3412 \text{ BTU's per KWH} \times 2.1 \text{ eff.}} = \frac{22,000,000}{3412 \times 2.1} = 3070 \text{ KWH}$$

$$\text{Total Cooling KWH EER8 Unit} = \frac{\text{Total Cooling BTU's}}{8 \text{ BTU's per watt} \times 1000} = \frac{35,000,000}{8 \times 1000} = 4375 \text{ KWH}$$

$$\text{Total Cooling KWH EER9 Unit} = \frac{\text{Total Cooling BTU's}}{9 \text{ BTU's per watt} \times 1000} = \frac{35,000,000}{9 \times 1000} = 3889 \text{ KWH}$$

Cost

Electric-strip heating	= 6448	KWH	x	4.7¢	= $303.06
Heat-pump heating	= 3070	KWH	x	4.7¢	= $144.29
		Difference per year			= $158.77
EER8 unit - Cooling	= 4375	KWH	x	4.7¢	= $205.63
EER9 unit - Cooling	= 3889	KWH	x	4.7¢	= $182.78
		EER8 vs EER9 yearly difference			= $22.85
Heating Savings - Heat Pump					= $158.77
Cooling loss - EER8 vs EER9 difference					= -$22.85
Net savings, using a heat pump					= $135.92

Heat pumps can be obtained with an EER of 8 while a "regular" air conditioning unit may have an EER of 9 or higher. The heating efficiency of a heat pump with an EER of 8 is still much higher than that of an electric strip heating unit/air conditioning system with an EER of 9. This is detailed by table 19-5 above.

Many things enter into the decision as to whether or not to install a heat pump, some known now and some that can reasonably be expected to happen in the future. The two main points are: (1) ratio of heating needs to cooling needs for the home and (2) present and future cost and availability of gas and oil. The future availability of gas is considered to be most uncertain and its replacement with manufactured gas will result in much higher unit costs than today. Rationing or complete cutoff for short periods may be expected now and at an increasing rate and severity in the future. The availability of oil and its future cost is also uncertain and, like natural gas, may be subjected to rationing and complete cutoff at any time due to severe winter drains or cutoff or reduction of the import of foreign oil.

Today, a gas-fired or oil-fired furnace is the least expensive heating system as to fuel price and is clearly the best least-cost heating system for very cold areas (SPF of 1.50 or less). If the home is to be all-electric in an area with a minimum SPF of 1.50, a heat pump should be considered even if cooling is not a problem. The possible use of a heat pump in various climatic zones is given by Table 19-6.

Because of the uncertain availability of natural gas and oil in the near future, many home owners are building to heat on an all-electric basis. Electricity can be generated at acceptable unit cost (per KWH) whereas manufactured gas will be very costly. In fact, the unit cost may rise on manufactured gas to make even electric-strip heating less expensive. Thus, the heat pump is being considered, recommended and installed in ever increasing numbers as their energy-saving potential is understood by home buyers (and by home builders).

A heat pump is a quality unit and must be compared as to cost with a comparable-quality "regular" air conditioner and not against the cheapest (and shortest-life) unit available. On a comparable-quality basis, a heat pump should cost between $200.00 and $400.00 more than its equivalent in a "regular" unit. The dollar savings possible on the heating bill made possible by use of a heat pump will be somewhat dependent upon the number of hours of heating required in the house locale and the SPF figure associated with the climatic conditions of the locale (see Table 19-3). Of course, the dollar savings is versus an electric-strip furnace. The dollar savings can run up to "a $100.00 or more *per month*" in areas experiencing winter minimums of not under 20°F, with a winter-time temperature seldom dropping below 30-35°F returning the maximum dollar savings. The payback time for a heat pump over a "regular" air conditioner may then be as little as one winter and certainly within 5 years in any area with an SPF of 1.00 or better.

Table 19-6. Heat Pump Use vs Climatic Conditions

Climatic Area	Min. SPF	Hvy	Mod	Small	None	Hvy	Mod	Small	None	Heat Pump Suggested
Long winter-short summer. Many days below −20°F.	1.0	x						x		No (2) (1) (3)
		x							x	No. (1)
Long winter-short summer. Few days below −20°F.	1.25	x	x					x		No (2) (1) (3)
		x	x						x	No. (1)
Long winter-short summer. Few days below 1°F.	1.5	x	x					x		Yes (2) (3) (1)
Moderate winter & summer. Few days below 35°F.	2.0		x	x				x		Yes (1) (3)
			x	x					x	Yes (1)
Mild winters & mild, long summers	2.25			x				x	x	Yes (1) (3)
				x				x	x	No (4)
Mild winter & hot, long summers.	2.25+			x			x			No (3)
					x			x	x	No (4)

(1) yes - if gas, oil or coal-fired furnace is not desired or possible.
(2) no - if window air conditioners can be used.
(3) yes - if whole-house air conditioning is needed.
(4) no - as a "regular" air conditioner can be used, one having a high EER.

OTHER HEATING SYSTEMS

Houses in general are heated by gas-fired or oil-fired furnaces and these systems are, at least as of now, the least costly in terms of energy dollars. Many houses equipped with a central air conditioner use electric-strip heating while others use a heat pump. Several other heating systems are in use today. These are:

Radiant Ceiling Heat — Electric heater strips are imbedded in the ceiling plaster and act to heat the house on a radiant basis. This system is rather inefficient and is seldom used now that electric power is so expensive. It also takes a long time to warm a room up thus it can cause discomfort if the room temperature is set back at night or when the house is unoccupied. This because the recovery time is so long when "normal" control is restored to the thermostat.

Radiant Floor Heat — Electric heater strips are imbedded in the cement floor of a slab foundation. The comments given for radiant ceiling heat hold equally well for radiant floor heat. Neither system should be used in line with their inefficiency, slow recovery time, and high use of electricity.

Baseboard Heat — Electric heater strips are imbedded in a special plastic that can be installed along or just above the baseboard. The plastic pieces range in length from 3 to 10 feet and can be painted to blend into the room decor. Control on a room-by-room basis is possible and thus baseboard heating is sometimes used in individual rooms.

Hydronic (Hot-Water) System — a wall-mounted unit that heats water by electricity (or sometimes, gas). Room air is fan pumped past the water pipes, with the air being distributed through baseboard convectors. These can be painted to blend into the room decor and local control is possible. The system is not really efficient except as used on an occasional basis.

Wall Panel Heaters — generally gas-fired or electrical — the unit mounts in the wall (without penetrating the opposite side of the wall). The units are generally equipped with a fan, are moderately efficient (especially if gas is used) and permit heating of a given room on an individual basis.

Window-Mounted Air Conditioner — Window-mounted air conditioners can be obtained equipped with electric heater strips. Other units are heat pumps, operating with supplemental heater strips in the same fashion detailed for full-house units. If only 115 volt AC is available in a room, a heat pump will develop a greater amount of heat without overloading the electrical circuit than would be possible with a unit equipped with electric-strip heaters.

Free-Standing Fireplace or Stove — These units are becoming increasingly popular for use as bedroom or sitting room heat sources. For ease of operation and storage of fuel, a coal-burning unit is usually used. Do not oversize the unit, a small cast-iron burning coal will warm a rather large room with ease.

OTHER COOLING SYSTEMS

Evaporative Coolers — These units filter water through a screen-like material through which the house air is blown under fan control. The units are practical only for areas where water (of the required purity) is available at a low price (or is free). The units might develop too much humidity if used with a house with an air-infiltration rate of one change per hour or less. In general, the modern electrically-powered refrigerant air conditioning systems are more efficient and, as a bonus, act to lower the humidity level of the house.

Window-Mounted Air Conditioners — The modern refrigerant-type air conditioner, if used as a window-mounted unit, can cool a rather large room or even several rooms such as in an apartment. The cooling output can be very high, especially if 220-volt power is available in the room. However, even 115-volt units can cool a rather large room very efficiently. The newer units are rather quiet and generally are not considered to be "sleep disturbers".

Whole-House Ventilation — Many have installed whole-house fans and use same for most or the major part of their cooling needs. For details, refer to "Whole-House Ventilation", page 15-6.

AREA HEATING AND COOLING

In many homes, the occupants are finding it increasingly expensive to heat or cool the entire house. And, since very often large parts of a house may not be occupied (such as bedrooms during the day and the living-eating area at night) heating and cooling of these separate areas on a separate basis is commonly being practiced.

Some close all the vents in the bedroom during the daytime while opening those in the living area and at nighttime the living area vents are closed while the bedroom vents are opened. This is not really a very efficient system since the air-conditioning system is sized and powered to operate with a minimum amount of air-outlet area. Closing off too many vents can be damaging to the air-handler motor due to excessive backpressure. Then too, for the system to operate to an acceptable degree, the separate areas must be capable of being shut off from each other by doors. A house thus must be built with this need for area separation in mind if the whole-house air conditioning system is to be used on a zone basis. Of course, two air conditioners can be used, one for the living area and one for the sleeping area.

A suggested better method would be to provide "extra" heating and cooling facilities on an area basis. Such as any of the heating or cooling systems that can be controlled on a local (room or small area) basis. These could be: baseboard heat, hot-water system, wall-panel heater, free-standing fireplace or stove, and window-mounted air conditioner. The thought is — the whole-house unit is either turned down (winter time) or up (summer time) so that it keeps the living area of the house as much as 20°F different from the bedroom area when bedtime arrives. The smaller heating or cooling units can then be turned on individually to condition the room air to a desired temperature. The net usage of energy is then usually less than that which would have been used by the whole-house air conditioner if operating as "normal". If the whole-house air conditioner can be turned off completely during any period area air-conditioning is being used, a much greater energy savings will be realized. As a bonus, each room (or small area) could be held to the temperature desired by the occupant of that room or area — either higher or lower than that developed by the whole-house air conditioner.

House Orientation and Landscaping

GENERAL

Recent tests and studies conducted by progressive home builders, power and light companies, government agencies, universities and colleges, and others have produced some powerful facts as related to energy-saving home construction and existing-home upgrading as to energy efficiency. In total, the tests and studies reveal the potential for energy savings in new-home construction breaks down somewhat as follows:

POTENTIAL ENERGY SAVINGS

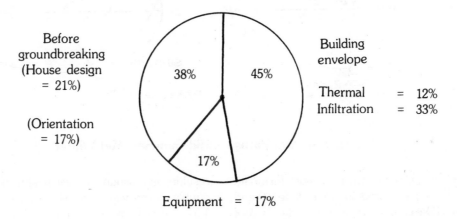

Equipment = 17%

Note that 38% of the potential energy savings occurs before the ground is broken, with house design averaging 21% of the savings and house orientation the remainder (17%). The building envelope (the house itself) accounts for 45% of the savings as an average and the equipment (appliances, air-conditioning system, hot-water system, etc.) accounting for 17% of the potential savings.

House design is covered under "House Design", page 9-1, Section 9 on a basic level. However, since the orientation of a building will influence its design in an inter-related way, both must be considered at the same time. House design as it relates to house orientation will thus be covered in this section.

HOUSE ORIENTATION

House orientation, as it relates to energy savings, is primarily concerned with the mid-summer or mid-winter path of the sun across the house and to take advantage of or to counter a prevailing wind. Of the two, orienting to achieve an optimum sun path is more important except where very high winds (usually winter-time wind) must be countered. Ideal house orientation, in brief, is achieved when minimum heat is input into the house from the summer sun and maximum heat is input from the winter sun. Sun heat can enter through the house walls by conduction and through the windows mainly as radiated heat. Today, with most outer walls insulated to at least R11, very little of the radiant heat captured by the outer sheathing will pass through the walls to act as a load on the cooling system or to act as a heat gain in the winter. Windows, unless equipped with reflective screens, can input a very high level of the sun's radiation which is turned into heat upon striking an absorbant material. Thus, in those areas where summer-time cooling is a problem, the house should be oriented to keep the sun off the largest window area for the maximum part of the summer season. For those areas where winter-time heating is the major problem, the house should be oriented to keep the sun on the largest window area for the maximum part of the winter season.

The sun in summer rises north of east and sets north of west and at noon is very high in the sky. By contrast, in winter the sun rises south of east and sets south of west, and at noon it is relatively low in the sky. The mid-summer and mid-winter paths are illustrated by figure 20-1. A study of figure 20-1 reveals that a house oriented so its long axis runs east and west will position the smallest wall area toward the rising and setting sun. Note that the sun altitude (slant) at noon time will cause the sun's rays to strike the south wall of the house, with the sun angle in the summer being such it can be easily shielded from the windows by a roof overhang. During the winter, the sun angle is much lower so the sun's rays pass under the roof overhang to enter the windows to deliver radiant heat to the house. Ideal house orientation is thus where the long axis of the house runs due east and west and the wall having the maximum window area faces due south.

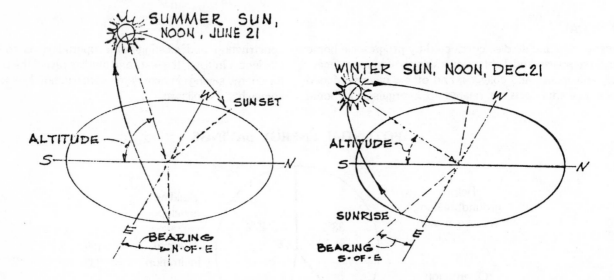

Figure 20-1. Sun Paths — Mid Summer, Mid Winter

From an energy-saving viewpoint, it is most fortunate that the sun angle is so high at mid summer (June 21) and so low at mid winter (December 21) since a moderate roof overhang (2-6" wide) will generally suffice to shade the south-facing windows in the summer and to allow the sun to strike the windows in the winter. This is illustrated by figure 20-2.

The radiant energy (solar heat) striking a wall will vary with summer and winter sun movement, the time of day and the house orientation. This is illustrated by figure 20-3 which gives the solar heat gain in BTUs per square foot, for eight hours per day at midsummer and midwinter for the four compass points. The charts are most revealing — consider the solar heat gain that would enter the house through a wall of glass.

Windows input heat into the house in two ways: (1) by conduction (thermal transfer) when the air temperature on the outside is greater than that of the inside and (2) by direct solar radiation when the sun is shining on the window. Single-glazed windows have an R value of about R-0.88 while an outer wall is insulated to at least R11,

resulting in a window-to-wall heat transfer ratio of 12.5. For double-glazed windows, which have an R value of about 1.54, the ratio is seven (1.54 to 11). Taking an unshaded south-facing window, the solar heat gain through the window can be as much as twice as much as the thermal gain through that glass all day. Solar heat gain through the windows in the summer acts as a heavy load on the aid conditioner while it is a true heat gain and lessens the heating load in the winter.

Ideal house design to optimize energy efficiency is then:

1. With the east or west walls being the smallest-area walls to reduce summer-time wall exposure to the sun.

2. Windows should be minimized or eliminated on the east and west walls or be thoroughly shaded against the morning or afternoon sun, respectively.

3. Roof overhang on the south wall should be wide enough to shade the south-wall windows in the summer time but not too wide to prevent the wintertime sun from striking them.

4. Windows in the north wall should be considered for light and cross ventilation only since they input almost no solar heat.

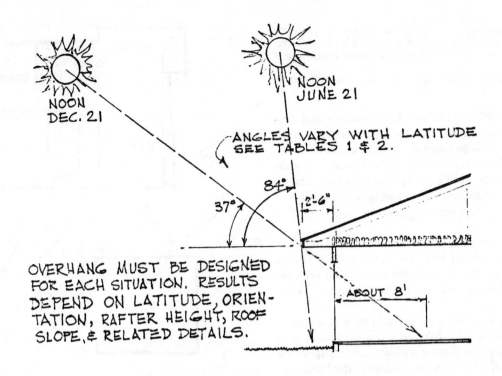

NOON
DEC. 21

NOON
JUNE 21

ANGLES VARY WITH LATITUDE
SEE TABLES 1 & 2.

84°

37°

2'-6"

ABOUT 8'

OVERHANG MUST BE DESIGNED
FOR EACH SITUATION. RESULTS
DEPEND ON LATITUDE, ORIEN-
TATION, RAFTER HEIGHT, ROOF
SLOPE, & RELATED DETAILS.

Figure 20-2. Window Shading With Roof Overhang

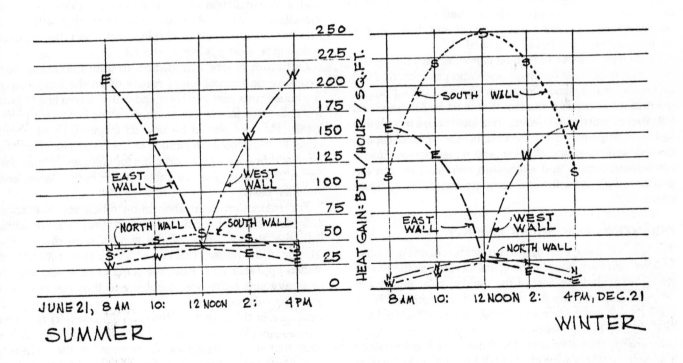

Figure 20-3. Solar Heat Gain on Exterior Walls

5. For proper placement of solar-gathering arrays, the roof should be slanted on the south side, if possible, to an angle about equal to the degrees of latitude of the house site.

6. Locating the garage at the west end of the house will add an additional shade against solar heat.

House orientation to optimize natural ventilation during the summer or to shield the living area from high wintertime winds may be more important, in some cases, than orientation to achieve ideal sun exposure. In such cases, a compromise might be made with the house being oriented to take advantage of prevailing winds while still realizing acceptable sun exposure on the larger window area.

House design can improve the effects of natural ventilation resulting from breezes blowing through the house. The best air flow is with the largest wall area set parallel to the direction of the outside breezes. When greater velocity inside is desired, the windows and doors on the leeward side (down wind) should be opened more than the windows on the windward (upwind) side. This is based upon the fact that there is a pressure build up on the windward side and a lower air pressure on the "shadow" (downwind) side of the house. A house may also be built with the garage partially separated from the house to provide a breezeway. This is illustrated by Figure 20-4. The air flow through the breezeway is increased in velocity since it is somewhat funneled down. This action plus having the windows properly opened (wider on the downwind side) causes a venturi effect and thus a higher air flow through the house is gained.

Of course, a house to be built cannot always be laid out on the lot to achieve optimum orientation as related to sun exposure and/or wind directions. For an existing house, the present orientation is a fact that must be accepted and adjusted to. Fortunately, a less than ideal house orientation can be compensated for by careful use of landscaping, window screening and shading, and house design. House orientation details and suggested solutions to sun exposure are given for the four compass quadrants by figure 20-5.

ORIENTING FOR SOLAR ENERGY

The use of solar energy for hot-water heating, house heating, and even house cooling will increase as the cost of energy rises and the cost of the needed solar equipment drops in response to sales volume and competition. Thus, even though solar energy use may not be planned for a new house, house orientation to optimize gathering of solar energy should be seriously considered. Further, since it appears so likely solar energy will be "a must" in the near future, thought should be given to designing a house to simplify installation of the solar gathering area (collectors) when they are decided upon sometime in the future. This might relate to strengthening of the roof, designing the roof

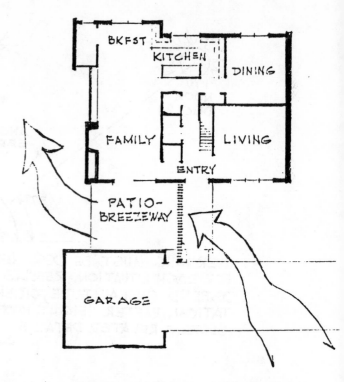

Figure 20-4. Enhanced Breeze Flow

to permit the collectors to be built into the roof structure itself and installation of piping and wiring to the potential installation point. A discussion as to this with your architect might greatly simplify and lower the cost of installing a solar system in the future.

Optimum house orientation to gain maximum sun exposure on the collectors results when the long axis of the house runs east and west and with the roof line to hold the collectors facing due south. Another important point, ideally the roof should be pitched (slanted) to be about equal to the degrees of latitude of the house site. The roof pitch and bearing of the collectors for latitudes 26° through 38° in 2° steps is given by Table 20-1 on both a winter and summer basis.

For maximum solar-absorbtion efficiency, the solar collectors should be installed to tilt (slant) in accordance with the altitude angle of the sun as occurring at the latitude of the house. This can be a very steep tilt angle as shown by Table 20-1. Also, the summer-peak and winter-peak altitudes differ considerably and thus the optimum angle for winter would be too low for maximum solar exposure in the summer. With sun altitude (tilt) reaching high angles (88° at a latitude of 26°), few roofs will have a pitch that steep unless specially designed by the architect. In general, maximum sun exposure is required by a solar system in the winter thus if the collectors are mounted to be tilted at least to the wintertime sun altitude (slant), wintertime efficiency is assured. If slanted steeper than that, somewhat improved summertime efficiency will be

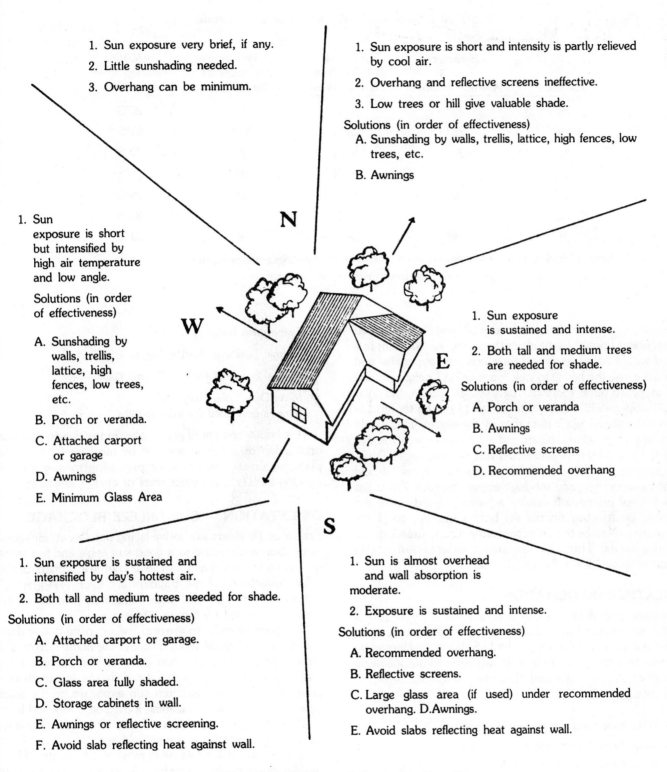

1. Sun exposure very brief, if any.
2. Little sunshading needed.
3. Overhang can be minimum.

1. Sun exposure is short and intensity is partly relieved by cool air.
2. Overhang and reflective screens ineffective.
3. Low trees or hill give valuable shade.

Solutions (in order of effectiveness)
    A. Sunshading by walls, trellis, lattice, high fences, low trees, etc.
    B. Awnings

1. Sun exposure is short but intensified by high air temperature and low angle.

Solutions (in order of effectiveness)

A. Sunshading by walls, trellis, lattice, high fences, low trees, etc.
B. Porch or veranda.
C. Attached carport or garage
D. Awnings
E. Minimum Glass Area

1. Sun exposure is sustained and intense.
2. Both tall and medium trees are needed for shade.

Solutions (in order of effectiveness)

A. Porch or veranda
B. Awnings
C. Reflective screens
D. Recommended overhang

1. Sun exposure is sustained and intensified by day's hottest air.
2. Both tall and medium trees needed for shade.

Solutions (in order of effectiveness)

A. Attached carport or garage.
B. Porch or veranda.
C. Glass area fully shaded.
D. Storage cabinets in wall.
E. Awnings or reflective screening.
F. Avoid slab reflecting heat against wall.

1. Sun is almost overhead and wall absorption is moderate.
2. Exposure is sustained and intense.

Solutions (in order of effectiveness)

A. Recommended overhang.
B. Reflective screens.
C. Large glass area (if used) under recommended overhang. D.Awnings.
E. Avoid slabs reflecting heat against wall.

Figure 20-5. House Orientation Details

Table 20-1. Sun Angle & Direction vs Latitude

Latitude	Summer June 31 Altitude @ noon	AM/PM Bearing from East or West	Winter December 21 Altitude @ noon	AM/PM Bearing from East or West
26°	88°	25°N	41°	26°S
28°	86°	26°N	39°	27°S
30°	84°	26°N	37°	27°S
32°	82°	27°N	35°	28°S
34°	80°	27°N	33°	29°S
36°	78°	29°N	31°	30°S
38°	76°	28°N	30°	31°S

Note: Altitude values are rounded off to even degrees, and bearings are approximate and will vary for all sites because of hills, trees or other "horizon barriers."

gained. A collector slant of between 30° and 80° is required dependent upon the latitude of the house. An 80° slant to a roof would be extreme and thus would be expensive and would cause the house to look "strange" in a neighborhood of standard pitch roofs (30° or less). Of course, the solar collectors can be mounted to be raised on the top end to reach a steeper pitch than that of the house. This would present a high-wind problem and would not be as attractive as if the collectors were laid flat on the roof. Thus, increasing the collector tilt by raising the top end should not raise the top end too high above the roof. For a flat roof, ideal orientation can be achieved regardless of the house positioning on the lot but, generally, good appearance dictates the collectors should run parallel to the house walls. Thus, sun-exposure orientation is still recommended for a flat-roof house.

WEATHER INFORMATION

Designing and laying out a house on a lot requires information about the weather patterns of the house area. These can be obtained from the U.S. Weather Bureau by contacting the nearest office. It is suggested the following weather data be requested. Be certain to specify the house location.

- Percentage Frequencies of Wind Directions
- Mean Annual Temperature
- Mean Length of Warm Season
- Mean Dates of First and Last Frosts
- Mean Annual Relative Humidity
- Mean Annual Possible Sunshine
- Mean Annual Precipitation

- Evaporation Rate
- Normal Seasonal Heating Degree Days
- Normal Seasonal Cooling Degree Days
- Mean Daily Solar Radiation (One is developed for each month)

This information is of great value in the design and sun orientation of a house and will be most useful to those planning on a new home or preparing to upgrade an existing house to a higher level of energy efficiency.

ORIENTATION — SUN-BREEZE BLOCKAGE

Far-sighted builders are today laying out new subdivisions to position each house to a good sun angle and to ensure maximum or near-maximum solar energy alignment of the solar collectors. These builders are even "staggering" houses so that no two houses completely face the other. This is illustrated by Figure 20-6.

This positioning both ensures the opposite house does not block the breeze from reaching the house across the street and provides for solar privacy. That is, with solar energy certain to be widely used in the future, house orientation to gain maximum sun exposure on the solar collectors will have no meaning if the sun is blocked from striking the collectors — even if only for a part of the day. Solar rights (privacy) is a new field and has not yet been established in the legal sense in most of the country. Thus, besides orienting the house for solar energy, one must take into consideration the possibility of sun blockage by a house built next door, in back or across the street. Two-story houses cast a rather large sun shadow as do large trees. When considering a lot, if lots on either side, in back or in front of the lot under consideration have not been

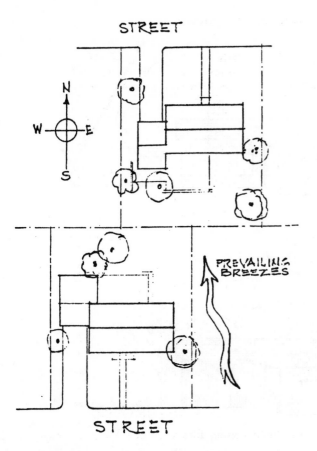

Figure 20.6 Sun-Breeze Blockage

built upon, it would be well to study the building restrictions related to these lots to determine if a two-story house can be built on any lot and may thus block the sun from your solar collectors. Ideally, the building restrictions should also relate to tall trees or shrubs since these, when full grown, can act as very severe sun shaders and make your solar system virtually useless. For those planning to install solar collectors on an existing house in an established neighborhood, serious thought should be given to the possibility a neighbor might plant trees or shrubs that would block the sun from your solar collectors. It has been suggested that it might be wise to get in writing from your neighbors that they will not plant large trees or shrubs and that they will sell their house with this as a restriction to the new owners. Admittedly, this could be most difficult to realize and it is hoped that local governments will soon establish solar rights — legal protection that nothing can be planted or erected that will block the solar rights of a neighbor.

The importance of breeze in maintaining an acceptable comfort level in a home without the need for air conditioning is such that this fact should be kept in mind when purchasing a lot and/or when orienting the house on the lot.

SUN SHADING

Sun shading of windows and walls is particularly needed in the south where short, moderate winters and long, hot, very sunny summers are normal. In the north and northwest areas and the sunny part of the eastern seaboard, sun shading (except for southern-exposed windows) is generally of less importance as related to window shading for energy-saving purposes.

Roof overhang is customarily used to shade house walls and windows and acts to prevent the summer sun from entering the windows while letting the winter sun (of a lower angle) to enter and help heat the house. A 30-inch roof overhang is somewhat standard but, in response to the need for energy saving, is often increased to 48" wide as a maximum in very sunny areas. This overhang width is about maximum as far as house appearance goes. If a wider overhang is considered necessary, the overhang should be converted into a porch or covered walkway. Alternately, an awning can be used, particularly for windows facing south. Tests have proven that it is seven times better to keep sunshine out of the house than to try to counter its effects inside with window shades, drapes, etc.

For additional details on sun shading, refer to "Window Shading," page 13-5, Section 13.

LANDSCAPING

The need for landscaping designed to reduce the heating and cooling loads of a house is all too little understood. Yet, this is an energy-saving feature of great potential and thus merits careful consideration. On the basis of just a few tests and measurements, heating and cooling load reductions as high as 25% to 35% are indicated over an unshaded house. Such excellent energy savings will be realized, of course, only with maximum use of the energy-saving potentials of landscaping.

To better understand how well-designed landscaping may reduce the heating and cooling loads of a house, a brief review of how a house may gain or lose heat is in order.

- *Solar Radiation*

  Heat can be developed in the house due to direct or indirect solar radiation entering through the windows—a heat gain in the winter, a cooling loss in the summer.

- *Air Infiltration*

  Drafts permit cooled air to escape outside in the summer and cold air to enter in the winter through cracks and joints in the building envelope and around windows and doors. The force of the drafts is in direct relation to the wind force and direction.

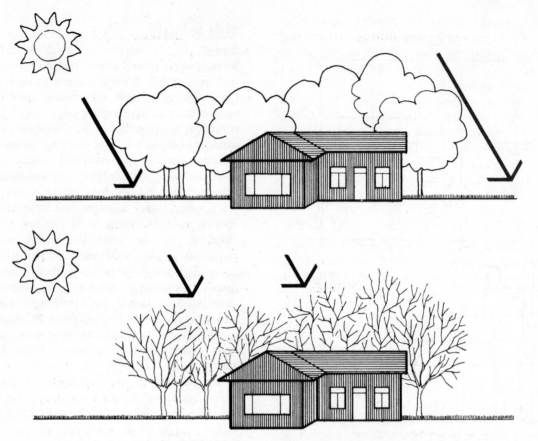

Figure 20-7. Deciduous Tree Landscaping Effect

• *Temperature Difference*

The amount of heat gained or lost through a wall, for example, is in direct relation to the amount of insulation (R factor) and the temperature difference between indoor and outdoor air. If the outer-wall temperature can be lowered in the summer by shading, the net effect is the same as if the wall insulation had been raised to a higher R value. In the winter, if the wall is unshaded, the solar radiation (sunshine) can raise the surface temperature. Again, the reduction of heat loss through the wall is the same as if the wall insulation had been raised to a higher R value.

To effectively reduce the heating and cooling loads of a house, landscaping must be designed to:

• Shade windows in the summer to prevent solar radiation from entering and to permit it to enter in the winter to heat the home. Solar radiation may be direct or indirect (reflected).

• Shade roof, walls and foundation of the house envelope to reduce the surface temperature in the summer from solar radiation thus reducing the cooling load.

Roof, walls and foundation should (ideally) not be shaded in the winter to permit solar radiation to raise the surface temperature and thus to reduce the heating load.

• Reduce winter wind velocities before they strike the house envelope since drafts are developed in direct proportion to the wind speed.

• Permit or channel wind to strike the house in the summer to optimize cross-ventilation and thus to reduce the cooling load.

LANDSCAPING WITH TREES

Trees are a most effective shading device and can, according to size, shade the whole house from roof to foundation. The best shading effect is gained by use of deciduous trees since they let the sun in during the winter as a heat gain and provide shade during the summer to reduce the cooling load. If a number of trees are grouped, a secondary effect will be noted. That is, the trees will not only provide shade and wind protection but will modify the outdoor temperature through evaporative cooling in the summer. This effect is illustrated by Figure 20-7.

Shade trees are stated to reduce solar gain by much as 40% to 80% dependent upon the number of trees, their leaf density and the amount of building envelope and window area shaded. Surface temperature on the outer walls have been recorded to have a drop of up to 10°F realized by tree shading. Trees are so important to energy savings it is recommended that if the lot does not contain trees, trees should be planted as soon as possible. Fast-growing deciduous trees are recommended. If the lot does contain trees, serious consideration should be given to fitting the house on the lot to minimize loss of trees.

In the southern latitudes, shade trees have been proven to be most effective on the east and west sides of the house. Farther north, shade trees are more effective on the west and south sides of the house. Tree placement in a given area might best be planned by observation of tree-shading effects as related to existing houses in the neighborhood.

LANDSCAPING WITH SHRUBS

Dense shrubs, such as Arborvitae, hemlock or spruce, when planted close to a building affect its outside surface temperature by blocking the wind, creating shade, and providing an insulation dead air space between the shrubs planted near the east, west and north walls, can return energy savings up to 20% over a house whose walls are not shaded and blocked by shrubs.

WINDBREAKS

In areas experiencing high wind speeds for long periods, planting a windbreak of dense-foliage trees is a most effective means of controlling wind speed and direction. The windbreak, dependent on its location to the house and its height and size, can act either to block the wind

from striking the house or as a funnel to direct the wind to windows and doors to optimize cross ventilation in the summer.

A windbreak diverts wind upwards and to the sides and thus creates a large relatively calm area on its leeward side and a small calm area on its windward side. This is shown by Figure 20-8.

A solid windbreak, such as a high solid fence, etc., deflects the wind in a manner that will produce a wake of air which contains large organized eddies. These eddies act to turn the air downward a short distance from the windbreak and can thus often cause rather severe drafts to occur within the house. Partially open windbreaks are thus recommended over solid windbreaks and these windbreaks are less likely to fail in a very high wind.

Some recent experiments at Princeton University were made using models of townhouses. Tests made with a wind tunnel and these models revealed that a five-foot-high wood fence would reduce air infiltration by 26% to 30%; a single row of evergreen trees as high as the house would reduce air infiltration by 40%; and the two used in combination indicated a possible air infiltration reduction of up to 60%.

The study also revealed that a double row of staggered trees is less effective than a single row, that 59% greater infiltration is created by winds coming at the corner of a building rather than perpendicular to one of the building's walls and that the best location for a

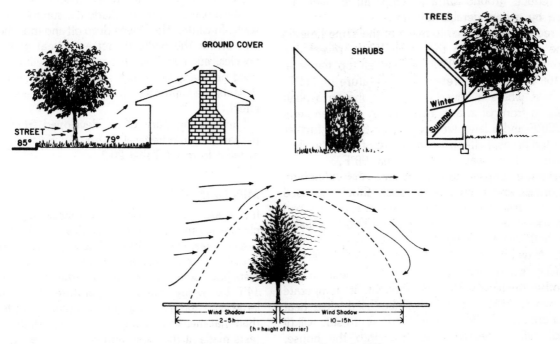

Figure 20-8. Tree Windbreak Effect

windbreak is at a distance of 1½ to 2½ windbreak heights upwind from the house.

Other tests have shown that a reduction in wind velocity from 15 mph down to 5 mph can reduce air infiltration around windows from 70 to 80%. Also, that reducing the wind velocity striking a window can reduce heat transmission through the window by one third.

LANDSCAPING WITH GROUND COVER

Ground cover about a house may consist of concrete or asphalt driveways, a concrete patio and walks, brick patio or walks, flower and garden plots, and plant ground cover such as grass, diachondra, etc. The ground cover about a house can act to reflect solar radiation into the house through the windows, to store up heat on a desired or undesired basis and (in the case of plant material) to reduce heat buildup from radiation by its evaporative cooling characteristics.

Light-colored materials such as concrete create a summer-time cooling load problem by reflecting the solar radiation onto the walls and windows and by storing up heat which it gives off after sundown to sustain the outdoor temperature. A concrete patio is particularly bad with relation to its effect upon the energy efficiency of the house. Dark-colored materials like asphalt and bricks tend to store a large amount of heat during the day (much more than concrete does) and to give this heat back after sundown. Plant material such as grass, etc. is ideal ground cover since it does not reflect solar radiation or store up heat during the day. The evaporative cooling effect related to a large lawn, for example, can actually reduce ground surface temperature over the lawn area by a considerable amount.

Some recent measurements made at the same time on the same day relating to the same house revealed a grass-top temperature of 89°F, an asphalt-top temperature of 106°F and a concrete-top temperature of 111°F. Another test where a house eave overhung an asphalt cover just in front of a lawn revealed an eave temperature of 120°F and a lawn temperature of 80°F. A further test reported an asphalt-top temperature of 125°F while a grass lawn 30 feet away measured only 98°F.

The given examples clearly indicate that concrete, asphalt, bricks and even crushed rock should be used sparingly. In particular, a concrete patio is especially bad in that it will reflect radiant heat into the house (causing a glare) and will store up heat to be released after sundown. A wood patio floor or deck should be used in most cases, since wood does not store heat to the degree other materials do. One thought, in temperate climates where solar radiation will be used as a heat source, a concrete walk or patio on the south side will (if unshaded) reflect desired solar heat into the house.

Shading of the patio in the summer can be gained by planting deciduous trees.

Landscaping particulars, developed from a pamphlet prepared by the Federal Energy Administration, are given in table form by Table 20-2.

LANDSCAPING WITH VINES

Deciduous vines are often used to shade and cool an outer wall. For masonry walls, clinging species such as Virginian creeper (Parthenocissus quinquefolia) and trumpet vine (Bignonia capreolata) are recommended. Their leaves are borne in an orderly shingle pattern on four-to-six-inch petioles. The leaf blades intercept and absorb the sun's rays, while between the vines and the wall a convection current carries the warm air up and away from the wall. Native and cultivated grape vines are also effective, especially when used on trellises, arbors or deck roofs extended from the house. Evergreen and sun-tolerant species including fig ivory can also be useful on brick walls. English ivy is also an effective climate-control vine when planted against a masonry wall or, if against a wooden wall, if planted on a trellis.

Clinging vines are not recommended to be planted directly against wooden walls since their stems and tendrils hold moisture and can thus cause the wood to deteriorate. However, the same cooling effect can be obtained by training twining vines like wisteria or climbing roses on a trellis. The trellises should be built so that they may be loosened from the wall and swung out to permit the wall to be painted.

Deciduous vines are most effective on southern and western walls, acting to shade the summer heat from the walls. In winter, the leaves drop off and thus the winter sun can strike the walls to act as a heat gain. Evergreen species, such as English Ivy (Hedra helix), are generally used on shady north sides where their year-round foliage deflects the winter winds and the stems have an insulating effect.

Landscaping particulars, developed from a pamphlet prepared by the Federal Energy Administration, are given in table form by Table 20-2.

MINICLIMATE

It is possible to a minor but worthwhile degree to alter the climate about a house by well designed landscaping. The use of trees, shrubs, lawns, bushes, garden plots, etc. can actually alter the climate about the house. Some recent tests have demonstrated a temperature drop of from 10 to 14°F below the true air temperature as measured over a large lawn and a temperature difference of 25 to 30°F lower than that measured over a nearby asphalt driveway. Other tests made at the same time on the same day relating to a

Table 20-2. Landscaping Particulars

Landscape Element	Effect Cold Climate	Effect Temperate Climate	Effect Warm Climate
Ground cover or grass	Neglible effect on all sides	On south side	On east, west & south sides
Paving	On south side	Shaded if on south side	Shaded if on east, west or south side
Shrubs against house wall	On east, west & north side	On east, west & north side	On all sides
Deciduous shade trees	Neglible effect on all sides	On south & West side	On east & west side
Evergreen trees	On east, west & north side	On east & west side	On east and west side
Windbreak (trees, bushes, fences)	On sides exposed to winter winds	On sides exposed to winter winds	Undesirable effect on all sides
Windbreak, used to funnel wind	Undesirable on all sides	On sides exposed to summer winds	Where cross-ventilation is desired

given house revealed a grass-top temperature of 89°F, an asphalt-top temperature of 106°F and a concrete-top temperature of 111°F. Another test where a house eave extended out to shade an asphalt cover just in front of a lawn revealed an under-eave temperature of 120°F and a lawn temperature of 80°F. A further test reported an asphalt-top temperature of 125°F while a grass lawn 30 feet away measured only 98°F. The cooling effect of lawns and other plant ground cover is such that the lawns of a block of homes has a total cooling effect equal to 70 tons of air conditioning.

The given examples clearly indicate that concrete, asphalt, bricks and even crushed rock should be used sparingly. In particular, a concrete or brick patio is especially bad in that it will reflect radiant heat into the house (causing both a glare and a load on the air conditioner) and will store up large amounts of heat to be released after sundown. A wood patio floor or deck would be much better since wood would not reflect much solar energy and does not store heat to the same degree as other solid materials. One thought, if solar radiation is to be counted on for winter-time heating, a concrete walk or patio on the south side will (if unshaded) reflect desired solar heat into the house. In the summer, the concrete walk or patio can be shaded by a deciduous tree which will lose it's leaves in the winter to leave the walk or patio unshaded.

DOLLAR BENEFITS OF LANDSCAPING

The energy saved (and thus the dollars saved) by landscaping designed to reduce the heating and cooling load of a house is difficult to calculate since so many variable factors must be considered. The local climatic conditions, house design, orientation on the lot, tree growth, amount of plant versus solid-material ground cover, strength and direction of wind, etc. must be taken into account.

Generally speaking, landscaping about the house is really worthwhile for beauty sake alone. Designing the landscaping about the house to optimize energy savings should not appreciably raise the landscaping cost and, as the examples given in this section indicate, meaningful energy savings can be realized while the house and grounds are beautified.

The subject of landscaping to achieve an acceptable balance between beauty and energy savings is so new and yet so important, it is suggested that additional reading be done. The Bibliography at the back of this manual lists subject-related books and articles.

Section 21

Energy-Saving Hints

GENERAL

It has been estimated that five percent of the nation's energy supply is used to operate major appliances, television, lighting and small appliances. This represents a considerable portion of the energy used in a home. In total, almost 20 percent of all the energy consumed in the United States is used in our 70 million households. More than half the energy we use in the home goes into heating and cooling. Heating water takes about 15 percent. Lighting, cooking, refrigeration and operating appliances account for the rest.

With 70 million households, even a small energy savings per household can amount to very sizeable energy savings per year. Let's be honest—during the days of cheap energy we developed wasteful habits, habits we must now correct. The old saying "Waste Not—Want Not" must be dusted off and considered as the watchword for now and the future. We can, most easily, by just practicing every practical energy-conservation measure, act to save energy on a large scale without unduly affecting our present living standards. If we do not become conservative minded as to energy use, if we do not become adherents to the "Waste Not—Want Not" outlook, we will surely see our wonderful living standards reduced as energy will become more expensive and scarce and energy-rationing measures will be introduced because we have not corrected our current wasteful energy-use habits.

The energy-saving hints to follow should be considered carefully and the thought inherent in each suggestion—"Waste Not—Want Not"—be accepted—not as a tiresome thing but as a natural thing. All can contribute to energy savings—young and old alike. The major contributor to energy savings will be the housewife, ruler of the house and kitchen. To all we say—why not make energy saving a game, a challenge in which all take part. A survey of the monthly energy bills can become the score card which tells how the challenge has been met.

MAJOR APPLIANCES

The major appliances are: refrigerator, oven, range (surface unit), dishwasher, clothes washer, clothes dryer, hot-water heater and disposal unit.

Refrigerator - Freezer

- Set refrigerator temperature to between 36-40°F and the freezer temperature to 0°F. Temperatures below this do not noticeably lengthen the storage life of food and do require more energy.

- A refrigerator or freezer operates at maximum efficiency when filled to capacity—but not overloaded. Be certain air vents inside unit are not blocked by food containers as good air circulation is required for cooling efficiency to be gained.

- If a refrigerator provides a switch for turning off the door-edge heaters, be certain switch is placed to "OFF" at all times except when room humidity is high (40% or greater). At this point, doors will be noted to stick.

- For manual defrosting units, defrost when the frost has built up to one-quarter inch in thickness. Frost thicker than that actually acts as an insulation and thus will increase the cooling load.

- Check seals around door (or lids) make an airtight fit. Check seal tightness by opening door (or lid), placing a piece of writing paper against weatherstripping and closing the door (or lid). Close door (or lid) and pull paper out slowly. It should pull out with slight resistance. If it slides out easily, improper sealing is indicated. This can be corrected by checking the setting of the door (or lid) lock, readjusting to achieve a tighter fit against the weatherstripping. If this does not correct the problem, replace weatherstripping. Kits are available and can be easily installed.

- Dusty condensor coils (at bottom or back of unit) reduce cooling efficiency. The coils should be cleaned at regular intervals with a vacuum cleaner, using a small nozzle hose. Be certain electrical plug is pulled from convenience outlet to avoid any chance of electrical shock.

- The unit (refrigerator or freezer) should have at least one-inch air space across the back and on both sides to prevent overheating and to ensure cooling efficiency. Keep units away from heat sources by locating units in coldest area. NEVER locate a refrigerator or freezer in a non-air conditioned part of the house and—most particularly—never in the garage unless it is insulated and air conditioned. For example, a 15 cubic-foot frost-free refrigerator uses 30% less energy if located in an area of 70°F temperature over the same unit located in an area of 90°F temperature.

- Before opening the door (or lid), stop a moment and recall what you want to remove. An open door (or lid) is a great energy waster.

- Heavy wrapping paper acts as an insulation and thus should be removed before the item is stored in a refrigerator or freezer. However, wrap (if needed) with aluminum foil or lighter paper to seal item against moisture loss.

- Prior to vacations, holidays and other periods of extended absence, plan to use up stored items in the refrigerator. The unit may then be emptied of non-perishable items (cold drinks, etc.) or any remaining perishable items can be stored in the freezer (if a separate unit). Next, put a package of baking soda in the unit and prop door *open*. *Turn off unit and remove plug from wall.* This will doubly ensure the unit cannot operate while you are gone. With the doors open, the energy loss would be fantastic.

- To defrost frozen foods, remove item(s) from freezer and place in refrigerator (usually overnight). This will help keep the refrigerator cool whereas if the items were defrosted on the counter top, the frozen items would act as a load on the heating system.

Oven

- Plan family menu so that most (or all) of the items for the main meal may be placed in the oven at the same time. Some may have to be removed before others. If possible, cook tomorrow's meal with today's. Only a small amount of warming up will then be needed for the next day's meal.

- Do not preheat oven too long—five to 10 minutes is usually long enough. If a food will take from one hour or longer to cook, do not preheat oven. Do not preheat for broiling or roasting.

- Do not open door (unless needed) to check for cooking or baking—use a timer and/or look through oven-door glass (if provided). Each time the door is opened, the oven temperature drops about 20 degrees. This drop can account for many items which "do not turn out right" even though the recipe was followed closely. In the summer, each time the door is opened the outflow of heat will tend to warm the kitchen area.

- Try to time your roasting or baking operations so that you can turn the oven off before the roasting or baking is fully completed, allowing the stored heat to complete the task.

- NEVER use the oven (or range) to heat the kitchen. They are most inefficient as a room heater since they are not provided with a fan to circulate the developed warmth.

- If oven is a self-cleaning type and needs cleaning, try to start the cleaning cycle immediately after the oven has been used. In the summer, if the oven cannot be cleaned after cooking the evening meal, plan to start the cleaning cycle in the morning when it will be less likely to overload the cooling system.

- Pyrolytic self-cleaning ovens use less energy for baking and roasting than do comparable models not so equipped.

- Use minimum amount of water possible when cooking. More water than necessary simply uses more energy without producing better results.

  One-quarter to one-half cup of water is as much as you should use in most cases.

Surface Unit (Range)

- Use a matching size burner—do not put a small pot on a large burner and vice versa.

- All cooking utensils (pots, frying pans, etc.) should have flat bottoms, straight sides and be equipped with tight-fitting lids.

- When cooking, cover saucepans to conserve energy and to reduce the flow of humidity into the kitchen area. Foods will cook more quickly with the lid on tight since the saucepan then acts somewhat as a pressure cooker.

- Learn to turn the burner off before the cooking is fully completed, allowing the stored heat in the burner to complete the task. This is of particular importance with an electric range.

- For a gas unit, if the flame is any other color than blue the unit is not operating correctly. The air-to-fuel mixture must then be adjusted. This should usually be done by an experienced person. If the gas flame shows traces of yellow, the burner holes may be clogged. These should be cleaned out—do not use a toothpick as the end can easily break off and clog the hole. Use a pipe cleaner or a thin piece of wire.

- Use the lowest setting possible for any cooking or frying job. Expert chefs who must cook at high speed use burners turned to HIGH but this requires constant attention and great experience. In the home, practice to learn the lowest setting needed for each particular cooking task. This will both save energy and result in less burned items.

- Use the smallest amount of water possible—one-quarter to one-half a cup of water (or other liquid) is all that is usually required. Turn burner to HIGH until liquid starts to boil—then turn down to the lowest setting that will make the water simmer. Once water boils, additional burner heat will not raise the water temperature above the boiling point since the added heat is passed off during the boiling process.

Microwave Oven

A firm, Recipes Unlimited, Inc. and publishers of The Microwave Times, conducted some energy-consumption tests using a range (surface unit), a conventional oven and a microwave oven to cook, roast and boil. The results are given by Table 21-1.

Table 21-1 Summary of Energy Usage

Recipe	Microwave KWH Used	Surface KWH Used	Oven KWH Used
Oven-Fried Chicken	0.54		1.92
Oven-Fried Fish	0.13		0.68
Souper Meat Loaf	0.24		1.02
Meatballs	0.14	0.26	0.74
Hungarian Goulash	1.20	0.70	
Baked Potatoes	0.24		0.84
Steamed Potatoes	0.24	0.30	
Apple Crisp	0.24		0.90
Pudding Mix	0.14	0.10	0.90
Frozen Apple Pie	1.16*		1.10
Boil Water - 2 cups	0.08	0.14	
Boil Water - 4 cups	0.22	0.28	
Boil Water - 6 cups	0.41	0.30	
Boil Water - 8 cups	0.50	0.30	

*Includes energy for conventionally browning crust.

Actual KWH figures may vary between brands and models. The given values, however, can be considered close approximates.

Energy consumption and energy savings as related to a microwave unit and a conventional oven and a range were found to vary with the quantity, type of food and cooking method used whether a microwave or conventional unit was used. In addition, the energy savings also depended upon what the tester considered a normal eating pattern and family size to be. This because the actual savings gained was often directly proportional to the food quantity and food type. The tests showed that energy savings of from 0 (none) to as high as 80% could be gained when using a microwave oven. The finds of the test were:

- The microwave oven is generally more efficient than the conventional oven or range.

- It is usually more efficient with low-moisture, quick-cooking foods and less efficient with smaller quantities (less than four cups) of high-liquid foods.

- If the microwave oven is used mainly for reheating and defrosting, little energy is saved but convenience is gained. If the family is small and most of the food is cooked in the microwave oven, the savings can average to as high as 75% or more on energy use. For a large family, cooking high-liquid and long-simmering foods, the conventional oven or range was clearly more efficient as to energy use.

- Energy consumption by a microwave unit is relatively constant while the unit is being used. Since its operation does not depend upon the oven reaching a desired temperature, no energy is wasted in bringing the oven area up to temperature. As much as 60 to 80 percent of the energy drawn by a conventional oven or range may be used to initially raise the oven or burner temperature to the desired level.

A recent survey of microwave-oven users revealed that 57% were "very satisfied," 34% were "satisfied" and only 9% indicated "dissatisfaction." It thus seems that a family must learn to properly use a microwave oven and to use recipes and family menus that take advantage of the microwave oven's capabilities. If you own or plan to install a microwave oven, it is recommended that you obtain both recipes and family menus that are special for microwave use. Such information can be obtained by subscribing to The Microwave Times, published by Recipes Unlimited, Inc., Box 1202, Burnsville, Minnesota, 55337, cost $4.00 per year. Also, the Campbell Soup Company offers a 24-page recipe book particular to microwave-oven use. Order by writing to "Make It in a Microwave," Box 355BA, Colingswood, New Jersey, 08108.

Dishwasher

- Unless provided with "low-load" settings, use only when full but do not overload. Scrape off food particles, rinsing items only if felt necessary, and store dishes and pots, etc. in dishwasher until a full load is stored.

- Use the kind of dishwasher detergent recommended by the manufacturer and use only the recommended amount. This ensures proper cleaning and rinsing efficiency.

- Do not use dishwasher to heat dinner plates, etc. Use the stored heat in the oven.

- When unit has finished last rinse cycle, unit will normally enter into the drying cycle. At this point, if the door is immediately opened (and the selector switch is set to "OFF"), the dishes and all will dry equally as well as if the unit had been left on for the drying cycle. A considerable electricity savings results. Some units are provided for an automatic door opening at the end of the rinsing cycle.

Disposal Unit

- Unit uses a relatively small amount of electricity but even so, it should be used only as needed. Do not run for long periods. Learn what items should not be put into the disposal units—such as corn cobs which require a long grinding cycle.

- Disposal units are built to operate with cold water—do not use warm water as warm water is not needed and will result in an energy loss.

Clothes Washer

- Select wash time and water load to match load and soil levels. Washing longer than necessary is wasteful of energy.

- Use the proper soap to match the water-temperature selected. Use cold or warm setting wherever possible instead of hot settings. Most of energy used by a clothes washer relates to its use of hot water.

- For heavily-soiled items, place in tub, turn on unit to fill to selected water level and then turn unit off. Put soap into water, turn on unit to agitate for one to two minutes and then turn unit off. Let clothes soak for 5 to 10 minutes and then complete wash cycle (5 minutes more of agitation should suffice).

- Load machine to capacity but do not overload. A large-capacity machine may suffice to wash all clothes in one load rather than in two smaller loads.

- Use highest speed spin cycle possible since this will spin-dry clothes to extract more moisture and thus will reduce drying time in the clothes dryer.

Clothes Dryer

- Do not overload dryer since to do so reduces its drying efficiency.

- Try to separate clothes by weight—drying all "light" (quick-drying) clothes in one drying cycle and all "heavy" (slow-drying) clothes in another drying cycle.

- If two or more drying loads must be accommodated, try to have next load ready to place in dryer when previous load is ready to take out of dryer. This will save the heat needed to bring the dryer up to drying level.

- Be certain to clean the lint filter after each load or two. Also, regularly check the dryer vent to assure it is not blocked or clogged. Do not vent unit into the air-conditioned area, always use a dryer vent to the outside of the house.

- For permanent-press items, use the "permanent-press" cycle and remove clothes as soon as the drying cycle is completed. This will ensure that "wrinkles" are not put into the permanent-press items.

Water Heaters.

- If a single hot-water tank is used, the thermostat can be set to a maximum of 130°F. If the dishwasher does not have a water-heater element, the thermostat may have to be set to 135°F. If a separate hot-water tank is used for bathroom purposes only, the thermostat on that unit can be set back to a maximum of 110°F.

Note: For electrically-heated units, be certain to turn off electricity at the circuit breaker before making the adjustment. Also, two thermostats are usually provided and both must be adjusted to the same temperature.

- A few gallons should be run out of the tank through the drain faucet (located at the bottom of the tank) two or three times a year. Be certain NOT to drain all or most of the water out—this is not necessary to clear the tank of sediment and if done without turning off the heating source (gas or electricity) can destroy the tank.

- For a gas-fired unit, observe flame when burner is full on. If flame is other than a blue color, the air to gas mixture is incorrect and must be adjusted. This must be done by an experienced person. Contact your gas company.

- Consider covering the tank with an insulation blanket— these are now available at hardware stores and lumber yards and can be self installed. This will substantially reduce the heat loss from the tank.

- If you are to be absent from home for two days or longer, turn off the water heater. For an electric model, switch related circuit breaker to OFF. For a gas-fired model, turn thermostat back to OFF.

Hot-Water Wastage

- Showers use considerably less hot water than do tub baths, especially if the shower head is equipped with a flow restrictor. This unit reduces the water flow to about 4 gallons per minute. Get used to taking colder and shorter showers.

- When shaving, for example, do not let the hot water run to rinse the razor. Partially fill basin instead.

- Single-handle faucets are very convenient but can be hot-water wasters unless the user always turns handle to cold water when hot water is not desired. In the children's bathroom, two faucets should be considered and the children should be trained to use only the "cold" faucet when hot water is not desired. Turning on the hot water for a short period will usually not bring hot water to the faucet but will wastefully fill the pipe with hot water.

- In the kitchen, do not use hot water with the garbage disposal unit. It is designed to operate with cold water and will last longer than if used with hot water. The unit will grind properly and stay "sweet" equally as well with cold water as against hot water.

- Never run the hot water in the kitchen to rinse dishes one at a time. In fact, a dishwasher, if turned off at the end of the last rinse cycle, will actually use less hot water and energy than if the dishes are done by hand and rinsed individually.

House Lighting

- Do not use a large wattage bulb if a smaller wattage unit will produce the needed lighting. For three-level bulbs, rotate 3-way switch to select only the required light level. Note that there is little apparent difference in light level between the 2nd and 3rd steps.

- If a light fixture has two or more bulbs, consider using only one bulb of the proper wattage. Fill "other" sockets with burned-out bulbs. For example, one 100-watt bulb produces more light per watt than two 50-watt bulbs.

- Never use "long-life" bulbs except in locations where replacement of the bulb is difficult or hazardous. A "long-life" bulb gives considerably less light per watt than a regular bulb of the same wattage.

- Use spot lighting such as a portable lamp when working at a table or desk rather than using the full lighting of the room.

- Fluorescent lighting is four times as efficient as incandescent lighting and is particularly effective in the kitchen and bathroom areas. They are also very effective in the garage. For "natural" lighting tones, use the "Deluxe" tubes which emit a light frequency somewhat comparable to that emitted by incandescent lamp bulbs.

- For outdoor lighting—such as illuminating a yard or garage drive area—use mercury-vapor lamps. These have a much higher efficiency than incandescent bulbs and a longer life as well. The units can be purchased equipped with a light cell that will act to automatically turn the lights on at dusk and off at dawn. These light-cell operated switches can also be obtained for installation into regular light sockets to control incandescent bulbs mounted outside the house.

- Do not leave lights turned on when going away on vacations, etc. Timers should be used that will turn lights on and off within the house in a somewhat "normal living pattern."

- If repainting or redecorating a room, consider using light colors since they reflect light rather than absorbing it and thus the room will require less lighting.

- Above all—do not leave lights burning when they are not serving a useful purpose. Form the habit of turning off lights when not needed.

House Heating

- Do not pamper yourself—turn the thermostat to 68°F, wear a sweater and a bit heavier socks and learn to live at that temperature. If the house is free of drafts (particularly at floor level), one can easily adapt to a 68°F room temperature and learn to like it. The change between the inside and outside temperature will then not be as shocking as if the room temperature were held to the 80°F or more that all too many households feel is necessary.

  If, for physical reasons (age, arthritis, etc.) a winter-time temperature of 68°F cannot be accepted, the thermostat should be raised in small steps until an acceptable temperature is reached.

- For each degree the thermostat is set to over 70°F, your heating bill will increase by about three percent. (See Table 21-2)

- If any drafts are felt, trace them down and correct them, otherwise physical comfort at a low thermostat setting cannot be attained.

- The filter in the heater system should be cleaned at regular intervals, perhaps monthly, and replaced if needed.

- For a gas-fired furnace, check the flame when the burners are on. If the flame is other than a blue color, the air-gas mixture ratio is not correct and must be adjusted. This should be done by an expert. Contact your gas company.

- Be careful not to overheat the house during cooking or when large parties are being held. Cut down the heater temperature rather than opening a window.

- An open door or window, even if only slightly open, can rob the house of a fantastic amount of heated air and cause bad drafts. Consider installing automatic door closers on "most-used" outer doors, particularly if young children are present.

- Remember—a fireplace does not produce a net heat gain when operated unless it is a special unit or a free-standing unit. For details, refer to Fireplaces, Section 17.

- Be certain the fireplace damper is tightly closed at all times the fireplace is not in use. Do not use the fireplace if the outside temperature is extremely low.

- If a fireplace is the heat-producing type, put the heater fan on continuous operation to move the heat from the fireplace room to the rest of the house.

- The thermostat can be turned down by up to 10 degrees at bedtime. This can be done manually or by an automatic device (see page 19-4, Section 19).

House Cooling

- Set the thermostat to keep the house at a minimum comfort level. Most people can adjust to a house temperature of 78°F. For each degree cooler than 78°F, your cooling bill will increase sharply.

- The filter in the cooling system should be cleaned at regular intervals, perhaps monthly, and replaced if needed.

- An open door or window, even if only slightly open, can permit the loss of expensively cooled air. Consider installing an automatic door closer on the "most-used" outer door, particularly if young children are present.

- Be certain the furnace damper is tightly closed.

Table 21-2. Thermostat Setting Savings

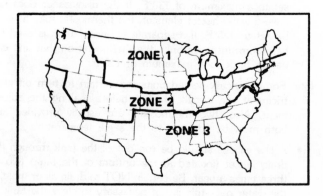

	ZONE 1	ZONE 2	ZONE 3
5° turn-down	14%	17%	25%
8° turn-down	19%	24%	35%

- The use of window fans to bring in colder air during the periods the outside temperature is below 80°F should be considered. The movement of this cold air will usually suffice to provide a comfortable sleeping atmosphere. Also, the air-conditioner fan can be set to continuous operation to move the outside air (if below 80°F) through the house.

The above table and figure, developed by the Department of Housing and Urban Development, indicates the energy savings made possible by "proper" setting of the thermostat. Note the savings detailed relate to heating. Somewhat lower but still worthwhile savings can also be realized on the cooling bills if the thermostat is turned up from the "normal" 72-75°F setting. Thus, by adjusting to a higher indoor temperature in the summer and a lower indoor temperature than thought "normal" in the winter, really meaningful energy (and dollar) savings can be realized.

Section 22

Choosing Your Building Contractor

YOUR DECISION

The perfect lot has been purchased, the house plans finalized and your education as to what constitutes an energy-saver home is complete. You accept the fact that there is a true energy shortage, that it is serious and that energy conservation must be practiced by all. And now you must select a building contractor to build your energy-saver dream home. Ideally, you must select a builder who:

- has had previous experience building energy-efficient homes.

- demonstrates genuine enthusiasm for the energy-saving features that you want built into your home.

- will be receptive to new ideas and can see that energy-saver homes are the homes of the future.

- realizes that if he builds your excellent energy-saver home, his building reputation will benefit and this will help him prosper in the rapidly changing world of building construction—the vital change from building energy-hog homes to that of building energy-saver homes.

- will enthusiastically work with you and assist you in your selection of energy-saving materials and building features.

- will quote you a fair price for the energy-saving features and materials you have selected.

If a building contractor experienced in building energy-saver homes cannot be located or is not available, you may have to work with one with little or no experience in this new phase of home construction. Here the critical point would be—enthusiasm. The building techniques related to true energy-saver home construction are straightforward and should pose no problems or troubles for a competent building contractor.

The author has acted as consultant on energy-saving construction materials and methods to both prospective home builders and building contractors. He found that all too often prospective home builders have been completely convinced of the need for energy-saving home

construction and have discussed their thoughts with one or more building contractors and found complete lack of enthusiasm. In fact, found a complete and positive rejection. Contractors displaying lukewarm enthusiasm or those who first expressed rejection and then said, "Oh well, if you want to build THAT kind of house, I can build it as well as the next guy," should be avoided.

In his talks with building contractors, the author found many immediately rejected the thought that a house could be built to achieve a very high level of energy conservation. The author knows the full facts of homes built by these out-of-date men and the energy bills run up by the homes they build. Other contractors were more receptive to the new ideas and are now incorporating some into their homes—better wall and ceiling insulation, double-glazed windows and metal-clad doors generally. A good start. It is to be hoped that they will soon see the need for the "full package" of energy-saving materials and methods—extreme care as to air infiltration, selection of an energy-efficient air conditioning system, insulated foundation, efficient hot-water systems, etc.

A survey was conducted by Professor Ranjit K. Banerji in 1976 as a part of the Home Energy Conservation Project at the College of Architecture, University of Houston. This survey related to the features home buyers and home builders felt were either very important or extremely important to energy efficiency in relation to home design and construction. Some interesting facts were revealed and the results are detailed by Table 22-1.

Table 22-1 Home Owner vs Home Builder Viewpoints

Rated Extremely/Very Important	Home Owner	Home Builder	Difference
Quality of construction	91%	63.5%	27.5%
Energy-saving design feature	61%	40%	21%
Efficiency rating of central air-conditioning system	68%	29.3%	38.7%
Builder's reputation	54%	84%	30%
Amount and type of insulation	78%	60%	18%
Total price of house	84%	94.7%	10.7%
Landscaping	44%	9.3%	34.7%

It is suggested that if you find a building contractor that is either experienced and enthusiastic or inexperienced but eager to gain experience as to building an energy-saver home, that you loan this manual to the contractor. In reading it, he should become even more enthusiastic and convinced. Of course, he need not read the manual to gain construction experience since, except for some points on draft prevention, the construction techniques are already completely familiar to him.

Many contractors have told the author that they are reluctant to build homes to the newest of energy-saving techniques since it increases the home cost and they find price resistance from the buyers. What it all comes down to is this—we are in a pioneering stage. We are changing, perhaps all too slowly, to cope with the ever rising cost of energy. While it has been said "Pioneering never pays" this should not hold for energy-saving construction. A builder should thus be both anxious and happy to work with a client who wants "the home of tomorrow built today." And, you should be both anxious and happy to work with the building contractor. Since your new home, when built, may well be tops in energy efficiency for your area, it would be well worthwhile to offer to work with the contractor as a customer-referral source. That is, you can offer to allow the contractor to use you as a reference when he is trying to guide others into building a real energy-saver home. Assuredly, if the contractor expects to receive good response from you as a reference, he will give an extra measure of personal attention to the energy-saving features incorporated into your home. You will both benefit by this cooperation.

There are three questions you must ask yourself and answer before you sign the building contract. These are:

- Do you believe completely that there is a severe energy problem and that a home must be built to achieve a very high order of energy efficiency?

- That the extra cost to raise the energy efficiency of your new home to that required by your climatic conditions and cost of energy is well worthwhile and will be repaid in energy-dollar savings in just a few years?

- Should you, can you, really settle for less?

OTHER INFORMATION SOURCES

If you are seriously contemplating building an energy-saver home, you are building exactly the type of home your local energy company (electrical and gas) wants to see built. Many electrical and gas companies have persons well versed in energy-saving materials and techniques and who would be most willing to discuss your new energy-saver home with you. More than willing—some may even want to work directly with you as to advice and to use your home as an example.

It is thus suggested that when you have your new home all thought out as to energy-saving features and construction techniques, that you call upon your local electrical and/or gas company and request a review of your plans. This service will most likely be free but it would be well to ask as to this point. If you visit your local energy company, it is suggested you bring along your copy of this manual to be used to establish the reason for your decisions as to energy-efficient home construction. The person you talk to over your house plans should be able to confirm your energy-saving decisions or to make points or suggestions based upon their more intimate understanding of local conditions. The discussion should be most informative and may serve to solidify your decisions.

BUILDING CONTRACT THOUGHTS

As has been pointed out, most houses are constructed to FHA Minimum Property Standards and this fact is stated somewhere in the building contract. A building contract relating to a home constructed to much higher insulation and air-infiltration standards should be very specific as to:

- *Insulation* - precise information should be given in full, detailing type of insulation (batts or blown-in), type of vapor barrier to be installed with manufacturer's name, number of inches or R value; type of installation, etc. This information to be given individually for walls (outer and, if applicable, inner walls), ceilings, under-floor and/or foundation (as applicable).

- *Windows* - desired windows should be listed in detail as to manufacturer's name, precise type by name and type number, if thermal-break type are to be installed, frame color (if aluminum type, only natural and bronze color is generally available), etc. Also, specify caulking and weatherstripping around window openings.

- *Outer doors* - full details should be given as to type (basically, if wood —solid or hollow-core—or metal-clad) and manufacturer's name and with precise facts given as to door trim, door glass or sidelights. If metal-clad doors are to be installed, magnetic weatherstripping should be specified. If wood, type of weatherstripping should be detailed. Also, specify caulking and weatherstripping around door openings.

- *Attic ventilation* - full facts should be given as to ventilation method (wind-drive turbines, motor-driven turbines, or fans), eave vents or gable vents, ridge venting, etc.

- *Air conditioning system* - equipment should be detailed as to manufacturer, model number, rating, type of thermostat, unit location (where installed inside or outside of house), etc. Also, location of forced-air and return-air vents should be detailed along with installation details on ducting (installed in attic, inside house or under floor). Insulation value of ducting should also be specified as to type, manufacturer's name, installation method, etc. If a gas-fired or oil-fired heater is used, source of combustion air should be given.

- *Hot-water system(s)* - equipment should be detailed as to manufacturer, model number and efficiency rating (if available). Location of unit (or units) should be clearly specified and (for a gas unit) how combustion air is to be obtained. If located in a closet, air tightness and insulation level should be specified. If unit (or units) is to be covered with an insulation blanket, this should be specified as to type, thickness, etc. If timers are to be installed (electric models only), this also should be specified as to model number, etc. If hot-water pipes are to be insulated, full details should be given.

- *Air infiltration prevention* - type of caulking material should be specified as to manufacturer and type by number. Caulking should be discussed with the contractor in detail as should be caulking and flashing of window and door openings. Pertinent facts from this discussion should be given in the building contract. It should be remembered that prevention of drafts is now considered to be a very important matter and must be thorough and handled with care.

In addition, it is seriously suggested the building contract specify that the building contractor (or his approved substitute) will personally conduct you all through the house when each of the following stages of construction are reached:

- *Foundation* - for a slab foundation, before walls are poured. For a crawl-space foundation, before the floor is laid down. This inspection will permit inspection of the insulation and vapor barrier installed and the construction techniques (such as under-floor installation of ducts and hot-water pipes).

- *House bare-framed* - complete house inspection just before wiring, piping and insulation is installed. Inspection will permit a check to be made on room layout, position of window and door openings, closet locations, etc. Check for caulking of the sole (slab foundation) or plate (wood floor) at this time. If outer sheathing is in place, check that caulking and taping has been accomplished as specified in the building contract.

If windows and outer doors are installed, check for flashing and caulking details.

- *House all framed* - with house all framed but *before* sheet rock is installed but after wiring, water piping and insulation is installed—check most carefully for:

  - type, thickness and R value of wall and ceiling insulation and installation method (batts are butted against each other without gaps, etc.).

  - check no gaps in the installation are found around door and window openings. If any are found, see they are properly filled.

Check air conditioning ducting for proper duct runs and insulation value.

If daylight can be seen through any portion of the outer walls or around any window or outer door opening, have repaired as needed to block air flow (draft). This is your last chance to achieve a tight house.

- *House closed in* - with sheet rock in place on walls and ceilings, hot-water and air-conditioning systems installed—house is ready for interior finishing. Check for vent locations, hot-water tank(s) location and insulation, timer installation, compressor location outdoors, attic ventilation system, etc. For a crawl-space or basement-type foundation, determine any pipes, ducting or wiring penetrating flooring is sealed off to prevent drafts.

A suggested thought—if you make personal inspections on your own at any time workmen are present, *do not* discuss anything with the workmen but deal only with the building contractor or his approved supervisor directly. He will much appreciate your courtesy in this matter.

RETROFITTING CONTRACT

The energy savings made possible by retrofitting a home to achieve a high level of energy efficiency will result in excellent dollar savings. So much so that the retrofitting cost will be repaid in a few years. And, since much of the retrofitting work can be accomplished on a do-it-yourself (DIY) basis, the cost can be lower than expected.

The percentage of the energy-saving upgrading work you do yourself will depend upon your handy-man experience. The "Energy-Use Checkout List", starting on page 23-29, can be used as a guide as to what your home may need in the way of energy-use upgrading. This Checkout List can be used to develop your own list of what you want to do on an overall basis. The "Best Do-It-Yourself Order" list on page 23-28 should be consulted so you may organize your upgrading plans on a "best dollar-spent to dollar-saved" basis.

It is suggested that you do not tackle any that you feel may be outside your handy-man experience. Generally speaking, blowing or foaming in wall insulation is a specialists task and should not be done on a DIY basis. Most other upgrading tasks are less difficult but you must be your own judge as to those you feel confident you can handle.

Should you decide to have some of all of the retrofitting items accomplished by a contractor, the next question is "Who and what will be the cost?" Even now, retrofitting a house to reduce it's energy consumption is a new field and not many contractors have the required experience. Regretfully, one must be most careful in selection of a contractor both to obtain an experienced contractor who will quote a fair price and one who can do the work in a workmanlike manner. Many who list themself in the phone book and newspapers as "energy experts" really do not qualify as to knowledge and experience.

And, a few have entered the field with the intent to "charge whatever the traffic will bear." The author knows of a contractor who quoted "$3,100 for a complete storm-window installation," based on 11 windows. This works out to about $282.00 a window against a somewhat average cost of perhaps $50.00 per window.

As a guide, a somewhat "average" price or cost will be given for each of the retrofitting items discussed in Section 23. These prices cannot be guaranteed and may vary, even widely, on a city-by-city and state-by-state basis. However, the figures should help you to determine if the retrofitting bid is "in order." One should always get at least two bids and, preferably, three to gain confidence in the bid charges.

How to Avoid Dishonest Contractors

Know your home improvement contractor:

- Personal recommendations from other customers; or a check with the Better Business Bureau, a consumer protection office or a local home improvement licensing office may be helpful.

- Membership in a trade association may also provide some assurance of reliability.

Be wary of a phone or door-to-door solicitations. Rip-off artists often use this approach to make a sale.

Get bids from at least three contractors. Make sure the work to be done is clearly spelled out in the bid so you can make a valid comparison.

Know what to expect in terms of the quality of materials and installation procedures.

Check to be sure that you get what you pay for by making careful inspections when the work is completed.

Obtain a certificate from the contractor stating that the materials used and the work performed are as described in the bid.

Don't pay in advance. A down payment of 25% is almost always sufficient.

Be especially wary of claims that promise a specific dollar saving. Conditions vary and such claims can be misleading.

Section 23

Energy-Saving Upgrading

GENERAL

The very best time to incorporate energy-saving features into a home is during the construction period. At that time it is easier, quicker and less costly to install insulation, hang energy-efficient doors, caulk all possible draft sources, etc. Regretfully, once the outer and inner walls are covered, certain draft sources will thereafter be inaccessible.

However, even after a house is completed, excellent energy savings can be realized for that house—energy savings whose dollar return will more than justify the capital outlay required for the upgrading. In a recent pamphlet, the American Institute of Architects said:

"In existing buildings, fuel consumption could be reduced as much as 50 percent from current levels."

"Using conservative estimates of 30 percent savings for existing buildings . . ."

The amount of energy that can be saved by upgrading the energy efficiency of a home will largely depend upon two things:

- The current energy-efficiency level of the home—what amount, if any, insulation has been installed in walls, over ceilings, under floors and in the foundation, what kind of windows and doors were originally installed and what is their condition, is the attic ventilated, etc.

- The number of energy-saving features fitted into the house during the upgrade operation and the quality of both materials and workmanship.

What type of house needs energy-saving upgrading? In a broad sense, every house built to the "old" standards of energy efficiency, even if just recently completed. The range of upgrading needed is then that related to a "fairly-well insulated, fairly-tight house" to a "completely uninsulated house with poorly fitting doors and windows and with numerous draft sources." Today one reads about moderate-size homes whose energy bills (gas and electricity, mainly) are unbelievably high—such as "over $300.00 last month."

In line with the saying "There is no such thing as too much insurance," one could also say "There is no such thing as too much insulation." But, of course, there is a limit on each—a practical and economical limit. The practical limit is—"How much can I spend today, next year, etc. on energy-saving features" while the economical limit is "How much in energy dollars will I save?". These points will now be explored.

First—the houses which have energy bills as high as "$300.00 last month" and even higher. An inspection of these houses will reveal that many are rather old (from 20 to 50 years old) while others are somewhat younger but have not been maintained. These houses fall rather roughly into two categories: (1) those too old or rundown to be worth upgrading and (2) those solid enough and capable of being upgraded at a reasonable figure.

How can homes that have been maintained rather well run up such high energy bills? First, because they are either not insulated or, if insulated, the insulation is thin, of an inefficient type, and compacted by age. Next—and this is of utmost importance—they may leak air at a fantastic rate through the window and door openings and through the entire house envelope.

An existing house should be upgraded as to energy efficiency for the same reasons a new house should be built to achieve energy efficiency. These reasons are:

- to realize energy bills as much as 50 percent reduced from pre-upgrading levels.

- to achieve the true house comfort realizable only with a well-insulated and draft-free house.

- to ensure the total of energy used in the house will not exceed future energy limits that might be imposed.

- to make the house competitive in the house-sales market if it must be resold.

While the American Institute of Architects states "30 percent savings" as related to upgrading an existing home, it is felt that this statement relates more to houses that will require only a moderate amount of upgrading. For houses containing little or no insulation, poorly fitting outer doors and windows, and a leaky house envelope, savings in excess of 50 percent or more are entirely possible and have been attained by many.

The four-house heating/cooling energy comparison detailed on Page 7-3, Section 7, revealed the heating-/cooling energy saved by two houses (A and B) as a result of energy-efficiency upgrading. The energy and dollar savings are detailed by Table 7-5 (page 7-4) for the year 1976 as against the year 1975. The dollar savings indicated were: House A = $152.52 per year—House B = $149.08 per year. The estimated upgrading cost was $500.00 for each house, thus a payback time of less than 4 years is indicated.

UPGRADING COSTS

The actual cost to upgrade the energy efficiency of a given home is somewhat difficult to arrive at since so many factors must be taken into account. These factors are:

- Current energy-efficiency level of the home.
- Energy-saving features needed to upgrade the home to a meaningful level.
- Labor costs—this can vary widely depending upon:
  - work performed by owner.
  - work performed by handy-man labor.
  - work performed by highly-skilled labor.
  - hourly labor cost in house area.

The cost could thus run from as little as $1.00 per square foot of living space to a possible maximum of $3.00. One thing should be kept in mind:

"You will never be able to get it done for less—and—your savings start only when the job is done."

Not all the required upgrading need be done at the same time and excellent energy savings can be realized with relatively small capital outlay if "first-things-first" is practiced. Thus, the upgrading steps to follow will give best estimates on the "dollar-spent, dollar-gained" aspect of each upgrading step. A person could start with the least expensive steps first up to the amount of money currently available for energy-efficiency upgrading. Then, when more upgrading money can be set aside, further steps can be completed.

The attitude that you "shouldn't do anything if you can't do it all at once" is not good reasoning. Remember—the sooner you do any upgrading, the sooner you start to realize dollar savings and increased home comfort.

Before you—the home owner—start to upgrade the energy efficiency of your home—educate yourself. The

Bibliography lists manufacturer's pamphlets that often can be obtained directly and for free by visiting any large lumber yard or hardware store. If not available at the lumber yard or hardware store, write the listed companies. These pamphlets are most informative and very instructive and should be read even if you aren't planning to do any of the work yourself. The education will assure you that you or any one you may hire is doing the work properly.

In particular, a manual titled "In the Bank or Up the Chimney" issued by the Department of Housing and Urban Development (HUD) is highly recommended. This manual contains detailed instructions on how to install insulation, to mount storm windows, caulk draft sources, etc. The cost is $1.70 and the manual is available in book stores and even handled by lumber yards. Or, it can be ordered by mail, addressed to Superintendent of Documents, U.S. Gov't. Printing Office, Washington, D.C., 20402. Ask for Stock Number 023-000-00297-3, Cat. No. HH 1.613: EN 2/3. Price $1.70.

A thought here to those who might plan to perform as much of the upgrading they feel they can competently handle. Why not discuss energy-efficiency upgrading with a neighbor who has a somewhat similar home and problem. The old saying "two heads are better than one" has real meaning here. The information contained in the pamphlets and brochures listed in the Bibliography will easily ensure, if carefully followed, that the job will be done right. And, the extra care and attention you will naturally bring to the job will definitely ensure good workmanship. However, certain jobs (such as blowing insulation into walls) might best be left to a contractor as it requires special equipment and techniques somewhat hard to acquire.

As a part of the upgrading information to follow, suggestions will be given as to whether the related upgrading operation can be performed by the home owner, by a hired handyman (at lower than trade pay scale) or if the operation might best be performed by a contractor.

The first step in determining what can be done to upgrade the energy-use efficiency of an existing house is to make a complete survey of the house. To assist, an "Energy-Use Checkout List" for an existing home is provided at the end of this section.

DRAFT ELIMINATION

Elimination (or reduction) of drafts is of utmost importance both as to energy savings and home comfort and is—most happily—relatively easy to accomplish, is inexpensive, and returns maximum savings. The answer is—caulking—using a high grade caulking material, absolutely *never the cheapest*.

Only recently has the extreme bad effect drafts have on the energy efficiency and comfort of a home been fully realized. Be assured, most building contractors are just not aware that a drafty house is both a cold house and an expensive house to air condition. The author has checked numerous houses under construction to determine the level of caulking employed at each house. These houses ranged from $30,000.00 to over $100,000.00 in cost. To the author's amusement (and despair) he usually found from 1 to 3 tubes of rather cheap caulking material are used during the construction phase, regardless of the house cost. Just before the house is painted, a fair number of tubes of caulking are used but—these are used to fill cracks under the eaves (soffits) and in the wood sheathing, etc. to make the

painting job easier. This caulking will have little or no effect upon drafts entering through the house envelope or windows and outer doors. Thus, just assume your house completely lacks caulking and caulk everything you can get to.

The importance of using high-grade caulking material *cannot* be overemphasized. Inexpensive caulking material is a total waste—of time and money—as it will deteriorate to dust in just a year or two at best. An excellent caulking material is a silicone product sold by GE and DOW Chemical and obtainable in a variety of colors, including clear and white. This caulking material has two drawbacks: it is relatively expensive (try to buy

Caulking should be applied outside around window and door frames . . .

. . . . and wherever else two different materials or parts of the house meet.

Figure 23-1. Exterior of House - Major Caulking Points
(Developed by Federal Energy Administration)

it in bulk case lot) and does not take paint (thus the various colors made available). However, its long life (guaranteed 10 and 20 years) more than outweighs its cost—use no others.

The caulking gun required is relatively inexpensive ($2.00 or less) and is easy to use. However, one should follow good caulking practices:

- Be certain surface to be caulked is *clean of dust, dirt, oil, flaked paint*, etc.—otherwise the material will not stick tightly.

- Cracks of ½" or more in width or depth should first be filled with a more solid material (oakum, etc.), leaving just enough surface room for a bead of caulking material.

- Cracks should be filled to leave a slight concave surface, do not pile up caulking material to make a top bead.

- When caulking a vertical crack, fill from bottom—not from top down. This enables you to lay a neater bead.

- Always try to hold caulking gun to the crack such that the material will be forced deep into the crack—a little on the surface just won't last.

Weatherstripping is of extreme importance in reducing drafts around outer doors and windows. However, since this weatherstripping is particular to doors and windows, full coverage will be given under those subtitles.

Caulking building envelope - outside house (See Figure 23-1.)

- Around each window—both as forced under the window trim where it lays against the wall and used to seal the window frame to the window trim.

- Around each outer door trim—forced under the door trim and door sash—and under the sill piece (lift sill piece if felt necessary, lay down a bed of caulking where sill meets floor, and resecure sill *firmly* to the flooring).

- Around exterior of house where walls sit on foundation top. If any openings are found that appear as draft sources, caulk them solidly.

- Cracks or breaks in outer siding should be caulked. For a wood outer covering, caulk any joints or overlays and cracks, etc. For a brick or stone outer wall, check for any place mortar is missing or thin and refill (either with proper colored mortar or silicone caulking material).

Inside house

- A draft can enter the house through holes made in the floor (crawl space or basement type foundations only) for electrical cables, water pipes, etc. Seal these openings in any manner possible—caulking material, cement, wood inserts, etc. or stuff with batt-type insulation. Really large drafts can enter through these floor openings.

- Inner or outer walls, even if insulated between the studs, can introduce noticeable drafts through the wall openings

related to the wall switches or convenience outlets. If a draft is noted or considered possible, eliminate by stuffing opening in back of electrical box with batt-type insulation. Alternately, foam-rubber gaskets can be fitted under the wall switch and convenience outlet plates to stop these drafts. For details, refer to "Wall Outlets and Switches," page 14-6, Section 14.

- Floor-level drafts of considerable volume can enter through the outer walls and under the sill and exit out around the baseboard trim. A check should be made for drafts entering in this manner. If any are noted they can be eliminated by prying the baseboard loose and caulking the edge of the entire sill (or sole plate) where it rests on the floor. The baseboard can then be replaced. If carefully done, the baseboard can be removed without damage and may not need repainting. Any nail holes could be touched up.

- Fireplace—check carefully to see if the fireplace has a damper and, if it does, see that it closes tightly. If a damper is not provided (and it often isn't), fill the flue opening with batt-type insulation during any periods the fireplace is not used. Another remedy—solid screens with glass doors are available that can be fitted tightly into the fireplace opening and closed when the fireplace opening is not in use. (This screen also permits the fireplace opening to be closed off even when it has hot coals. This means warm air from the house will not be lost during the period the fire is dying down.)

- Recessed (bullit) lights in the ceiling can act to offer free passage of air between attic and house interior. Note that these lights must not be covered with insulation. Thus, if a recessed light provides an air passage, it is recommended that the passage be sealed with insulation material and the light disabled (or never turned on).

Exhaust fans must be equipped with a positive-action damper otherwise a very large flow of air can occur between the house interior and the outside. Any exhaust fan not equipped with a properly-operating damper should be repaired or replaced.

Caulking material cost—$10.00 to $20.00.
Labor time—4 to 8 hours. Low-skill work, easily done.
Return—can be very good dependent upon the number of drafts eliminated or reduced.

For additional details on draft prevention, refer to "Air Infiltration", Section 14.

NOTE

The art work (figures) on pages 23-5 through 23-23 were taken from "In the Bank or Up the Chimney" by HUD.

INSULATION INSTALLATION COSTS

The costs figures for insulation material and labor costs for installation are rising. Insulation is in short supply and costs can vary on both a local and seasonal basis. Labor costs are also likely to vary across the country. Therefore, exact figures cannot be given for either insulation materials or installation costs.

To a certain degree the cost to upgrade the energy efficiency of your home should not be your first consideration. The certain knowledge that energy costs will rise almost endlessly and that insulation material and labor costs will most likely never be lower than they are today should be kept in mind. Estimated payback periods of even up to 10 years should be considered from the viewpoint that increased energy costs will surely result in increased dollar savings in the future and thus an estimated payback period of 10 years as of today may actually be reduced to 8 or even 7 years or less.

ATTIC INSULATION

Dollar Return. Suggested insulation levels (R-Values) are given for five (5) climatic zones by figure 9-3, page 9-9. Alternately, the amount of insulation considered practical to install in your area for walls, floors and ceilings may be determined by neighbor experience and recommendation or by inquiring at your local power company. Keep in mind the future cost of energy when determining the amount of insulation to install.

For R-Values per inch for different kinds of insulation, refer to "Insulation", page 5-3, Section 5.

Vapor Barrier. An uninsulated attic will most certainly not be equipped with a vapor barrier. If the attic floor, walls or roof are already insulated and more is required, be certain not to install a vapor barrier or vapor-barrier backed batts (or blankets) over the existing insulation. If attic insulation is already installed, determine if a vapor barrier exists under the insulation. If not, it would be well to provide a vapor barrier even if more insulation is not installed. For vapor barrier details, refer to "Vapor Barriers", page 5-9, Section 5.

Ventilation. The "new" outlook on energy-saving home construction stresses attic ventilation to reduce humidity build up in the winter and heat build up in the summer. To determine if your attic is properly ventilated to the "new" standards, review "Attic Ventilation", page 15-2, Section 15. If ventilation volume is considered inadequate or true cross-flow ventilation is not provided, this must be remedied to ensure maximum energy-saving efficiency is realized by the attic insulation.

Roof Leakage. Wet insulation loses most of its insulation efficiency and holds moisture (resulting in a humid attic area). Thus, check the roof for leaks, repairing all leaks before the insulation is installed.

Measurement - Insulated Area. The attic area to be insulated must be rather accurately measured so that you may obtain the proper amount of insulation. Note that unopened bundles of batts or blankets or bags of loose-fill or blown-in material can usually be returned. Of course, check with the supplier on this. Foamed-in material is a special case since it must be installed by a contractor who will bid his job on an R-Value per square-foot basis.

Attic-measurement details for each type of attic will be covered separately in the individual attic sections to follow. Once the square footage to be insulated is determined, the amount of insulation required can then be determined. For R-Values per inch for different kinds of insulation, refer to Table 5-3.

Tools Required.

1. Temporary lighting
2. Temporary flooring
3. Duct or masking tape (2" wide)
4. Heavy duty staple gun and staples, or hammer and tacks
5. Heavy duty shears or linoleum knife to cut batts or blankets and plastic for vapor barrier

Safety Measures.

1. Provide good lighting.
2. Lay boards or plywood sheets down over the tops of the joists or trusses to form a walkway (the ceiling below won't support your weight).
3. Be careful of roofing nails protruding through roof sheathing.
4. If you use glass fiber or mineral wool, wear gloves and breathing mask, and keep the material wrapped until you're ready to put it in place.

Attic Types. Most attics fall into one of the following categories:

- Unfinished - Without Floor
- Unfinished - With Floor
- Flat/Mansard Roofed
- Finished
- Combination - Finished/Unfinished

UNFINISHED ATTIC - WITHOUT FLOOR

Unfinished Attic without a floor. (Attic isn't used at all): (this includes Attics with *roof trusses* in them.)

Measurement. The attic area, in most cases, can be measured without going up into the attic. Most houses are constructed as one or more rectangles or as a square. The length and width of the house can be measured and multiplied together to obtain the overall square-foot size of the house. For L-shaped or U-shaped houses, measure each rectangular portion separately as to width and length, multiply the values, and add up all values. Next, measure the width and length of all area that are not air conditioned (such as the garage, a porch, etc.). This square footage must then be deducted from the overall square-footage figure to arrive at the total area requiring insulation. This figure is then multiplied by 0.9 to compensate for the wood framing. For a two-story house, if any air-conditioned second-floor area is above the garage (for example) and the floor and outer walls of that area are insulated, the attic floor over that area must be insulated. In this case, the garage area cannot be deducted from the overall area.

The resultant square-footage figure then identifies the total area of the attic to be insulated.

Installation Method. An unfinished attic floor, dependent upon ease of access, can be easy or difficult to insulate. Generally speaking it is a rather unskilled task and can usually be considered a DIY (do-it-yourself) job. Full insulation detailed are given by figure 23-2.

It should be noted that some insulation sellers (Wards, for example), will loan use of a blower machine if blown-in material is purchased from them. Also, note that if the needed R-Value of insulation is to be made up using two layers of batts or blankets and the attic contains roof trusses, the second layer may not easily fit across the first layer at right angles. In such a case, blown-in insulation should be considered to be blown in over the first layer to raise the insulation to the desired level.

PREPARATION

Put in temporary lighting and flooring, check for leaks and check need for ventilation and vapor barrier. Seal all places where pipes or wires penetrate the attic floor. **NOTE:** Some manufacturers may recommend using polyethylene in a continuous sheet across the joists or trusses. If you aren't adding insulation that covers the tops of these framing members with at least 3½" of insulation, laying a continuous sheet may cause condensation along them: lay strips as shown instead.

UNFINISHED ATTIC - WITH FLOOR

Unfinished Attic with a floor. (Attic can be used for storage.)

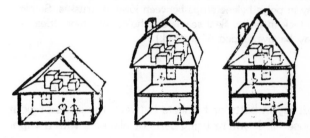

Figure 23-2. Unfinished Attic Insulation Installation

1

Install temporary flooring and lights. Keep insulation in wrappers until you are ready to install. It comes wrapped in a compressed state and expands when the wrappers are removed.

2

Check for roof leaks, looking for water stains or marks. If you find leakage, make repairs before you insulate. Wet insulation is ineffective and can damage the structure of your home.

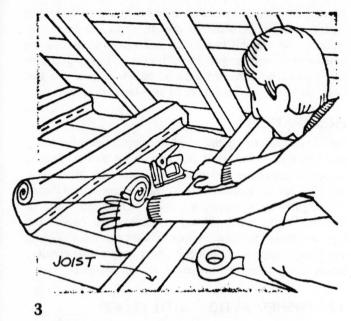

JOIST

3

Install separate vapor barrier if needed.
Lay in polyethylene strips between joists or trusses. Staple or tack in place. Seal seams and holes with tape. (Seams may be overlapped 6" instead.)

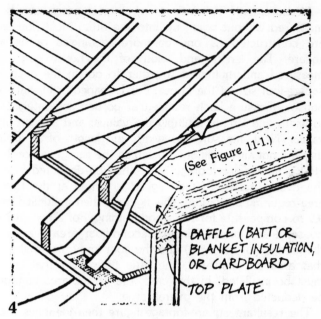

(See Figure 11-1.)

BAFFLE (BATT OR BLANKET INSULATION, OR CARDBOARD

TOP PLATE

4

If you're using loose fill, install baffles at the inside of the eave vents so that the insulation won't block the flow of air from the vents into the attic. Be sure that insulation extends out far enough to cover the top plate.

Either lay in batts or blankets between the joists or pour in loose fill. If you're using batts or blankets with a vapor barrier, place the barrier on the side toward the living area.

OR

5

Lay in blankets or batts between joists or trusses. (Note: batts and blankets are slightly wider than joist spacing so they'll fit snugly). If blankets are used, cut long runs first to conserve material, using leftovers for shorter spaces. Slide insulation under wiring wherever possible.

LOOSE FILL

6

Pour in loose fill insulation between the joists up to the top of the joists. Use a board or garden rake to level it. Fill all the nooks and crannies but don't cover recessed light fixtures or exhaust fans.

The space between the chimney and the wood framing should be filled with *non-combustible* material, preferably unfaced batts or blankets. Also, the National Electric Code requires that insulation be kept 3" away from light fixtures.

Cut ends of batts or blankets to fit snugly around cross bracing. Cut the next batt in a similar way to allow the ends to butt tightly together. If needed R-Value requires a second layer, place it at right angles to the joists.

The flooring in an unfinished attic somewhat complicates insulation installation. The first decision to be made is—"Will you ever finish the floored area?" If the answer is "yes", it should be more economical, at this time, to insulate the rafters, end walls, and collar beams rather than to insulate under the floor boards. The attic will thus be ready for finishing and will not require insulation. For details, see "Between Rafter Installation" that follows.

If the answer is "no", the next question is—"Can the floor boards be pulled up without undue damage to them?". If they can, batt, blanket, or loose-fill can be easily and economically installed. If the boards cannot be pulled up, the underfloor insulation must be installed by a contractor by being blown in. If you really want to insulate the attic yourself, you might consider getting a contractor bid for blowing the insulation under the floor boards and compare this bid with the insulation job you could do on a "finish the attic later" basis.

Underfloor Installation. The attic floor area to be insulated can be determined in the same manner detailed for an unfinished, unfloored attic. If the attic flooring covers only a part of the attic and the floor boards cannot be pulled up, two types of insulation may be used—batts or blankets for the uncovered portion and blown-in for under the attic flooring. Thus, two measurements must be made. This can be done by measuring the entire area as previously described and then measur-

ing the floored area. This area can then be deducted from the entire-area figure to arrive at the actual area requiring batts or blankets and the under-floor area.

The area not covered by flooring can be insulated as detailed by figure 23-2 as may the floored area if the boards can be pulled up. For under-floor installation, contractor-installation is recommended. If batts, blankets, or loose-fill insulation is fitted between the joists upon which the floor boards rest, do not raise the insulation height to where the insulation is above the top of the joists. Otherwise, insulation compression with an attendant loss of insulation efficiency will occur when the floor boards are replaced.

Between-Rafter Installation. This installation method is economical only if you plan to finish the floored portion of the attic at some later time or if the floor boards cannot be pulled up and the contractor price for under-floor installation exceeds the between-rafters cost as accomplished on a DIY basis.

Installation can be accomplished in either of two ways. (1) Batts of blanket insulation as installed between the rafters from the floor line right up to the top (ridge line). Next, batts or blankets are fitted between the wall studs at each end wall, running from the floor line up to the roof. This is a simple method but does use more insulation since the insulation is brought right up to the ridge line and roof.

(2) The second method required the installation of col-

lar beams, made of 2 x 4's and fitted across between the rafters at the desired height (usually about 7' up from the floor level. These beams will act to provide support for batt or blanket insulation and thus less insulation is required since the rafter and end-wall insulation need only run up to the collar beams.

Measurement details are as follows:

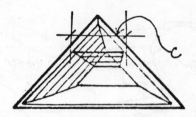

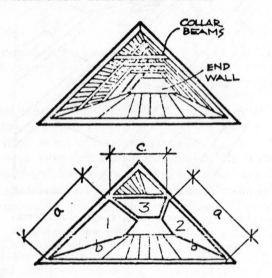

Rafter area = width (a) x length (b) x 0.9 = total, one side (items 1 & 2) total (one side) x 2 sides = total rafter area
Ceiling area = width (c) x length (b) x 0.9 (total area, item 3) End wall = see below

Figure out the area of each end wall you want to insulate. Measure (d) and (e) and multiply to determine the area. Multiply by (.9) to correct for the space taken up by the studs, then multiply by the number of end walls.

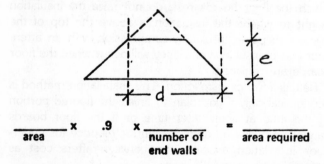

$$\underline{\hspace{2cm}} \times \ .9 \ \times \ \underline{\hspace{2cm}} = \underline{\hspace{2cm}}$$
area   number of   area required
            end walls

Calculate the length of 2x4 stock you'll need for collar beams. Measure the length of span you need between rafters (c) and count the number of collar beams you need to install. Multiply to get the length of stock you need. You can have the lumber yard cut it to length at a small charge. If you cut it yourself, allow for waste. If you plan to finish your attic, check with your lumber yard to make sure 2" x 4"'s are strong enough to support the ceiling you plan to install.

Collar-Beam Installation. First, check roof for leaks, looking for water stains or marks. Make any needed roof repairs before you insulate. Determine need for ventilation. Put up adequate temporary lights.

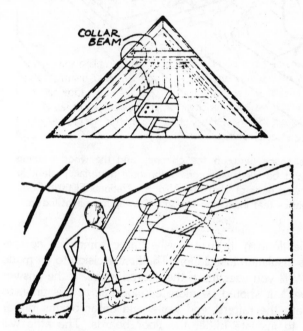

1. Install 2x4 collar beams spanning from rafter to rafter at the ceiling height you want. Every pair of rafters should have a collar beam spanning between them.

   Note: If you're installing new insulation over existing insulation:

   Between the Rafters and Between the End Wall Studs, cut the old insulation loose where it has been stapled, push it to the back of the cavities, and slash the old vapor barrier (if any) before you lay the new insulation over it.

   Between the Collar Beams, lay the new insulation above the old. Lay it over the tops of the collar beams in an unbroken layer at right angles to the beams. Use insulation that does not have a vapor barrier for this part of the job. If you can't get insulation without a vapor barrier, slash the vapor barrier before laying it down, so that moisture won't get trapped in the insulation.

2. Install batts or blanket sections in place between the rafters and collar beams. Install with the vapor barrier

on the inside, the side toward you. Don't try to use a continuous length of insulation where the collar beams meet the rafters. It will only result in gaps that are very hard to fill. Install batts in the end walls the same way. Be sure to trim carefully to fit the angles on the end walls.

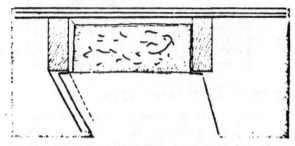

3. Install batts or blanket sections by stapling the facing flange to the *edge* of the rafter or collar beam. Don't staple to the outside of the rafters; the vapor barrier will have a break at every rafter; and you may compress the insulation against the sheathing, reducing its insulating value.

FINISHED ATTIC

Finished Attic that can be used for living or storage.

A finished attic may be somewhat more difficult to insulate than an unfinished one, depending upon ease of access. The following are generally insulated:

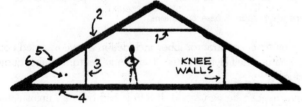

1. Attic Ceiling
2. Rafters
3. Knee Walls
4. Outer Attic Floors, or
5. Outer Attic Rafters
6. End Walls

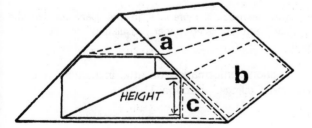

Measurement. Measure as follows:

a - Attic Ceiling (1) = length x width x 0.9

b - Outer-Attic Rafters (5) = length x width x 0.9
(There may be several such areas—add totals together.)

c - Outer-Attic Gables (6) = length x width x 0.9
Since Area is a triangle, total must be divided by 2 to obtain actual area. This total is then multiplied by 4 (there are 4 gable) to arrive at the overall total.

- Knee Walls (3) = length x width x 0.9 x 2 (for 2 walls)

- Outer-Attic Floor (4) = length x width x 0.9 x 2 Insulate floor only if over an air-conditioned area and Outer-Wall Rafter insulation is not used.

Attic Ceiling. Can be insulated only if accessible by means of a door or hatch way. If attic ceiling is not insulated, insulate as detailed by figure 23-2 for an unfinished attic. If attic ceiling is insulated and more is required, do not use vapor-barrier backed insulation over existing insulation. Insulation used can be either batts, blanket, loose-fill, flown-in or foamed-in type. Vapor barrier must be installed and face inside of room.

Inner Rafters. If not covered, can be filled with batt or blanket material, with vapor-barrier side towards inside of room. If area is covered and covering cannot be removed, can be filled with blown-in or foamed-in insulation as detailed for walls. Refer to "Walls", page 23-12.

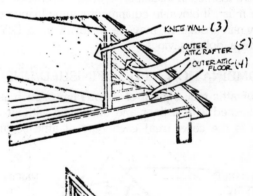

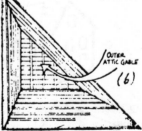

Knee Walls. If not covered on the back side, can be filled with batt or blanket material—with vapor-barrier side towards inside of room. If covered on back side and covering cannot be removed, can be filled with blown-in or foamed-in insulation as detailed for walls. Refer to "Walls", page 23-12.

Outer-Attic Rafters or Outer-Attic Floor. To completely insulate the living area below the attic floor from the attic area, either the attic floor or the rafters must be insulated. If the outer-attic rafters are to be insulated, install batt or blanket material between rafters as previously detailed for Attic Ceiling except vapor-barrier side must face towards the attic. If the floor is to be insulated, batt, blanket, loose-fill, blown-in or foamed-in material may be used. Vapor barrier must face living area below attic floor.

End Walls. If not covered or if covered and the covering can be removed, insulate with batt or blanket material as detailed for walls. Refer to "Walls", page 23-12. If the stud cavities are covered and the covering cannot be removed, fill with blown-in or foamed-in insulation as detailed for walls. Vapor-barrier side must face inside of room.

Floor. With the entire outside of the finished attic section insulated, the area under the attic floor need not be insulated.

Ventilation. Attic ventilation, especially in older houses, is usually inadequate or may be totally lacking. Proper ventilation, both as to air-flow volume and cross-flow ventilation, must be provided and be adequate to reduce the summer load on the air-conditioning system.

Installation Method. Where ease of access is provided, insulation can be rather easily installed. In any case where foamed-in insulation is used, contractor installation is a must. If blown-in equipment can be loaned or rented, blown-in insulation may be installed on a DIY basis at quite a dollar savings.

COMBINATION ATTIC - FINISHED/UNFINISHED

Your attic may consist of various types, such as finished, unfinished with a floor and unfinished without a floor. If this is the case, treat each type of attic separately.

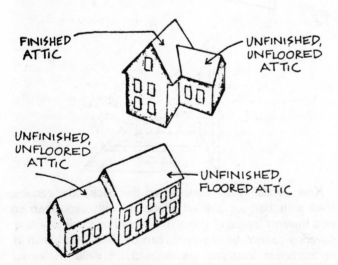

FLAT/MANSARD ROOFED

If your home has a flat roof, or a mansard roof, it will be harder and more expensive to insulate than the others—talk to a contractor.

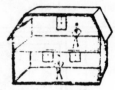

COST ESTIMATES—ANY ATTIC

Labor costs can be determined only on a local basis. Labor time is most difficult to estimate, with ease of access to the attic area being of prime importance as related to a low-hour labor time. However, it should be noted that insulation may be poured in, blown in or foamed in much more quickly than if batt or blanket material is used. Blowing insulation into an attic is a relatively simple task, requiring primarily that you blow in "just enough" per square foot to achieve the desired insulation (R-Value) as specified on the material bag. One caution—exercise extreme care not to blow insulation material such that it covers the eave (soffit) vents (if existing). Note caution related to item 4, figure 23-2.

Some average costs for the Austin, Texas area as of September 1979, are as follows:

6" vapor barrier batts, not installed	= 18¢ per square foot
6" batts, no vapor barrier, not inst.	= 16¢ per square foot
6" vapor barrier batts, installed	= 35¢ per square foot or more*
12" vapor batts installed, 1 vapor barrier	= 55¢ per square foot or more*
6" rock wool blown in (R19)	= 32¢ per square foot
8" glass wool blown in (R19)	= 32¢ per square foot
12" rock wool blown in (R38)	= 45¢ per square foot
16" glass wool blown in (R38)	= 55¢ per square foot

*Depending upon access conditions.

Labor time—contractor labor included in above installed cost estimates. Self-laying batts—too many factors make quote difficult.

Return—can be very good. If R19 is laid over an uninsulated ceiling, payback period will be less than 5 years. R19 laid over R19 does not return savings at same rate as first R19—has a payback period up to 10 years except when electric-strip heating is used.

Suggested instruction material—"In the Bank or Up the Chimney" and as listed under "Insulation" in the Bibliography.

For additional information on attic insulation, refer to "Walls and Ceilings," Section 11.

OUTER WALL INSULATION

Upgrading the insulation efficiency of an outer wall is expensive, so costly in most cases that a payback period of up to 10 years is indicated. Yet, energy loss through the walls is costly, a cost that goes on and on with the years and increases as energy costs rise.

An outer wall in an existing house may either be insulated to a less-than needed level or have no insulation at all. If the wall contains insulation between the studs, extra insulation *must not* be pumped or blown into the wall cavity since to do so would simply compress the existing and new insulation and result in a net lower-than-before R value.

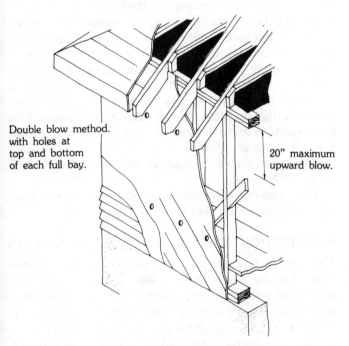

Double blow method.
with holes at
top and bottom
of each full bay.

20" maximum
upward blow.

Figure 23-3. Outer Wall Access to Cavities

Installation Method. If the outer wall does not contain insulation, insulation may be pumped or blown into the wall cavities. Two basic methods are used:

1. The upper board of the siding is removed to gain access to the wall cavities, the material is pumped or blown in and the board is replaced.

2. If the above cannot be done, holes (usually 15/16ths in diameter) are drilled midway between each stud pair (16-inch stud spacing is standard) high up in the outer wall covering. The insulation is then blown or pumped in and the holes are filled with wood plugs. See figure 23-3.

Note

In some areas, a piece of wood is nailed as a fire break between each stud pair halfway up between the wall cavity. In this case, the entry (drill holes or remove siding board) must be done at the top and again at the bottom

above the foundation top. Local building codes will indicate if fire blocking is required and is thus present in the walls of the house.

Two types of insulation material are used. First—a foam type (ureaformaldehyde) pumped in under high pressure, acting to expand and harden in seconds. This material can raise the R-Value of a 3½" stud wall to about R11.5. Secondly, a glass fiber or rock wool material can be blown in, raising the R-Value of a 3½" wall to between R8 and R10. Cellulosic fiber also may be blown in, acting to raise the R-Value of a 3½" wall to about R10 or better. Note that the R-Values given are effective values and take into account the insulation-value reduction due to the wood framing in the walls.

Brick-veneer houses can be treated in much the same manner as for a house having wood or other type of outer siding. In such a case however, it may be easier (and thus cheaper) if the holes (figure 23-3) are drilled in the inside walls since to remove bricks is difficult and can result in breakage. The holes in the inside walls can be covered with a wide moulding board to make an attractive cover for the holes.

Considerable experience and good equipment is required to properly pump or blow insulation into an outer wall. It is thus recommended that a contractor be employed for such an installation.

Note

Do not guess if walls have insulation—you must know before additional material is pumped or blown in. To check, open circuit breaker to remove power from a wall switch or outlet. Remove plate and try to see into the wall cavity. Fish around with a wire to bring out insulation material, if present. If still not positive, drill small hole through inner wall and see what the drill brings out. A clean drill means no insulation.

The siding, in some cases, can be removed with only minor (and repairable) damage occurring to the siding material. In this case, the siding and then the outer sheathing can be carefully removed and batt or blanket insulation can be fitted into the wall cavities. Note that if a vapor barrier is needed, vapor-barrier backed material should be used. Be certain to open circuit breaker or remove fuse related to wiring in wall being worked on.

If it is desired to raise the R-Value of the wall above that which can be realized with material completely filling the wall cavities, the original outer sheathing can be replaced with insulation (rigid-foam) panels. A one-inch thick panel of Styrofoam will raise the insulation value by about R5.6 and a one-inch thick piece of TF-400 will raise it by about R8.

If the wall cavities are filled with insulation and a higher R-Value is desired or if insulation cannot be pumped or blown into the wall, another insulation method can be used. That is, rigid panels of Styrofoam or TF-400 or other types may be nailed directly over the interior-wall covering. For one-inch thick panels, Styrofoam will raise the R-Value by about R5.6 and TF-400 by about R8. Since this will bring the wall surface out from the switch and convenience outlet boxes, spacers would have to be used. That is, longer bolts would be required, with spacers fitted over them to bring out the switch or wall socket part to be flush with the new wall line. Enough slack in the wiring will surely permit the switch or convenience outlet parts to be moved out up to two inches, if needed. Note that the insulation panels *must* be covered for fire hazard and damage reasons. This can be accomplished by covering the panels with sheet rock (⅜" thick) or by paneling. Other rigid-foam panels are available with sheet rock or paneling already glued to the panels. Note that TF-400 panels are aluminum-foil covered on both sides. This can present a problem if a vapor barrier is presently installed in the wall cavities. Check with the TF-400 manufacturer's representative for preventative measures.

Vapor Barrier. If a vapor barrier is required (see "Vapor Barriers, page 5-9, Section 5), a low-permeable paint can be used to paint the inner wall surfaces. This paint can then be painted over with a more typical wall paint.

Measurement. The square footage of the wall area to be insulated can be obtained as follows: Measure length and height of each wall. Multiply these two figures to obtain the overall square footage. Next, measure the height and width of all windows (and doors if part of a wall). Calculate the square footage for each and deduct the total from the overall square footage. Also, if part of the wall faces an area not being air conditioned, deduct the square feet of this area from the overall total.

Costs. Blowing or pumping insulation into the wall is a fairly expensive operation. The care taken in the installation coupled with a wide experience determines to a large degree the insulation efficiency (R-Value) of the finished wall. It is thus recommended that an insulation contractor with a good reputation be employed. Ask for customer references—a good firm will have same.

The basic price will vary depending upon:

- Square footage to be filled.
- Ease of access (remove top siding board or drill holes).

Prices are on the increase and insulation is actually in short supply. Actual cost figures are thus a matter of local conditions. Prices in the Austin, Texas area for late 1979 were:

> 35¢ per square foot for a 3½" deep wall—if owner removes siding board or drills holes and replaces

siding board or repairs holes. Hole plugs provided by contractor.

> 50¢ per square foot—contractor does all.

Return: Installation costs can be high but excellent savings will be returned with added comfort being realized as an added benefit. A payback period of 10 years or less is indicated even at today's energy prices.

Removal of the outer siding and sheathing can permit batt or blanket insulation to be used. Material cost is thus lower than for a blow-in or foamed-in operation. However, labor costs would be very high unless accomplished on a do-it-yourself basis. The payback time might run from a minimum of 5 years (low labor costs) to 10 years or less (contractor does all).

Installation of rigid-foam panels against the inner surface of the outer walls is a fairly expensive operation. The foam panels must be covered. If sheet rock (gypsum board) is used, surface must be spray coated and leveled out (nailing dents obscured). This can be moderately expensive and must be done (usually) by a contractor. Covering the rigid-foam panels with paneling would be less expensive as to labor costs. A payback time of from 5 to 10 years is indicated.

Suggested instruction material—see "Insulation Panels" in the Bibliography.

For additional information on wall insulation R values, etc., refer to "Walls and Ceilings", Section 11.

FOUNDATION AND UNDERFLOOR INSULATION

The energy loss through the foundation walls is the greatest in the winter and the least in the summer. The amount of foundation wall above the ground level has a large effect upon the energy loss through the wall since earth is a relatively good insulator. The dollar-spent versus dollar-return for foundation and under-floor insulation is generally less than that related to insulating or raising the insulation level of ceilings and walls.

SLAB FOUNDATION WALLS

Installation Method. Concrete is a very good conductor of heat thus if the slab walls are exposed to the elements (especially if the walls are high), a fairly high heat loss or gain can result. Slab walls can be insulated by gluing insulation panels (1" to 2" thick) to the walls by a special glue. The earth near the wall should first be dug down to the frost line and the insulation should extend from that point right up flush with the wall siding (see figure 23-4).

Since the insulation panels (Styrofoam, TF-400 etc.) are fragile and will burn, they must be covered with a noncombustible material. Asbestos board, ¼" thick, is often used—glued directly to the insulation panels. Or, a thin coating of cement (stucco) can be troweled completely over the panels.

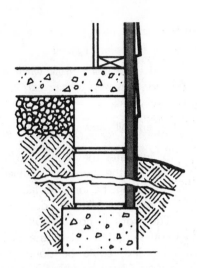

Figure 23-4. Slab Foundation Wall Insulation Details

Insulation panels 1" to 2" thick can be used. A 2" thick panel of Styrofoam will raise the insulation value of the wall to about R11+ and 2" panel of TF-400 to about R15+. The installation is easy but fairly time consuming and can be done by anyone with moderate carpentry experience.

Cost. 1" thick panels of Styrofoam cost about 25¢ per square foot and 1" thick TF-400 panels about 35¢ per square foot. Asbestos board (¼" thick) would run about 25¢ per square foot while stucco (for materials only) would be fairly inexpensive though it would take more labor. A 1500-square foot house would have about 240 square feet (maximum) of slab foundation wall to insulate. For 1" panels on a do-it-yourself basis, a total cost of about $100.00 is estimated. For 2" paneling, add about $35.00. For contract costs, price would be about double.

Return. Initial cost in relation to return is relatively high and the savings realized are such that a payback time of 5 years or more is indicated on a do-it-yourself basis at today's energy costs.

Note. Adding 2" of insulation to the wall plus the outer covering may bring the wall out past the wall siding. If so, a piece of trim (1" x 2") can be nailed to be flush with the paneling and to blend the wall and siding together. Caulk the trim where it touches the insulation panels and the wall siding.

Other Methods. If desired, slab foundation walls can be insulated rather economically by heaping dirt against the walls. A raised flower bed, for example, can be used to cover the walls and thus prevent heat transfer into and out of the walls since dirt is a rather good insulator compared to concrete. The dirt level should be kept at least six inches below the wood frame of the house to prevent termite or insect invasion.

Another inexpensive means to insulate foundation walls is through the use of dense shrubs, planted close to the walls. The shrubs tend to keep the sun's rays off the walls and thus act to lower the temperature immediately against the foundation walls. In winter, the shrubs act as a barrier to wind action and thus tend to keep the foundation walls warmer than if they were bare to the wind.

If the foundation walls are very high (on steep hills some may be 10 feet or more high), thick vines could be planted and trained to cover the entire foundation wall. The insulation effect of shrubs or vines has been tested and found to be excellent. Further, since concrete (in mass) is not overly attractive, the shrubs and vines also tend to make the home more attractive.

CRAWL-SPACE FOUNDATIONS

Sealed Crawl Space. If a crawl space is sealed (not ventilated), the outer surface of the foundation walls can be insulated or shielded in the same manner detailed for slab-foundation walls. Alternately, the inner surface of the foundation walls can be insulated as follows:

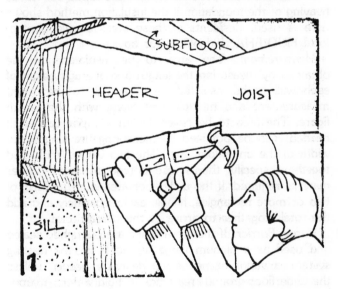

Drawing 1: Where the joists run at right angles to the wall, press short pieces of insulation against the Header—they should fit snugly. Then install the wall and perimeter insulation by nailing the top of each strip to the Sill using the ½" x 1½" nailers. Make sure the batts fit snugly against each other, and that you cut them long enough to cover 2 feet of floor as in Drawing 2.

Drawing 2: Where the joists run parallel to the wall, you don't need the short pieces of insulation, just install the wall and perimeter insulation by nailing the top of each strip to the Band Joist, using the ½" x 1½" nailers.

When all batts have been installed, lay down the polyethylene vapor barrier, tucking it under the batts all the way to the foundation wall. Tape the joints of the vapor barrier or lap them at least 6". Finally lay 2 x 4 lumber along the wall on top of the batts to weight the batts in place. (Rocks work well, too) Plan your work to minimize stepping or crawling on the vapor barrier.

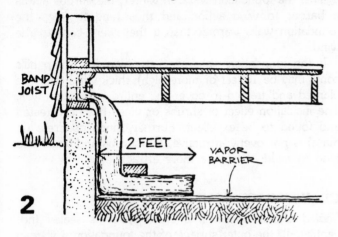

NOTE: This method of installation should not be used for homes in Alaska, Minnesota, and northern Maine. The extreme frost penetration in these areas can cause heaving of the foundation if the insulation method shown here is used. Residents of these areas should contact local HUD/FHA field offices for advice.

Measurement. The area to be insulated can be obtained by measuring the length and average height of each wall to be insulated. Next, add 3' to the height measurement and multiply that figure with the length figure. The area to be covered with a vapor barrier (if needed) can be obtained by measuring the length and width of the underfloor area. The two values, multiplied together, specify the square-footage of vapor-barrier material required. If the underfloor area is in the form of two or more rectangles, handle each separately and add the totals together to arrive at the overall total.

Vapor Barrier. If the crawl-space area is tightly sealed and used as a plenum (large air duct) for the heating system, a vapor barrier is not generally needed unless the underfloor ground-area tends to hold water. A vapor barrier, if used, should be installed to good practices—overlapped 6" at seams or taped at the seams and weighed down with boards, rocks or sand at the foundation wall edges.

Tools Required.

1. Hammer and nails

2. Heavy duty shears or linoleum knife

3. Temporary lighting

4. Portable fan or blower to provide ventilation

5. Tape measure

6. Duct or Masking Tape (2" wide)

Safety Measures.

1. Provide adequate temporary lighting

2. Wear gloves and a breathing mask when working with glass fiber or rock wool

3. Provide adequate ventilation

4. Keep lights, fan, and all wires well off wet ground

Cost. Costs to insulate the outer surface of the foundation walls will be the same as detailed for slab-foundation walls. Insulating the inner surface can be time consuming and somewhat difficult due to cramped working spaces. The work is not difficult and could be done as a do-it-yourself item. Also, the laying of the vapor barrier, if needed, could be done in the same manner. The cost would then be only the material which should not be high.

Return. Initial cost in relation to return is relatively high and the savings realized may be such that a payback time of 5 years or less is indicated for a do-it-yourself job or about 10 years or less for a contractor job.

VENTILATED CRAWL SPACE

The floors, not the foundation walls, of a ventilated (open) crawl space foundation must be insulated. The insulation method is the same as detailed for "Underfloor Insulation" that follows except for the following special problems.

- Limited Working Height. Working laying on your back with your arms overhead can be very tiring. Thus, it is suggested that you use batt or blanket material that can be stapled to the floor joists (item 4, figure 23-5). An electric staple gun can be rented and is recommended for ease of operation and speed.

- Vapor Barrier. If the house is set on pier and beams, the resulting excellent cross ventilation will reduce any chance for humidity build up. However, if the house sets on foundation walls, numerous vents must be built into the walls—placed to ensure cross ventilation. If the ground tends to hold moisture and the house area experiences moderate to heavy rainfalls, a vapor barrier should be installed. The vapor barrier might best be laid down after the insulation is installed to prevent damage. Any rips or tears in the plastic film must be repaired if proper vapor-barrier action is to result. Note that this vapor barrier, if laid, does not remove the need for a vapor barrier under the floor. This underfloor vapor barrier is usually gained by using vapor-barrier backed insulation batts or blankets.

The vents in the foundation wall can be closed (tightly) in the winter to make the most of the underfloor insulation. However, if the furnace obtains combustion air from the crawl-space area, some of the vents must be left open. Check with your local HUD/FHA office.

UNDERFLOOR INSULATION

Worthwhile energy savings and increased comfort (warmer floors) will be realized if floors over the following areas are insulated:

- Ventilated Crawl Space
- Ventilated Basement
- Heated Area Over Garage, Porch, or other cold unheated area

The "new" standards of underfloor insulation recommends R19 (6" batts) for any area experiencing moderate to severe winters. The FHA Minimum Property Standards specifies a minimum of R11 (3" batts) and this is now considered adequate only in areas experiencing mild winters. Underfloor insulation is particularly effective in preventing heat loss from the house in the winter.

Underfloor installation of insulation is not difficult except for crawl space with less than 30" of underfloor clearance. Underfloor installation is thus a do-it-yourself task, if desired.

Measurements. The area to be insulated can be determined by measuring the length and width of the area and multipling the two to obtain the overall square footage total. It may be necessary to divide the floor into smaller areas as related to measurements and to add the individual square-footage totals to arrive at the overall total. If wire mesh or chicken wire (see below) is to be used to hold up the insulation, the overall square-footage total identifies the amount of mesh or wire required. This total also identifies the amount of vapor barrier (usually a plastic film) required to be laid on the ground of a crawl space (ventilated or unventilated). The square-footage actually to be covered with insulation can be determined by multiplying the overall total by 0.9 to compensate for the area covered by the floor joists.

Installation Methods. The batt or blanket insulation fits between the floor joists, vapor-barrier side up towards the living area. Three basic methods for holding the insulation material up between the joists are available. These are illustrated by figure 23-5.

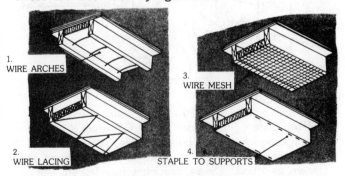

1. WIRE ARCHES
2. WIRE LACING
3. WIRE MESH
4. STAPLE TO SUPPORTS

Figure 23-5. Underfloor Insulation Installation

The batts fit between the floor joists, vapor barrier up towards the living area. Three methods of installation are used:

- Batts are pressed up between joists and held up by nailing wide-meshed wire (chicken wire) or wire lacing across the joists.
- Batts are pressed between joists and held up by spring wires (wire arches) pressed between the joists.
- Special batts are provided that have a stapling flange that fits against the joist bottom, allowing easy stapling.

Start at a wall at one end of the joists and work out. Staple the wire to the bottom of the joists, and at right angles to them. Slide batts in on top of the wire. Work with short sections of wire and batts so that it won't be too difficult to get the insulation in place. Plan sections to begin and end at obstructions such as cross bracing.

Buy insulation with a vapor barrier, and install the vapor barrier facing up (next to the warm side) leaving an air space between the vapor barrier and the floor. Get foil-faced insulation if you can; it will make the air space insulate better. Be sure that ends of batts fit snugly up against the bottom of the floor to prevent loss of heat up end. Don't block combustion air openings for furnaces.

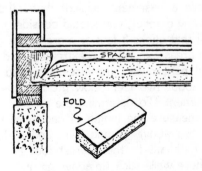

Floor joists are generally spaced apart on 16" or 24" centers and batt and blanket material sized to fit snugly between either spacing is available. If your joists are spaced any other distance apart, a great deal of cutting and fitting will be required. Note that blown-in or foamed-in material could be installed between the floor joists only if they are covered to make a closed cavity between the joists. In certain cases, such as for a finished garage ceiling, the underfloor area may be closed off. In this case, blown-in or foamed-in material must be used if the ceiling covering cannot be removed.

Tools Required.

1. Heavy duty shears or linoleum knife
2. Temporary lighting with waterproof wiring and connectors
3. Portable fan or blower to provide ventilation
4. Tape measure
5. Heavy duty staple gun and staples

Safety Precautions.

1. Provide adequate temporary lighting
2. Wear gloves and breathing mask when working with glass fiber or rock wool
3. Provide adequate ventilation
4. Keep lights and all wires off wet ground

Cost. The initial cost in relation to return can be fairly high except if all work is completed on a do-it-yourself basis. Material costs are rising and cannot be specified.

Return: A payback period of 5 years or less is considered "average" if all work is done on a do-it-yourself basis. If the work is completed by a contractor, the cost may be such that a 10 year or less payback period will be needed.

For additional information, refer to "Foundation and Floors", Section 10.

INSULATING BASEMENT WALLS

If you have a basement (sealed) that is heated and/or cooled in any manner, you should consider insulating any outer wall that sticks 2 feet or more above ground level. Except in areas experiencing extremely cold winters with deep frost penetration, the insulation need only extend down to about two feet below ground level.

Measurement. To determine the amount of insulation required, measure the length of each wall that sticks 2 feet or more above ground level and add the lengths together. Estimate to the nearest foot how far on the average these walls stick up above ground. For example, suppose your house is on a slope like pictured above. The average height of these walls above ground is three feet. The average height plus the total wall length when

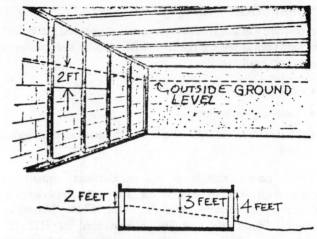

multiplied together will specify the number of square feet to be covered. If the insulation is to extend down to floor level, height averaging will not be required.

Installation. Basement walls that are below ground level have a tendency to be damp. If your walls are damp or have been noted to become damp during the rainy season, the walls must be waterproofed before the insulation is installed. This can be done somewhat easily by coating the walls with a moisture-proofing material.

Unless the walls have stud framing to fit the insulation between, a stud wall must be built up. A wall made up of 2 x 4 studs will permit installation of 3" thick batts for a total of R11. If 2 x 6 studs are used, a 6" thick batt (R19) can be installed. Erect stud (furred) wall as follows:

First - nail bottom plate (P) to floor, using concrete nails. Nail top plate (TP) to floor joists. Cut studs (S) to fit exactly between top and bottom plates. Toenail studs as shown. Space studs to be either 16" or 24" apart at centers, as desired. The 24" spacing will use less studs at a savings.

2

Cut blankets into sections long enough to extend from the top plate to 2 feet below the ground line. Staple them into place between the studs, with the vapor barrier towards the living space. **NOTE:** in northern climates there will be added benefit to installing the insulation the full height of the wall.

3

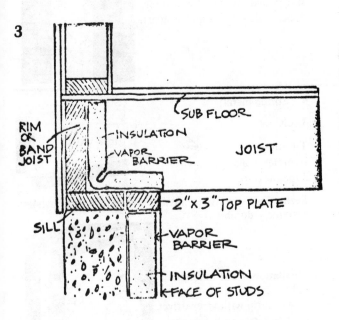

Install another small piece of insulation above the furring and against the sill to insulate the sill and band joist.

4

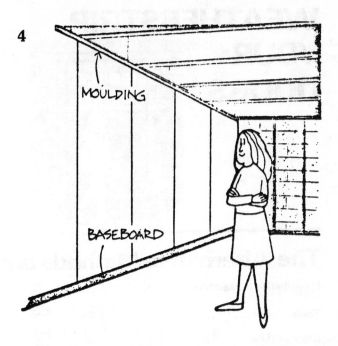

Install finish wall board or panelling over insulation and furring, if desired.

Cost. The initial cost in relation to return is relatively high, particularly if all work is done by a contractor. The work seems moderately complex but it really is fairly easy to accomplish. Even covering the stud wall with wall board (sheet rock) or paneling is an easy task.

The costs are dependent upon the following:

- All work done by contractor - maximum cost.
- All work done on a do-it-yourself basis - least cost.
- Stud wall is covered. Since this does not really relate to increasing the energy efficiency of the walls, this cost should be considered separately.

The stud wall need not be built out of top-grade lumber, No. 2 and even No. 3 pine (if carefully picked) can be used.

Return. The return will be directly related to the amount of wall exposed to the elements and the severity of the winters in the house area. As an estimate, if all work is done by a contractor, a payback period of 10 years is likely. If you do all the work and do not cover the stud wall, a payback period of 5 years or less seems assured.

OUTER DOORS

A poorly fitting outer door, operating with defective or missing weatherstripping, can be one of the worst energy wasters in the entire house. Air infiltration through such a door can put an unbelievable load on the air

WEATHERSTRIP YOUR DOORS

AN EASY DO-IT-YOURSELF PROJECT

You can weatherstrip your doors even if you're not an experienced handyman. There are several types of weatherstripping for doors, each with its own level of effectiveness, durability and degree of installation difficulty. Select among the options given the one you feel is best for you. The installations are the same for the two sides and top of a door, with a different, more durable one for the threshold.

The Alternative Methods and Materials

1. Adhesive backed foam:

Tools

Knife or shears,
Tape measure

TOP VIEW

Evaluation — extremely easy to install, invisible when installed, not very durable, more effective on doors than windows.

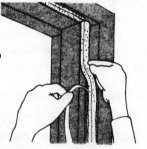

Installation — stick foam to inside face of jamb.

2. Rolled vinyl with aluminum channel backing:

Tools

Hammer, nails,
Tin snips
Tape measure

TOP VIEW

Evaluation — easy to install, visible when installed, durable.

Installation — nail strip snugly against door on the casing

3. Foam rubber with wood backing:

Tools

Hammer, nails,
Hand saw,
Tape measure

TOP VIEW

Evaluation — easy to install, visible when installed, not very durable.

Installation — nail strip snugly against the closed door. Space nails 8 to 12 inches apart.

4. Spring metal:

Tools

Tin snips
Hammer, nails,
Tape measure

TOP VIEW

Evaluation — easy to install, invisible when installed, extremely durable.

Installation — cut to length and tack in place. Lift outer edge of strip with screwdriver after tacking, for better seal.

Figure 23-6. Door Weatherstripping Details (Side 1)

Note: These methods are harder than 1 through 4.

5. Interlocking metal channels:

Tools

Hack saw,
Hammer, nails,
Tape measure

Evaluation — difficult to install (alignment is critical), visible when installed, durable but subject to damage, because they're exposed, excellent seal.

Installation — cut and fit strips to head of door first: male strip on door, female on head; then hinge side of door: male strip on jamb, female on door; finally lock side on door, female on jamb.

6. Fitted interlocking metal channels: (J-Strips)

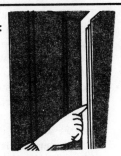

Evaluation — very difficult to install, exceptionally good weather seal, invisible when installed, not exposed to possible damage.

Installation — should be installed by a carpenter. Not appropriate for do-it-yourself installation unless done by an accomplished handyman.

7. Sweeps:

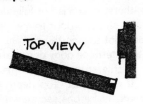

Tools

Screwdriver,
Hack saw,
Tape measure

Evaluation — useful for flat threshholds, may drag on carpet or rug.

Installation — cut sweep to fit 1/16 inch in from the edges of the door. Some sweeps are installed on the inside and some outside. Check instructions for your particular type.

8. Door Shoes:

Tools

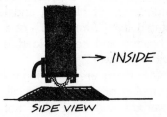

Screwdriver,
Hack saw,
Plane,
Tape measure

Evaluation — useful with wooden threshhold that is not worn, very durable, difficult to install (must remove door).

Installation — remove door and trim required amount off bottom. Cut to door width. Install by sliding vinyl out and fasten with screws.

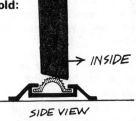

9. Vinyl bulb threshold:

Tools

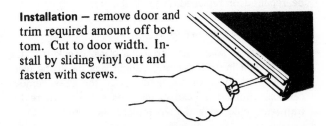

Screwdriver,
Hack saw,
Plane,
Tape measure

Evaluation — useful where there is no threshhold or wooden one is worn out, difficult to install, vinyl will wear but replacements are available.

Installation — remove door and trim required amount off bottom. Bottom should have about 1/8" bevel to seal against vinyl. Be sure bevel is cut in right direction for opening.

10. Interlocking threshold:

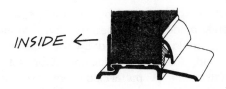

Evaluation — very difficult to install, exceptionally good weather seal.

Installation — should be installed by a skilled carpenter.

Figure 23-6. Door Weatherstripping Details (Side 2)

conditioner, summer and winter. A recent report by the U. S. Department of Housing and Urban Development (HUD) stated that "Almost 70% of a typical single-family dwelling heating and cooling load is traceable to outer doors (and windows)."

Many outer doors are operating with old and inefficient weatherstripping or with none at all. Other outer doors are so warped and bent that not even the best of weatherstripping would make them draft tight. Outer doors should be examined as follows:

- First—determine door is relatively straight. If bent or warped to other than a very minor degree, the door must be repaired or replaced. Also, if the door sections have become loose so that the door can be easily bent, the door must be repaired or replaced.

- If the door is sound and contains glass, check that the glass is tight in its frame and cannot leak air. If the glass trim is lifted, loose or not tight against the glass, remove carefully. Spread a bead of caulking material where the trim was removed and then replace the trim.

- Unless the weatherstripping is relatively new and in excellent condition (and fits the door tightly), refit or replace the weatherstripping. Use a good grade weatherstripping if replacement is needed. For installation details, refer to figure 23-6.

- The threshold (sill) should next be checked. Determine that the door fits tightly against the threshold weatherstripping when the door is closed. If the door bottom mounts plastic or rubber wipers, check their condition. If worn, cracked or with pieces broken off, replace. If the threshold contains a plastic or rubber "bumper," check its condition and replace if necessary. Also, check that the threshold sits flat against the floor. If not, remove screws holding threshold to the floor and caulk where the threshold will be replaced. Tighten screws down hard. See figure 23-6.

A good way to check the air tightness of a door is at nighttime. With the door closed at night, stand outside and have someone shine a flashlight inside around the door where it fits into the frame (jamb). If any light can be seen, a draft point is indicated and should be repaired.

If a door is so warped, bent and broken that repairs cannot be completely made, it must be replaced. If at all possible, the door should be replaced by the "perfect door"—the metal-clad, foam-core insulating door with magnetic weatherstripping. A metal-clad door can be somewhat more expensive than a comparable quality wood door and the installation is more difficult and thus more expensive if done by a carpenter. If installed as a do-it-yourself project, the cost will be less. Installation is as follows:

- Some metal-clad doors are available on a prehung basis—already being hung in a metal remodel door-frame. To install this door, the door stops must first be removed. The door and remodel frame is then fitted right into the existing door opening and the supplied new stops (with magnetized weatherstripping installed) are nailed in. Manufacturer's literature details method. Such a door costs around $100.00, complete with remodel frame, weatherstripping and hinges. A new threshold may also be required.

Note: Metal-clad doors can be painted and antiqued as desired and cannot be told from wood doors.

- At somewhat less expense (about $20.00 less) installation can be made. The door and door stops are removed and the new metal-clad door is fitted into the frame. The hinges on the metal door may not fit into the existing hinge frame cutouts so new hinge cutouts may be needed. To accomplish this, fit door into frame and shim up so door "rides" on threshold just enough to make a good wiping contact. Mark where outer edge of hinges touch the door frame. Using a hinge as a template, cut out enough wood so each hinge lays flat like old hinge did.

The magnetic weatherstripping must next be fitted. First, secure weatherstripping to the stops previously removed, magnetic side towards door. With door mounted, fit stops against door so the weatherstripping is not fully depressed (almost but not fully). Nail stops to door frame, using only 2 or 3 nails per stop and not driving the nails all the way in. Check door action to determine door opens and closes easily and that the weatherstripping can make total contact with the door. If not, adjust stop depth to door. When operation is correct, nail stops securely. Note that this method requires a fair level of carpentry skill.

Rather large drafts can flow into and out of a house around the door trim. The remedy is to completely fill in between the outer door trim and the house siding. If the space between the trim and siding is large, fill first with a solid caulking material to within about ¼" and fill the remainder in with top-quality caulking material. Do both side pieces and the top and bottom pieces. For details, see figure 23-7.

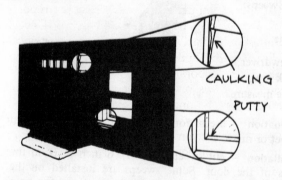

Figure 23-7. Door and Window Caulking Details

Storm Doors. Storm doors may be required in areas that experience rather severe winters or in areas of moderate winters if the door faces north into strong winds. If a storm door is to be installed, use a prehung door and be careful to caulk the door jamb where the storm door frame will mount. Buy a good quality door, one that has tight joints that will not leak air. If you can see through the joints, the door will leak air and be relatively ineffective. Of course, installing a storm door does not mean the regular door can be ill fitting, missing weatherstripping, etc. since the stormdoor insulating effect requires a tight air seal—tight to the outside and inside of the house.

Cost. About $3.00 to $4.00 per door for good-grade weatherstripping if self installed. A threshold, if replaced, could add an additional $5.00 to $6.00. Storm doors are relatively expensive, costing from $40.00 and up for a prehung type, self installed. Installation is relatively easy and requires only minor carpentry experience.

Return. Can be excellent if outer doors were in bad condition or required weatherstripping. A storm door, especially to cover a door facing north in areas of severe winter, can also return excellent savings. A payback time of less than a year is indicated for weatherstripping, and less than five years for a storm door.

Replacement of an outer door with a good-grade solid-core wood door would cost about $50.00 to $60.00 installed—a simple task. If a metal-clad door is installed, the door may cost up to $100.00 (in a prehung frame, without glass inserts), with installation adding up to $30.00 or more. A payback time of up to five years (or more) is indicated.

Suggested literature—"In the Bank or Up the Chimney."

WINDOWS

A poorly fitting window, operating with defective or missing weatherstripping, can be one of the worst energy wasters in the entire house. Air infiltration through such a window can put an unbelievable load on the air conditioner, summer and winter. A recent report by the U. S. Department of Housing and Urban Development (HUD) stated that "Almost 70% of a typical single-family dwelling heating and cooling load is traceable to outer windows (and doors)."

Many windows are operating with old and inefficient weatherstripping or with none at all. Wood-framed windows may be warped or cracked badly around the joints such that even the best of weatherstripping cannot make them draft tight. All windows should be examined as follows:

- Wood windows, opening type—determine if wood is relatively straight, all joints are tight and window moves freely in frame. If not, remove window from frame (inside stops may have to be removed) and repair as needed.

Inspect weatherstripping, if any. If defective (or was never installed) replace using the bronze-spring type. Measure both sides and cut material to exact length. For double-hung windows, two pieces will be needed for each side. Nail weatherstripping every 6" and lift outer edge of seal so it stands up and will press against window sash. Do not cover pulleys in the upper channel. If only half of a double-hung window is ever opened, unused section could be caulked tight and thus would not need weatherstripping. See figure 23-8.

Measure across top and bottom of sash and install exact length pieces, spring edge to the outside. Lastly, attach a strip to the upper sash bottom rail, spring edge pointing down. Counter-sink nails so they won't catch on the lower sash top rail.

A slider window should be weatherstripped in the same general manner, treating the slider as a double-hung laid on its side.

- Wood windows, fixed type—check for cracks around window frame and caulk as needed. See figure 23-7.

- Wood windows, all types—check putty seal around each pane. If defective or missing, repair as needed. See figure 23-7.

- Metal windows, opening type—check weatherstripping. This is usually the fur-strip type that fits into a small channel. If defective or missing, replace entire strip. Channel openings may have to be widened (with a screw driver, etc.) for an inch or two at the top and bottom to permit the old weatherstripping to be removed and the new installed.

Check condition of plastic pieces that hold glass in frame. If loose or any gaps are noted, caulk lightly using a clear caulking material—such as silicon.

Rather large drafts can flow into and out of a house around the window trim. The remedy is to completely fill any gap between the outer trim and the house siding. If the space is large, fill with a solid caulking material to within about ¼" and fill remainder with a top-quality caulking material. Do both side pieces and the top and bottom pieces.

Storm windows may be required in areas that experience rather severe temperature changes or high winds. Storm windows, if properly installed, can reduce the heat loss or gain through a single-glazed window by about half. This level of energy saving is, however, gained only if the storm window and the window it covers are essentially air tight. Thus, the installation of a storm window does not mean the regular window can be ill-fitting, missing weatherstripping, etc. since storm-window insulating effect requires a tight air seal—tight to the outside and inside of the house.

Thin spring metal

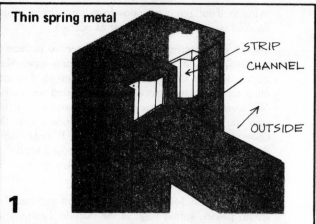

1

Install by moving sash to the open position and sliding strip in between the sash and the channel. Tack in place into the casing. Do not cover the pulleys in the upper channels.

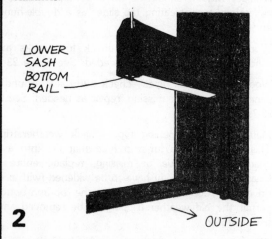

2

Install strips the full width of the sash on the bottom of the lower sash bottom rail and the top of the upper sash top rail.

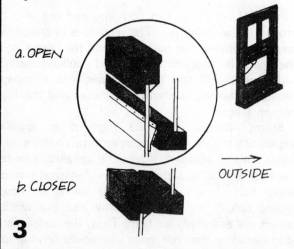

3

Then attach a strip the full width of the window to the upper sash bottom rail. Countersink the nails slightly so they won't catch on the lower sash top rail.

Rolled vinyl

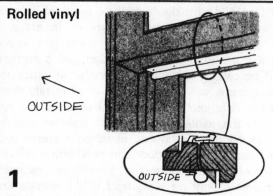

1

Nail on vinyl strips on double-hung windows as shown. A sliding window is much the same and can be treated as a double-hung window turned on its side. Casement and

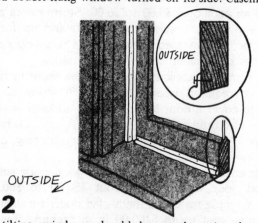

2

tilting windows should be weatherstripped with the vinyl nailed to the window casing so that, as the window shuts, it compresses the roll.

Adhesive-backed foam strip

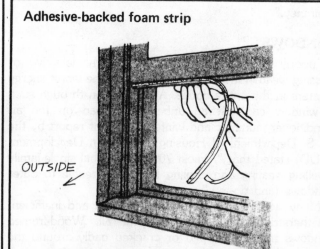

Install adhesive backed foam, on all types of windows, only where there is no friction. On double-hung windows, this is only on the bottom (as shown) and top rails. Other types of windows can use foam strips in many more places.

Figure 23-8. Window Weatherstripping Details

Two basic types of storm windows are available: home-made or factory made of plastic film and factory-made aluminum frames with glass inserts.

- *Plastic storm windows.* If home-made, use 6-mil thick polyethylene plastic obtainable in rolls. Buy a roll width equal to the widest window. An air gap of about 1" should separate the plastic film and the window glass. The plastic, cut to size, can be attached to the inside of the window frame by means of a 2" wide masking tape. Alternately, the plastic can be attached to the window trim, using ¼" x 1¼" slats nailed to the trim with finishing nails. In either case, the plastic must fit air-tight to be fully effective. Plastic may have to be replaced yearly.

Factory-made plastic-film storm windows are now available in the larger hardware stores and lumber yards. These units are designed to fit against the window on the inside of the house. The windows are fitted in using provided plastic strips and are available in all standard sizes. These windows are highly recommended.

- *Storm windows, metal framed.* Two types are available, known as a (1) picture window (a single-piece, non-opener unit) and (2) a triple-track unit (a two-piece unit with screen, one piece of which can be opened). Triple-track units of standard size are usually available from stock whereas most picture windows and non-standard sized triple-tracks must be ordered. The windows must be fitted onto the existing window frame to achieve an air-tight fit (as near as possible) if the full insulation benefits possible are to be gained. For installation details, refer to "Storm Window Installation" that follows.

STORM WINDOW INSTALLATION

Triple-track storm windows are of two types: (1) half-hung in that the lower portion can be slid open and (2) sliders which permit one piece to be slid open. Triple-track windows all come equipped with screens that fit over the window portion that can be opened. The storm window frame is made such that when the unit is installed over the existing window, an air gap of from ½ to 1 inch is provided. A tight seal between the storm window and the existing window assures very slow air movement through the air gap between the windows and thus provides for maximum insulation against heat and sound transfer.

Storm windows are fitted over the existing window using plastic weatherstripping pieces. For proper fit, the existing windows must be measured exactly as to width and height. Unfortunately, not all existing metal-framed windows are alike but almost all are built to accept a storm window. Most aluminum-framed windows are constructed as illustrated by Figure 23-9.

For half-hung and picture windows, the width is measured across the bottom lip and the height is measured from the top to the bottom (under the lip to the frame itself). A certain amount must then be deducted from the width and height measurements to allow for the plastic weatherstripping. The plastic material provides about 3/8" movement and thus permits a small adjustment to be made. Generally, the width and height measurements should be reduced by 1/4" to 3/8". That is, if the top to bottom measurement was 36" total, the required size would be 36" minus 1/4" or 3/8". The same deduction holds true for the width measurement.

For half-hung and slider windows, the exact measurement from the bottom of the existing window to the cross piece must be made. The measurement is always made from the bottom up to the cross piece for half-hung units. Slider windows are generally standard with the cross piece at half way across the width of the unit but it is best to measure and give the figure when ordering. If the windows are ordered without the cross-piece measurement being given, the manufacturer will assume the cross piece is exactly in the middle. For measurement details, see Figure 23-10.

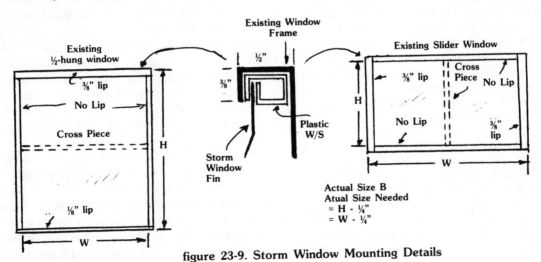

figure 23-9. Storm Window Mounting Details

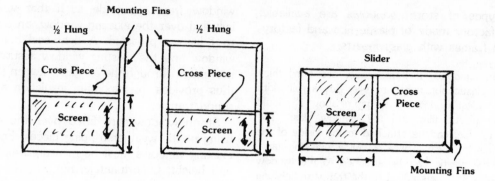

Figure 23-10. Cross-Piece Measurement Details

Slider windows do not (generally) have lips on top and bottom, being provided with lips on both sides (vertical portions). Some picture windows may not be provided with lips on either top or bottom or both sides. In this case, the window cannot be installed using plastic weatherstripping.

Storm windows may be installed in either of two ways, depending upon the installation features provided by the existing window. That is, either with or without use of plastic weatherstripping.

1. Plastic weatherstripping - obtainable from the window supply company. The weatherstripping should be cut to fit completely across the top and bottom fins of the storm window. When cut, the pieces should be pressed on the fins with the flattest side outside (pointing away from the existing window). Pieces for both sides should then be cut, fitting snugly against the top and bottom pieces when slipped onto the side fins.

The window is then placed "inside" the existing window frame. For window frames provided with under-lip areas, slip plastic under lip to start (half-hung units, mainly). When the window is in place, push weatherstripping to make a tight seal against the existing window frame. As a final touch, small bead of clear silicon caulking material could be run around weatherstripping where it touches the existing window frame—this to ensure an air-tight fit. Also, run a bead of the caulking material across the mitered seams of the storm-window frame to seal the seam.

2. No weatherstripping possible - in this case, the window (a picture window) must be measured for size from the extreme top and bottom and both sides. A deduction of ¼" to ⅜" is then made. The storm window must then be screwed to the existing window frame using self-tapping screws. First, drill holes in the storm window fins—just large enough to take the self-tapping screw (use a small size screw). Next, lay a *small* bead of caulking material around existing window frame where the storm window fins will lay. Lastly, place storm window over existing frame and true up. Then, using a smaller drill, drill through the pre-drilled holes in the fins into the existing window frame. Install self-tapping screws and tighten window against the caulking material.

Storm window installation can be a bit "tricky" as to "are lips present or not," "what is the correct installation measurements," "can weatherstripping be used or not," etc. It is thus suggested that you visit a company handling storm windows and discuss your windows directly with these knowledgeable people. An order for storm windows for the whole house should entitle you to ask that the storm-window people send a man out to measure your windows and to advise on their installation. This service might also be offered if the company hopes to receive orders from your neighbors after your installation has proven the worth of storm windows. If you cannot get direct knowledgeable help in this manner, it is suggested that you initially order only one window—a small one, preferably. This window can be used to gain experience and—should a mistake be made—will not result in a major loss.

If the top and bottom parts of a half-hung window are the same size or the lower part is smaller than the upper part, the bottom part can usually be removed from inside for cleaning. The screen can also be removed from the inside. If the window ledge inside the house is extra wide, the lower piece may not be removable from the inside. The slider part of slider windows can usually be removed from inside if the window is not set too deeply in the wall (as may be the case with 2 x 6 wall framing). If the windows cannot be removed from inside, the entire window must be removed from the outside. If installed with weatherstripping, the plastic pieces can be pushed away from the existing window frame and the entire storm window can be removed as a unit. If the window is held with self-tapping screws, the screws must be removed.

If it is not desired to remove the entire storm window, the window pieces can be removed by unscrewing the cross piece. This will permit both window pieces to be easily removed by a bit of "juggling." When replacing the cross piece, be certain NOT to tighten the self-tapping screws too tightly as this will strip the threads in the existing window frame. If this should happen, replace the present self-tapping screw with the next larger size.

Be sure to remove the existing window screens before installing a storm window since the storm window has its own screen. The existing window screen cannot be used with the storm window thus if a screen is desired, it must be ordered.

Costs. Weatherstripping, bronze-spring or fur type, about $1.00 per window on a do-it-yourself basis. Plastic film storm windows, about 50¢ per window, do-it-yourself. Single-pane storm windows, from $10.00 and up dependent on size installed on a do-it-yourself basis. Add about $6.00 per window for contractor installation. Triple-track storm windows, from $20.00 and up dependent on size installed on a do-it-yourself basis. Add about $6.00 per window for contractor installation.

Results. Can be excellent. Just sealing the air leaks through the windows themselves and the window trim can make a remarkable savings in energy costs at very little expense. Storm windows should result in energy savings making their cost repayable in about 5 years or less, dependent on climatic conditions and condition of existing windows.

Suggested literature - "In the Bank or Up the Chimney."

HOT WATER-SYSTEM

Hot-water heating uses large quantities of energy especially when electric heating is used. Meaningful savings of energy as related to hot-water heating may be accomplished as follows:

- Most hot-water heater thermostats are set at the factory to 145°F and even up to 150°F. This is much too high and can be reduced to 135°F or even 130°F with no loss of dishwasher efficiency. Reducing the water temperature saves energy in three ways:

1. Heat loss through the tank walls

2. Heat loss through pipes

3. Heat loss in water left in pipes after use.

Electric hot-water heaters usually have two thermostats; one at the top and bottom of the tank. Do not adjust unless all power has been removed. Gas-heated units may have thermostats that are marked only as to HOT with an arrow to show how to increase or decrease the temperature. In this case, a thermometer must be used to measure the water temperature.

- Tank loss can be reduced by wrapping a special insulation blanket around the tank. Or, if the tank is enclosed in a closet, the closet walls can be lined with insulation batts (3" being recommended). Cost—about $20.00 with a good return.

- If the hot-water pipes can be reached and are not insulated, pipe insulation should be installed.

- If the hot-water tank and heater are near the end of their anticipated life span (from 5 to 15 years depending on

quality and use), it is suggested the unit be replaced with a newer and more efficient model.

- Zoning as related to hot-water use may also be worthwhile especially if the existing tank is nearing replacement time. For additional details, refer to "Hot-Water Zoning," page 9-2, Section 9.

- A gas-fired unit, if located inside the living space, should not draw combustion air from the living area since this will waste expensively conditioned air. If presently using inside air and mounted over a ventilated crawl space or basement, a hole can be cut in the floor to draw the combustion air from under the house. Otherwise, the air should be brought to the combustion chamber by a duct system from outside the house. This, of course, assumes the unit is mounted in a closet with a tight-fitting door.

- If a gas-fired unit needs replacement, a "pilotless" model is recommended, equipped with an automatic electronic ignition system that incorporates a flame-failure safety switch. Pilot lights, over a year's span, can consume a very large amount of gas.

- If an electric hot-water heater is used, energy savings can be realized by installing a timer which acts to turn off the heating element(s) during long periods of non-use. There are generally two periods each day when little or no hot water is used:

  - the sleeping hours from about 10PM to 6AM

  - work or school time from about 9AM to 4PM

The timer can be set to open the heater circuit at a preset time and to close the heater circuit at a further preset time. Some timers provide for two such timed periods, others just for one.

The timer saves the energy used to keep the hot-water up to a set temperature during long periods of non-use. The temperature of the water will drop somewhat during the non-use period but will be rapidly brought up to desired level when the heater circuit is restored. For further information, refer to "Timed Use," page 16-3, Section 16.

Users of this system report energy savings sufficient to payoff the cost in as little as 6 months. The timers cost between $20.00 and $30.00 plus installation. The timer should be installed by a person experienced in electrical installation.

For additional details on hot-water systems, refer to "Hot Water Systems," Section 16.

Costs. Exact costs are somewhat difficult to determine since many local factors must be considered—local costs, amount of upgrading done by owner, etc.

Pipe insulation - easy to install, buy from plumbing supply house if possible—cost about 6¢ to 8¢ per foot. Good return.

Insulating blanket - range from $10.00 to $20.00. Installation is easy since instructions are given with the blanket. Return should be good.

Zoning would be worthwhile if long runs of pipe are currently being used and hot-water unit is near replacement time. Savings on hot water heating costs and comfort gained are high—returns are good and a payback time of 5 years or so is indicated.

Bringing in outside air to combustion chamber for a gas-fired model can be inexpensive (cut hole in floor) to moderately costly ($25.00 to $50.00 to run duct outside). Payback time should be fairly good.

Pilotless model extra cost would certainly be worthwhile and should have a good payback period. Exact cost depends upon unit purchased, size, etc. so each installation would be unique.

Returns. As indicated above.

Recommended instruction material - manufacturer's literature—obtain from local plumbing-fixture firms.

AIR-CONDITIONING SYSTEMS

Air-conditioning systems can use up to half the energy consumed in a home, in particular when electric-strip heating is used. Meaningful savings of energy as related to heating and cooling may be accomplished as follows:

- Duct systems, forced air and return - if the ducts do not run inside the house, they must be insulated to at least R8. If the ducts are insulated and run outside the house (in attic and under house) and the duct material is 1" thick or less, more insulation is required. Vapor-barrier batts, 2" thick (R9) being recommended, can be fitted completely around the ducts (or to the best degree possible) with vapor-barrier side out (looking at you). When making the installation, *check ducts first* to *determine* if there are any *leaks* in the duct walls. If so, repair with a 2" wide contact tape.

  Also, be sure each *subduct* running to a *vent fits tightly* on the *vent*, otherwise conditioned air (hot or cold) will be wastefully lost back into the attic or crawl space-basement. This holds for both the forced-air output ducts and return-air input ducts.

- Gas or oil heater - such units should be inspected yearly and the flame adjusted for proper and most efficient burning. For additional details, refer to "Basic Facts—Heating System," page 19-2, Section 19.

- The filter in the return-air input to the air conditioner should be checked at least two or three times a year and cleaned or replaced as needed. A clogged filter is a bad energy waster so much so that some newer air conditioners have a circuit that measures the return-air flow and turns on a light if it is low (filter is clogged).

- Electric-strip heating is the most expensive means of heating a house. If the home is all-electric and a heat-strip furnace is used, if the air conditioner is nearing replacement time, earlier replacement with a heat pump might be considered. The heat pump, developing up to 2.5

times more heat per dollar of electricity than a heatstrip furnace, is so much more efficient a heater than an early replacement might be warranted. Actually, replacement of the compressor and some rewiring may be all that is required. If the heating bills with an electric-strip heater, are very high it would be well worthwhile to discuss replacing the unit with a heat pump. Check with two or more reputable dealers. For additional details on heat pumps, refer to "Heat Pumps," page 19-6, Section 19.

- Setting the thermostat back at night can realize sizeable energy savings. For details, refer to "Thermostats," page 19-4, Section 19.

- If a gas heater needs replacement, a "pilotless" model is recommended, equipped with an automatic electronic ignition system that incorporates a flame-failure safety switch. Pilot lights, over a year's span, can consume a very large amount of gas.

Costs. Exact costs are somewhat difficult to determine since many local factors must be taken into account, such as—how much work is done by owner, etc.

Duct insulation—about 16¢ to 18¢ on a do-it-yourself basis, double or more if done by contractor depending on ease of access to ducts.

Thermostat night-time setback—costs from $20.00 to $100.00 plus depending on model (resistor strip or clock) and if installed by a contractor.

Replacement of an electric-strip heater with a heat pump can be expensive and is warranted only if the existing air conditioner (or condensor only) needs to be replaced. The heat pump savings vary depending on climatic conditions. For actual savings and payback information, refer to "Heat Pumps," page 19-6, Section 19.

If a gas-fired unit is replaced with a pilotless model, the extra cost for this feature should give a good return.

Returns. Indicated above.

Suggested instruction literature - visit large plumbing firm and obtain literature on a local basis.

ATTIC VENTILATION

The very large buildup of heat that can occur in an unventilated attic can reflect a very large load on the air conditioning system. For full details on attic ventilation, refer to "Attic Ventilation," page 15-1, Section 15.

LANDSCAPING AND SHADING

The solar energy streaming down on a house, winter and summer, can be either a heat loss or heat gain. In colder climates with long winters and short, rather moderate summers, solar energy can be useful and result in lowering of the heat load. In the warmer climates with short winters and long, hot summers, solar energy can reflect a very large load on the cooling system and is thus not desired.

For landscaping and shading details as related to efficient heating and cooling systems, refer to "House Orientation and Landscaping," Section 20.

FIREPLACE

New and updated fireplace accessories are now appearing on the market that can turn an existing fireplace into a heat source capable of developing a rather large volume of heat. A "standard" fireplace, unless specially equipped, can never qualify as a true heat producer. If it is desired to use an existing fireplace as a practical heat source, review "Existing In-Wall Fireplace—Accessories," page 17-2.

DISAPPEARING STAIRCASE

A disappearing (folddown) staircase, if located within the air-conditioned portion of the house, can be a very serious energy waster. First: the staircase door must be weather-stripped to make the door fit air tight against the ceiling covering (gypsum board—sheet rock). In actual fact the staircase door should be treated as if it were an outside door. Unless made weathertight, warm air will pass out of the house through the leakage around the door and cold air will flow in. This air exchange rate can be very severe.

Secondly, the door itself must be insulated otherwise it will appear as a 2-foot by 5-foot un-insulated part of the ceiling. The door can be covered on the inside using a rigid-foam insulation board. A 1-thick piece can be fitted onto the door, cemented with a heavy glue. This can raise the insulation value of the door to as high as R8, a worthwhile improvement.

BEST DO-IT-YOURSELF ORDER

On a do-it-yourself basis, the best dollar-spent to dollar-saved order is thought to be:

1. **Draft Elimination**—caulking and sealing all draft sources. For full details on draft sources, refer to "Air Infiltration Points," Section 14. For details on how to eliminate draft sources, refer to "Weatherization," Section 14 and to "Draft Elimination," page 23-2.

2. **Hot-Water System**—increase efficiency by raising insulation level and insulating hot-water pipes where possible. Reduce tank temperature—to 125°F for kitchen use and to 90°F for unit used only for bathrooms. If unit needs replacement, consider installing a dual-tank system and/or (for gas-fired models), a pilotless unit. Refer to "Hot-Water Systems, page 23-26 and review "Hot Water Systems," Section 16.

Heating hot water using the hot gases from the air conditioner or heat pump is now very practical. If your present hot-water bill is $20.00 per month or higher, use of a preheater in conjunction with the air conditioner or heat pump is cost practical if the cost is below about $400.00. A savings of about 75 to 90% is advertised thus the "regular" hot-water heating bill would be reduced by this amount.

3. **Outer Doors**—repairing or replacing defective outer doors (preferably with metal-clad insulating units using magnetic weatherstripping) can save large amounts of energy. The door weatherstripping should be checked carefully and replaced or adjusted as needed. For details, refer to "Weatherstrip Your Doors," page 23-19 and review "Outer Doors," Section 12.

4. **Windows**—repairing or replacing defective windows and/or installing storm (insulating) windows. Repair or replace weatherstripping as needed. Refer to Figure 23-8 and review Section 13.

5. **Attic Insulation**—if necessary, bring up to recommended R value for house area. Do not overinsulate. Refer to Figure 5-2 for recommended "minimum" values.

6. **Underfloor and Foundation Insulation**—if necessary, bring up to recommended R value for house area. Do not over-insulated. Refer to Figure 5-2 for recommended "minimum" values.

6. **Underfloor and Foundation Insulation**—if necessary, bring up to recommended R value for house area. Do not over-insulate. Refer to Figure 5-2 for recommended "minimum" values.

7. **Landscaping and Window Shading**—plan landscaping to shade windows and walls in summer—to leave windows unshaded in winter.

8. **Outer Wall Insulation**—if not insulated, insulate to "minimum" levels given by Figure 5-2 for various climatic areas. If walls are already insulated, do not add more.

9. **Attic Ventilation**—plan attic ventilation to provide a good air flow through attic in wintertime to prevent water condensation and summertime lowering of heat buildup in attic.

10. **Air Conditioning System**—bring heating and cooling systems up to designed efficiency. Review "Heating and Cooling Systems," Section 19.

EXISTING HOME
ENERGY-USE CHECKOUT LIST

1.0   OUTER WALLS

1.1   Insulation

1.1.1   Insulation level — R value?   ____ Refer to Table 5-3.

1.1.2   Proper R value for House area?   ____ If less than recommended value for house area, increase as needed. See Figure 5-2

1.1.3   Below recommended minimum value?   ____

If walls are insulated, more cannot be added.

1.2   Outer Sheathing (Brick, Stone, Aluminum, Paneling,etc.)

1.2.1   Is in weathertight condition?   ____ If yes, proceed to Check No. 1.2.2

                                                          ____ If No, repair as needed.

1.2.2   Any penetrations thru walls tightly sealed by caulking, etc.)   ____ If yes, proceed to Check No. 1.2.3

                                                          ____ If no, seal tightly as needed.

1.2.3   Outer sheathing sealed to foundation walls—to prevent drafts?   ____ If yes, proceed to Check No. 1.2.4

                                                          ____ If no, caulk and seal as necessary.

1.2.4   All wall junctions or corners tightly sealed to prevent drafts?   ____ If yes, proceed to Check No. 2.0

                                                          ____ If no, caulk or seal as necessary.

2.0   CEILINGS — OVER AIR CONDITIONED ROOMS   —   ACCESSIBLE ATTIC

2.1   Insulation — Over Ceiling (attic floor)

2.1.1   Insulation level — R value?   ____ Refer to Table 5-3. See Figure 5-2.

2.1.2   Proper R value for house area?   ____ If less than recommended value for house area, increase increase as needed. See Figure 23-2.

2.1.3   Below recommended minimum value?   ____

2.1.4   Insulation is complete—no gaps or breaks noted? ____ If incomplete, fill gaps or breaks to required R value. See "Thermal Blanket," page 11-1.

2.1.5   Insulation covers outer-wall top plates?   ____ See Figures 11-1 and 23-2(4).

2.1.6   Eave vents, if used, are not covered with insulation?   ____ If vents are covered, insulation should be cleared away to fully open vents.

2.2   Vapor Barrier

2.2.1   Vapor barrier provided?   ____ If not, refer to "Vapor-Barrier Installation," page 5-9. See Figure 23-2(3).

    Vapor-barrier type batts used?   ____

    Plastic film used?   ____

    Room side of ceiling painted with vapor-barrier paint?   ____

2.2.2   If vapor-barrier batts are used, are any gaps or breaks in insulation noted?   ____ If yes, vapor-barrier type batts should be installed in gap or break area.

2.3   Ceiling Penetrations

2.3.1   If any spotlights penetrate ceiling, are they covered with insulation?   ____   If yes, this creates a fire hazard and insulation must be be cleared away. Refer to "Recessed Spotlight," page 14-8.

2.3.2   Do any electrical boxes penetrate ceiling?   ____   If yes, are they caulked and sealed to be draft proof. If not, caulk and seal as necessary.

2.3.3   Do any chimney pipes penetrate ceiling?   ____   If yes, do they fit draft tight. If not, seal or caulk as necessary to make draft proof.

2.4   Disappearing Staircase

2.4.1   In ceiling over a/c room?   ____   If not, proceed to Check No. 2.5.

2.4.2   Is door weatherstripped properly?   ____   If not, repair or replace weatherstripping.

2.4.3   Is door itself insulated to at least R8?   ____   If not, refer to "Disappearing Staircase" page 23-28

2.5   Top-Plate Penetrations—Inner and Outer Walls

2.5.1   Any unsealed holes in top plates?   ____   If yes, caulk or seal as required to make completely draft draft proof.

     For electrical wiring?   ____

     For water pipes?   ____

     For TV or telephone cable?   ____

     Open knot holes?   ____

     Cracks or breaks in top plate?   ____

2.6   Air-Conditioning Vents and Ducts

2.6.1   A/C ducts insulated to at least R8?   ____   If not, refer to "A/C Systems," page 23-27.

2.6.2   Any tears, rips or breaks in duct walls?   ____   If yes, repair with contact tape.

2.6.3   All duct seams solidly sealed with contact tape?   ____   If not, seal with contact tape as needed.

2.6.4   All ducts fit tightly into the ceiling or wall air vents?   ____   If not, install properly—use contact tape (etc.) to hold duct into air vent solidly.

2.6.5   Any gaps between air-vent sheet metal and ceiling or wall covering?   ____   If yes, seal air vent using caulking material or contact tape, as needed.

These steps are most important and should be made carefully—on all sides and under the duct system.

3.0   WOOD FLOORS — OVER BASEMENT OR CRAWL SPACE

3.1   Any floor area over heated basement?   ____   If yes, this underfloor area need not be insulated.

3.2   Any floor area over unheated, ventilated crawl space or basement?   ____   If yes, underfloor area must be insulated. Refer to Table 5-2, See Figure 5-2.

3.3   Any floor area over unheated but not ventilated crawl space or basement?   ____   If yes, foundation walls (crawl space) or basement walls should be insulated. Refer to Check No. 4.0, then return to Check No. 3.4.

3.4   Vapor barrier under floor?   ____   If underfloor area is not insulated but insulation is required, vapor-barrier type batts are recommended. Refer to "Vapor-Barrier Installation," page 5-9.

If a vapor barrier under the floor is not provided and insulation is not to be installed, a vapor barrier should be laid on the ground if the underfloor area is not well ventilated. Refer to Check No. 4.

4.0 CRAWL SPACE — NOT VENTILATED

4.1	Entire floor of a/c part of house is insulated?	—— If yes, proceed to Check No. 4.3.
4.2	Inside of foundation walls are insulated?	—— If not, insulated all foundtion walls. Refer to "Crawl-Space Foundations," page 23-14.
4.3	Vapor barrier provided under floor?	—— If yes, proceed to Check No. 5.0.
4.4	Vapor barrier laid on ground under entire under-floor area?	—— If no, vapor barrier should be installed. Refer to "Vapor-Barrier Installation," page 5-9.

5.0 CRAWL SPACE — VENTILATED

5.1	Entire underfloor area of a/c part of house is insulated?	—— If yes, proceed to Check No. 5.2. If not, should be insulated. Refer to "Underfloor Insulation," page 23-16.
5.2	Vapor barrier under floor?	—— If yes, proceed to Check No. 5.3. If not, refer to Check No. 3.4.
5.3	Ample underfloor ventilation provided in all foundation walls?	—— If not, ventilation should be improved to recommended standards. Refer to "Underfloor Ventilation," page 10.7.

6.0 BASEMENT — NOT VENTILATED

6.1	Entire floor under a/c part of house is insulated?	—— If yes, proceed to Check No. 6.3.
6.2	Inside of foundation wall and/or outer basement walls are insulated?	—— If not, insulate as required. Refer to "Insulating Basement Walls," page 23-17.
6.3	Vapor barrier provided under floor?	—— If yes, proceed to Check No. 7.0.
		—— If no, lay a vapor barrier on top of all underfloor ground area. Refer to "Vapor-Barrier Installation," page 5-9.

7.0 BASEMENT — VENTILATED

7.1	Entire underfloor area of a/c part of house is insulated?	—— If yes, proceed to Check No. 7.2.
		—— If not, insulate as required. Refer to "Underfloor Insulation," page 23-16.
7.2	Vapor barrier under floor?	—— If yes, proceed to Check No. 7.3.
		—— If no, refer to Check No. 3.4. Then, proceed to Check No. 7.3
7.3	Ample underfloor ventilation provided in all foundation and basement walls?	—— If not, ventilated should be improved to recommended standards. Refer to "Underfloor Ventilation," page 10-7.

8.0 ATTIC — NOT AIR CONDITIONED

8.1 Insulation — Attic Floor

8.1.1	Insulation R value proper for house area?	—— If not, insulation should be increased. Refer to Table 5-3. See Fig. 5-2.
8.1.2	Insulation is complete — no gaps or breaks noted?	—— If any are noted, fill with insulation to required R value.
8.1.3	Insulation covers outer-wall top plates?	—— If not, cover with insulation if top plates are accessible. This relates to both inner and outer walls.
8.1.4	Are eave vents covered with insulation?	—— If yes, remove insulation — eave vents must be open at all times.

8.2   Vapor Barrier — Attic Floor

8.2.1   Vapor barrier provided?   _____   If not, one must be provided. Refer to "Vapor-Barrier Installation," page 5-9.

8.2.2   Vapor barrier complete — no gaps or tears?   _____   If any are noted, repair as needed.

8.3   Ventilation

8.3.1   Ample ventilation provided.   _____   If not, increase as needed. Refer to "Underfloor Ventilation," page 10-7.

8.3.2   Air venting set up to provide a good air flow through _____ attic?   If not, add ventilation as needed.

If top-ridge venting is used, gable-end vents should not be used.

8.3.3   Eave vents and top-ridge venting used with cathedral _____ or sloped ceilings and with flat roofs?   Ideally, these ceilings need ventilation to prevent moisture condensation. See Figure 15-4.

8.4   Air Conditioning Ducts and Vents

8.4.1   A/C ducts insulated to at least R8?   _____   If not, increase insulation. Refer to "A/C Systems," page 23-27.

8.4.2   Any tears, rips or breaks in the duct walls?   _____   If so, repair with contact tape.

8.4.3   All duct seams solidly sealed with contact tape? Any loose?   _____   If so, repair with contact tape.

8.4.4   A/C ducts all fit tightly into ceiling or wall vents?   _____   If not, repair or fix as needed.

8.4.5   Any gaps between air-vent sheet metal and wall or _____ ceiling covering?   If so, repair or refit to make a tight seal (draft-proof).

Checks 8.4.1 thru 8.4.5 are very important — check carefully.

8.5   Disappearing Staircase (can be a serious draft source)

8.5.1   In air conditioned part of house?   _____   If not, proceed to Check No. 8.6

8.5.2   Is door weatherstripped to make a draft-proof seal to _____ ceiling?   If not, weatherstrip. Refer to "Disappearing Staircase," page 23-28.

8.5.3   Is door itself insulated to at least R11?   _____   If not, insulate as needed. Refer to "Disappearing Staircase," page 23-28.

8.6   Top Plates — Inner and Outer Walls

8.6.1   Any unsealed holes in top plates?   _____   If yes, seal or caulk as needed.

8.6.2   Any open knotholes, unsealed cracks or gaps in top _____ plates.   If yes, seal, repair or caulk as needed.

9.0   ATTIC — AIR-CONDITIONED PORTION

9.1   Insulation

9.1.1   Proper R value for house area?   _____   If not, increase insulation as needed. Treat all walls as outer walls. See Figure 5-2 — Refer to Table 5-3

Check walls, ceiling and floor.

9.2   Air-Conditioning Ducts and Vents

9.2.1   Any ducts or vents used?   _____   If yes, check per Check No. 2.6.

9.3 **Door to Non-A/C Portion of Attic**

9.3.1 Any such door used? _____ If so, treat as an Outer Door. Check per Check No. 10.0.

10.0 **OUTER DOORS**

10.1 **Door Condition**

10.1.1 Door solid, not warped or bent, all joints tightly sealed —no holes? _____ If yes, proceed with Check No. 10.1.2. If not, repair or replace door.

10.1.2 Glass inserts in door — complete, tightly sealed — in in good condition? _____ If yes, proceed with Check No. 10.2. If not, repair glass, reputtied, etc., as needed.

10.2 **Door Weatherstripping**

10.2.1 Weatherstripping complete—makes a tight, draft-proof seal — is in good condition? _____ If not, adjust, repair or replace weatherstripping. Refer to "Outer Doors," page 23-18.

Best test — at night, use a flashlight on one side of door with observer on other side. Shine flashlight up and down sides and across bottom and top. If any light is seen, weatherstripping is defective.

10.3 **Outer Trim Around Door Opening**

10.3.1 If trim can be removed without damage, remove one side piece and check for:

Insulation between door frame and door-opening framing. Is cavity filled with insulation? _____ If not, remove all door trim and fill cavity with insulation—do not depress. Replace trim.

This can be a very serious energy-loss point.

10.3.2 Any gaps existing between door trim and door frame or house wall? _____ If yes, caulk or seal as necessary to achieve a draft-free seal.

10.4 **Door Sidelights (if any)**

10.4.1 Is glass tightly sealed or puttied? _____ If not, repair as necessary.

10.4.2 If trim can be removed without damage, remove one side piece and check for:

Insulation between sidelight frame and rough opening in wall. Is cavity filled with insulation? _____ If not, remove all sidelight trim and fill cavity with insulation — do not depress. Replace trim.

10.5 **Door Threshold**

10.5.1 Threshold securely tightened to floor? All complete and in good shape? _____ If not, repair or replace threshold. Seal between threshold and floor to achieve a draft-free seal.

10.5.2 Door bottom and threshold make an air-tight seal? _____ If not, repair or replace threshold as needed — or, repair sweep on bottom of door, etc.

11.0 **WINDOWS AND GLASS DOORS**

11.1 **Opening-type Windows**

11.1.1 Carefully examine each window for:

Windows loose in slides. _____

Any glass panes loose, putty missing, etc. _____ Refer to "Windows," page 23-22.

Window frame (wood) is in good shape—joints tight, etc. _____

Weatherstripping on windows is in good shape and complete? _____

Glass cracked? _____

If window cannot be satisfactorily repaired, it may require replacement or to be covered with an insulating (storm) window. Refer to "Storm Window Installation," page 23-24.

11.2 **Fixed (Non-Opening) Windows**

11.2.1 Carefully examine each window for:

Glass loose in frame?	____	Repair if needed.
Any putty or seal missing?	____	Repair if needed.
Glass cracked?	____	Repair if needed.

If window cannot be satisfactorily repaired, it may require replacement or to be covered with an insulating (storm) window.

11.3 **Sliding Glass Doors**

11.3.1 Carefully examine each door for:

Doors loose in slides?	____	Repair if needed.
Any glass loose, seal missing, etc.	____	Repair if needed.
Door frame (if wood) is in good shape—joints tight, etc.	____	Repair if needed.
Weatherstripping on door is in good shape and complete?	____	Repair if needed.
Glass cracked?	____	Repair if needed.

If door cannot be satisfactorily repaired, it may require replacement.

11.4 **Insulating (Storm) Windows**

11.4.1 Carefully examine each for:

Tight fit of insulating window frame to prime window window frame?	____	If not, install properly, Refer to "Storm Window Installation," page, 23-24.
Window itself fits tightly to the aluminum frame?	____	If not, fix.
Small weep holes in bottom lip of prime-window frame are open?	____	Must be open to prevent moisture condensation between prime and storm window. If blocked, open.

12.0 **AIR CONDITIONING EQUIPMENT**

12.1 Carefully check for

Filter is clean?	____	If not, replace or clean as required.
Plenum (large ducts connecting to air handler) is tightly sealed.	____	If not, seal with contact tape.
Duct material is not broken or holed, etc.	____	If so, repair with contact tape.
Turn off air handler at circuit breaker. Check fan belt for tightness.	____	If loose, tighten or have tightened by a/c man.
If unit does not develop "normal" amount of cool air, Freon level may be low.	____	Have checked and replenished by a/c man.
Is compressor shaded from sun?	____	Improved efficiency is gained if compressor is shaded Any shade built over compressor must allow air to freely move over the compressor coil.
Is air flow to compressor blocked in any way?	____	
With unit running, check for air leaks through access door to filter or access door to fan area.	____	If any leaks are noted, check gaskets to each access door —repair or replace gasket as needed.
Is compressor dirty—covered with dust, etc.	____	Carefully open circuit breakers (two may be used) to remove **all** electricity from unit. Use hose with high-pressure nozzle to clean unit. Return circuit breaker(s) to ON.

13.0 **FURNACE — GAS OR OIL FIRED**

13.1 Carefully check for:

Filter is clean?	____	If not, clean or replace as needed.

	Plenum (large duct connecting to air handle) is tightly sealed.	____	If not, seal with contact tape.
	Duct material not broken or holed, etc.	____	If so, repair with contact tape.
	Flame is proper height (not too high) and of proper color?	____	If not, adjust or have adjusted as needed.
	Pilot light is proper height (not too high)?	____	If not, adjust or have adjusted as needed.

13.2 If furnace is mounted in air conditioned part of house, is it mounted in a closet? ____ Unit should be mounted in a closet to keep unit from drawing its combustion air from within the air conditioned part of the house.
Refer to "Combustion Air Input to Furnace," page 19-4.

13.3 Is combustion air obtained from outside air-conditioned part of house. ____ If not, obtain outside air for combustion air if at all possible.

13.4 If unit obtains air from outside air-conditioned area and unit is mounted in a closet, is door air tight? ____ If not, weatherstrip door to prevent unit from pulling in air from air-conditioned portion of house.

14.0 FIREPLACE — MASONRY IN-WALL UNIT

14.1 Check damper closes tightly. ____ If not, damper must be repaired or replaced.

14.2 If glass-door screen is used, is screen fitted tightly into fireplace opening — must be very air tight. ____ If not, seal screen into opening as tightly as possible. Excessive air leakage around screen will make it ineffective.

15.0 HOT-WATER SYSTEM

15.1 Are hot-water lines insulated? ____ If not, insulate all lines that can be reached. Even very short runs should be insulated. Refer to "Piping Loss," page 16-00.

15.2 Is hot-water tank insulated with insulation blanket or stored in an insulated closet? ____ If not in closet, wrap tank with insulation blanket. If in closet, closet walls should be insulated as should the door. Refer to "Tank Loss," page 16-2.

15.3 Thermostat(s) setting - 125°F to 130°F at sink faucet? ____ If dishwasher raises the final-rinse water temperature, a sink-faucet temperature of 125°F is OK — otherwise, set for 130°F. Electric hot-water heaters have two thermostats— be certain to adjust both equally.

A separate hot-water tank used for bathrooms only? ____ The thermostat on this unit can be set down to as low as 95°F.

15.4 Gas-fired unit used? Is pilot light of proper height and color? ____ If not, adjust or have adjusted as needed.

Is flame of proper color and height? ____ If not, adjust or have adjusted as needed.

15.5 Has four or five gallons of water been drained out of tank within 6 months to remove sediment? ____ If not, turn off unit—drain out five gallons of water (use a hose). Turn unit back on. DO NOT DRAIN AN ELECTRICAL UNIT IF IT IS ON.

15.6 Water-use reduction washers installed in shower heads? ____ If not, such heads are recommended to be installed.

16.0 AREA VENTILATION

16.1 Bathroom vent — check for following:

Damper closes tightly? ____ If not, damper must be repaired or vent replaced.

Vent itself fits tightly into the wall or ceiling — no gaps or air leak points? ____ If not, unit should be sealed to be draft proof.

16.2   Kitchen Vent-a-Hood — check for following: (accounts for 6% of air infiltration)

     Unit is equipped with a damper—damper closes tightly? _____ A tight-closing damper must be provided in the vent pipe. If not, repair damper or install one if missing.

     Hood itself fits tightly to the wall and ceiling? _____ If not, caulk and seal around entire vent to make it draft proof.

17.0   WHOLE—HOUSE FAN

17.1   Frame of fan fits tightly against ceiling cover? _____ Unit should fit air tight. If not, seal as needed —clear silicon caulking material can be used.

17.2   Do shutters close tightly? _____ If not, repair—shutters must close to be nearly air tight.

17.3   Shutter area insulated during non-use periods? _____ If not, shutter area should be insulated. Refer to "Whole House Ventilation," page 15-6.

18.0   DRAFT SOURCES

18.1   Double check the following:

     Outer doors are as draft-proof as possible? _____ If not, repeat Check No. 10.0.

     Outer windows and glass sliding doors are as draft-proof as possible? _____ If not, repeat Check No. 11.0.

     All penetrations through the outer walls have been caulked or sealed. _____ If not, repeat Check No. 1l0.

     Outer wall junctions with foundation and at corners are draft free? _____ If not, repeat Check No. 2.0

     All penetrations through ceiling (vents, light boxes, etc.) are draft proofed? _____ If not, repeat Check No. 2.0.

     All penetrations through floor (wood or slab) are sealed? These may be pipes running to kitchen or bathrooms. _____ If not, seal as needed by caulking, etc.

     Wall switches and electric outlets have been sealed? Use gaskets for switches and outlets—insert plastic plugs in any unused outlet socket. _____ If not, seal as indicated.

     Sole plate sealed to floor (slab or wood)? _____ If not, and drafts are noted, seal sole plate as needed.

     Dryer vent—check damper operates and vent fits tightly into wall opening. Caulk to seal if needed. _____ A potentially bad draft source (3%).

     Recessed spotlights — if not really needed, should be cut off at circuit breaker box, with breaker tagged. Space between light and shield can then be sealed with insulation. Do not use flammable material. _____ A potentially bad draft source (5%).

Bibliography

GENERAL INFORMATION

"Some Little Known Facts About Wood"—free pamphlet, Write to American Wood Council, 1619 Massachusetts Ave., N. W., Washington, D.C. 20036

"Saving Energy in the Built Environment" free pamphlet, No. 6N904

"Hold Onto Your Heat (and Keep Your Cool)" free pamphlet, no number.

"Prescriptive Standards: No Rx for Energy Conservation in Building"—free pamphlet No. 6N816
Request from the American Institute of Architects, 1735 New York Ave. N.W., Washington, D.C. 20006

NEW HOME DESIGN AND CONSTRUCTION

"The Arkansas Story"—Owens/Corning Fiberglas Corp., Home Building Product Division, Fiberglas Tower, Toldeo, Ohio 43659 - $2.00

"44 Ways to Build Energy Conservation Into Your Homes"— Owens/Corning Fiberglas Corp., Home Building Product Division, Fiberglas Tower, Toledo, Ohio 43659—Publication No. 5-BL-7055-A.

"Energy Conservation in Buildings: Techniques for Economical Design"—C. W. Griffin. Order from Construction Specifications Institute, Washington, D.C. Price $20.00

ENERGY UPGRADING IN EXISTING HOMES

"In the Bank . . . Or Up the Chimney"—Can be obtained at local lumberyards, Hardware stores and book stores. Or, order from Superintendent of Documents, U.S. Government Printing Office, Washington, D.C. 20402. Stock No. 023-000-00297-3, Cat. No. HH 1.613: EN 2/3-Price $1.70.

"How to Save Money by Insulating Your Home"—Order from National Mineral Wall Association, 382 Springfield Ave., Summit, New Jersey, 07901—Price $0.70.

"Insulation Manual, Homes/Apartments"—Order from National Association of Home Builders Research Foundation, Inc., P.O. Box 1627, Rockville, Maryland 20850—Price $4.00.

"Energy Conservation Checklist"—pamphlet No. FEA/D-75/633—Order from Federal Energy Administration, Washington, D.C. 20461.

"Project Retro-Tech Home Winterization Manual and Job Book"—Federal Energy Administration, Conservation Division, 2626 W. Mockingbird Lane, Dallas, Texas 75235.

INSULATION MATERIALS AND INSTALLATION TECHNIQUES

TF-400 Insulation Panels - Form 1644—Free pamphlet, order from the Celotex Corp., Tampa, Florida 33622.

"Insulwal" panels, insulated wall panels—interior type. Order information from Panel-Era Company, 3447 Main St., Salt Lake City, Utah 84115 or 8001 Carpenter Freeway, Dallas, Texas 75247.

Insulated wall panels, interior or exterior type—"Energy Saving Wall Systems for Masonary Construction"—free pamphlet No. 1738 Rev A. and "Energy Saving Wall Systems for Frame Construction," free pamphlet No. 1739 Rev. A. Order from the Celotex Corp., Tampa, Florida 33622.

"How to Insulate for Maximum Return"—Code No. 30-21-102U. Send self-addressed, stamped, legal-size envelope to Certain-Teed Corp., Box 860, Valley Forge, Pa. 19482.

"How and Where to Install JM Fiber Glass Insulation" - free pamphlet No. HIGI772-12-75—request from Johns-Manville, Greenwood Plaza, Denver, Colorado 80217.

"Design Information and Specifications from Amspec"—Form No. 4108. Suggest requesting under your firms letterhead. Booklet details all types of Styrofoam insulation, including installation details for new buildings. Other information provided by Amspec, Inc., is:

"How to Apply Styrofoam SM Brand Insulation in Foundation Applications"—Form No. 4107.

"Improve the Thermal Efficiency of a Wall"—Form No. 4105.

"Near Perfect Insulation for Wall Construction"—Form No. 4100.

"Totalwall Insulation System"—Form No. 4091.

"Cavity Wall Insulation Installation"—Form No. 4106.

Order from Amsep Corp., 450 West Wilson Bridge Road, P.O. Box 466, Columbus, Ohio 43085.

"Polycel One"—foam sealant. Obtain pamphlet from local insulation firm, lumber yard or hardware store. Or, write to Coplanar Corp., 1631 San Pablo Ave., Oakland, Calif. 94612.

"Foamed-In-Place Thermal and Acoustical Insulation"—Rapco-Foam Form N. 7.14/RA. Request from Rapperswill Corp., 305 East 40th St., New York, N.Y. 10016.

HomeFoamers—franchised network of foam insulation specialists. Refer to "Insulation" in your phone book for local firm.

For information on mineral wool insulation, write to the National Mineral Wool Association, 382 Springfield Ave., Summit, New Jersey 07901.

For information on cellulose insulation, write to the National Cellulose Insulation Manufacturers Association, 400 West Madison St., Chicago, Ill. 60606.

WINDOWS AND STORM WINDOWS

"Energy Conservation with Windows"—free pamphlet from the Federal Energy Administration, Washington, D.C. 20461.

"Window Design Strategies to Conserve Energy"—$3.75—U.S. Government Printing Office, Washington, D.C. 20402

For information on storm windows and storm doors, write to the Architectural Aluminum Manfacturers Association, 35 East Wacker, Chicago, Ill. 60611.

Obtain manufacturers pamphlets and material from local window firms, lumber yards or hardware stores.

METAL-CLAD OUTER DOORS

Remodeling door units - design to fit directly into door opening of an existing home. Write for Catalog No. 72RM. For new-home installations, write for Catalog No. 74WF, Wood-Frame Catalog—Catalog No. 74SF for Steel-Frame Catalog and No. 73PD for Patio-Door Catalog. Obtain by writing to Pease Ever-Strait Division, 7100 Dixie Highway, Fairfield, Ohio 45014.

Obtain Manufacturers pamphlets by applying at local lumber yards.

WOOD-DOOR WEATHERSTRIPPING

Obtain Macklanburg Duncan Co., pamphlet from local lumber yard or hardware store.

HEAT PUMPS AND AIR CONDITIONERS

Obtain manufacturers literature from local air-conditioning firms.

"Heat, Cool and Save Energy with a Heat Pump"—send self-addressed, stamped, legal-size envelope to Air-conditioning and Refrigeration Institute, 1815 North Fort Meyer Drive, Arlington, Virginia 22219.

"Energy Efficiency in Room Air Conditioners"—free pamphlet - request from Consumers Information Center, Pueblo, Colo. 81009.

"7 Ways to Reduce Fuel Consumption in Household Heating—Through Energy Conservation"—Phamphlet No. C13.2:F95, $0.35—Order from U.S. Government Printing Office, Washington, D.C. 20402.

"11 Ways to Reduce Energy Consumption and Increase Comfort in Household Cooling" - Pamphlet No. C13.2:EN2, $0.40—Order from U.S. Government Printing Office, Washington, D.C. 20402.

"Energy Conservation with Heat Pumps"—free pamphlet—request from The Federal Energy Administration, Washington, D.C. 20461.

For data on heat recovery units used in conjunction with an air conditioner to preheat hot water, write to the following:
Sun-Econ, Inc.
Northway 10 Ushers Rd.
Ballston Lake, N.Y. 12019

G.S.T. Industries, Inc.
6605 Walton Way
Tampa, Fla. 33610

ATTIC VENTILATION

Ridge venting—free pamphlet—Vent-a-System—discusses ridge venting and details installation. Request from HC Product Co., P.O. Box 68, Princeville, Ill. 61669 or obtain at local lumber yard or hardware store.

Attic powered ventilators—free pamphlet—Form No. P7650—request from Leslie-Locke at any of the following addresses:
11550 West King St., Franklin Park, Ill. 60131
4701 Granite Drive, Tucker, Georgia 30084
9201 South Freeway, Fort Worth, Texas 76134
500 South Schnoor Ave., Madera, Ca. 93637

or obtain from local lumber yard or hardware store.

LANDSCAPING FOR ENERGY CONSERVATION

"Energy Conservation with Landscaping"—free pamphlet—request from The Federal Energy Administration, Washington, D.C. 20461.

"Climate and House Design"—No. 69 IV II—$3.00—obtain through any United Nations field office.

"The Weather Conditioned Home"—Conklin, Groff - New York: Reinhold, 1958 - Obtainable in large public libraries.

"Design with Climate"—Olgyay, Victor - Princeton University Press, Princeton, New Jersey—obtainable in large public libraries.

"Site Planning for Solar Energy Utilization"—American Society of Landscape Architects Foundation, Washington, D.C. - National Technical Information Service.

ENERGY SAVING TIPS

"Tips for Energy Savers"—Free pamphlet—request from Office of Public Affairs, Federal Energy Administration, Washington, D.C. 20461.

"Energy-Efficient Home Appliances—gives facts on electrical power drain on major appliances. 50¢—order from Association of Home Appliance Manufacturers, 20 North Wacker Drive, Chicago, Ill. 60606.

SOLAR ENERGY

For free information on solar energy, call or write the National Solar Heating and Cooling Information Center. The Center will answer specific questions and will send related printed material. Write P.O. Box 1607, Rockville, Maryland 20850 or phone toll-free 800-523-2929. In Pennsylvania, phone 800-462-4983.

"Buying Solar"—Booklet, $1.85. Order from The Federal Energy Administration, P.O. Box 35228, Dallas, Texas 75235.

"The Solar Home Book" - Bruce Anderson, Cheshire Books, Church Hill, Harrisville, N. H. 03450—Price $7.50.

"Minimum Property Standards (MPS) for Solar Heating and Domestic Hot Water Systems"—Publication No. 4930.2, Price $12.00. Booklet may be reviewed at any HUD field office or order from the U.S. Government Printing Office, Washington, D.C. 20402.

"How to Build a Solar Water Heater"—a full-detail description and plan—order from Florida Conservation Foundation, Inc., 935 Organe Ave., Suite E, Winter Park, Florida 32789—price $2.50 including postage.

"Solar Energy for Space Heating and Hot Water"—booklet detailing types of solar heaters available and giving general economics of solar heating. Order from U.S. Government Printing Office, Washington, D.C. 20402, costs 35¢.

For details on how to build a combination space heater/hot water heater using solar energy as developed by NASA, write to the National Technical Information Service, U.S. Dept. of Commerce, Springfield, Virginia 22161. Costs $4.25.

"Home Mortgage Lending and Solar Energy"—explains financing plans available for solar-energy installations for space heating. Put out by the Department of Housing and Urban Development. Order from the Government Printing Office, Washington, D.C., 20402, costs $1.40.

A great deal of useful information can be obtained in pamphlet or booklet form from various manufacturers of insulation, thermal-type doors and windows, fireplaces, air conditioners and heat pumps, etc. This material can be ordered through the House Beautiful, House Remodeling or Houses and Plans magazines. These magazines contain a list of pamphlets and booklets that may be ordered by filling in a form contained in the magazine. The magazine publisher then forwards the individual requests to the related companies who mail the material directly to you. This saves having to write individually to each manufacturer. Waiting time is from 4 to 8 weeks.

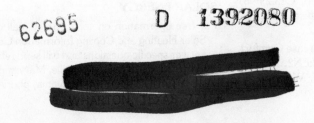